PRACHI

Strictly in Compliance with the Latest NCERT Content

Excellence in

SOCIAL SCIENCE

As per National Education Policy (NEP) 2020 and National Curriculum Framework for School Education (NCF-SE) 2023

Dr. Ruchi Pande
M.A. (History), Ph.D

6

Prachi India Pvt. Ltd.
SMART BOOKS FOR SMART LEARNING

Latest Edition

Prachi India Pvt. Ltd.
SMART BOOKS FOR SMART LEARNING
309, ALLIED HOUSE, INDER LOK, DELHI–110 035
PH. : 011-47320666 (8 LINES)
website : www.prachiindia.com
e-mail : info@prachiindia.com
query : feedback@prachiindia.com

Printed at : Goyal Offset Works Pvt. Ltd. Haryana

SECTION-F. (Map Skill-based Questions) [1 x 5 = 5]

37. **(*a*) Two places A and B have been marked on the given outline map of the world. Identify them and write their correct names on the lines drawn near them.**

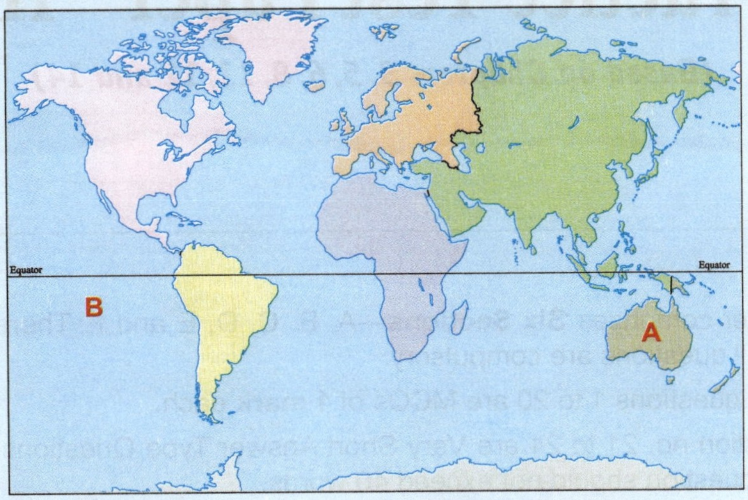

(*i*) The smallest continent.

(*ii*) The largest ocean.

(*b*) On the same outline map of world, locate, name and label any three of the following :

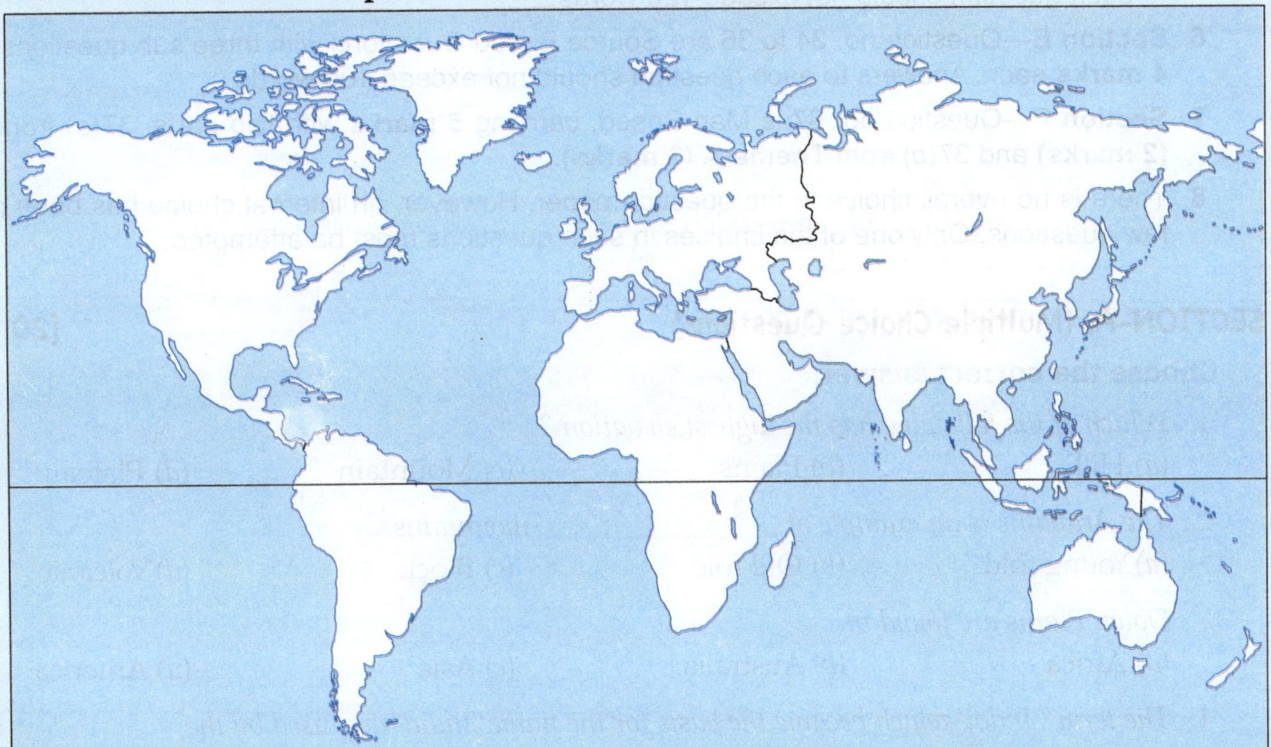

(*i*) The largest continent

(*ii*) The dark continent

(*iii*) The "S" shaped ocean.

(*iv*) The ocean which is almost triangular in shape.

Practice Test Paper–II*

(Based on Chapters 3, 5, 6, 8, 11, 12 and 14)

Time : 3 Hours **Max. Marks : 80**

General Instructions :

1. The question paper comprises **Six Sections**—A, B, C, D, E and F. There are 37 questions in the Question paper. All questions are compulsory.
2. **Section A**—From questions 1 to 20 are MCQs of **1 mark** each.
3. **Section B**—Question no. 21 to 24 are Very Short Answer Type Questions, carrying **2 marks** each. Answers to each question should not exceed 40 words.
4. **Section C**—Question no. 25 to 29 are Short Answer Type Questions, carrying **3 marks** each. Answers to each question should not exceed 60 words.
5. **Section D**—Question no. 30 to 33 are Long Answer Type Questions, carrying **5 marks** each. Answers to each question should not exceed 120 words.
6. **Section E**—Question no. 34 to 36 are Source Based Questions with three sub questions and are of **4 marks** each. Answers to each question should not exceed 100 words.
7. **Section F**—Question no. 37 is Map Based, carrying **5 marks** with two parts, 37(*a*) from **Theme-B (2 marks)** and 37(*b*) from **Theme-A (3 marks)**.
8. There is no overall choice in the question paper. However, an internal choice has been provided in few questions. Only one of the choices in such questions must be attempted.

SECTION-A. (Multiple Choice Questions) [20 x 1 = 20]

Choose the correct answer.

1. *Which of the following has the highest elevation ?*
   (*a*) Hill (*b*) Plains (*c*) Mountain (*d*) Plateau
2. *The Aravallis is an example of ______________ mountains.*
   (*a*) Young fold (*b*) Old fold (*c*) Block (*d*) Volcanic
3. *Down Plains are found in*
   (*a*) Africa (*b*) Australia (*c*) Asia (*d*) America
4. *The term " Indoi" which became the basis for the name "India" was used by the*
   (*a*) Greeks (*b*) Chinese (*c*) Persians (*d*) Buddhists
5. *The Southern boundary of the Indus-Saraswati Civilization in India is at*
   (*a*) SutkagenDor (*b*) Alamgirpur (*c*) Manda (*d*) Daimabad
6. *Which of the following Indus-Saraswati sites is not in Gujarat ?*
   (*a*) Lothal (*b*) Banawali (*c*) Rangpur (*d*) Dholavira

*Chapters are choosen according to five themes covering each aspect of the subject.

SECTION-B. (Very Short Answer Type Questions) [4 x 2 = 8]

21. Conventional symbols make a map very simple and understandable. Justify this statement.
22. Earth is called a blue planet. Do you agree with this statement ? Justify why.

Or

Not all water available on Earth is fit for human consumption. Justify this statement.

23. Members of a family are interdependent on each other for their everyday needs. Justify this statement.
24. Community led programmes help to strengthen social bonds. Justify this statement.

SECTION-C. (Short Answer Type Questions) [5 x 3 = 15]

25. The lines dividing the time zones are not fully straight. Give reasons why.
26. If it is 12:00 noon at the Prime Meridian, it will be 1:00 p.m. at 15°E. Explain why.

Or

It is 5:30 p.m. in India when it is 12:00 noon in London. Explain why.

27. What is a timeline in history ? Explain how it is useful for historians and students.
28. The separation of powers is called the system of checks and balances. Explain why.
29. Explain the significance of non-economic activities in the development of an individual.

SECTION-D. (Long Answer Type Questions) [4 x 5 = 20]

30. Rashmi wants to visit her aunt's place but does not know the way to her home. What will help her more in this situation—A globe or a map ? Explain why.

Or

Geographic Coordinates help us to find the exact location of any place. Justify this statement.

31. Analyse the importance of oceans for humans and marine life.

Or

Discovery of fire was one of the greatest achievements of early man. Justify this statement. State the different uses of fire for early man.

32. Several factors were responsible for the popularity of Buddhism both in India and abroad. Analyse this statement. Discuss those factors that made Buddhism popular among the masses.

Or

A family is our first school where we learn great lessons and values for life. Justify this statement. Describe some of the lessons and values that our family teaches us.

33. A government is an institution that makes political decisions to run a country. Justify this statement. Explain any three functions of the government that are necessary to run a country.

Or

Value Addition makes any product more useful and valuable for the customers. Justify this statement. Give an example where value is added at every step of production.

SECTION-E. (Source Based Questions) [3 × 4 = 12]

34. Read the source given below and answer the questions that follow :

Historians rely on a variety of sources to reconstruct the past. Primary sources, such as diaries, letters and official documents, provide firsthand accounts of historical events. These sources are invaluable because they offer direct insights into the thoughts, actions and experiences of people who lived during the period being studied. Secondary sources, on the other hand, are interpretations and analyses of primary sources by historians and other scholars. They help to contextualise and explain historical events, making them more accessible to a broader audience. Additionally, archaeological evidence, such as artefacts, buildings and inscriptions, provides physical evidence of past civilizations and cultures. Oral histories, passed down through generations, also offer valuable perspectives on historical events and cultural traditions. Each type of source has its strengths and limitations and historians must critically evaluate and corroborate these sources to create a comprehensive and accurate understanding of the past.

(*a*) Identify the different types of sources mentioned in the passage.

(*b*) Which archaeological evidences are mentioned in the passage ?

(*c*) Why are primary sources invaluable ?

35. Read the source given below and answer the questions that follow :

Oceans are vital for regulating the Earth's climate by absorbing and distributing heat, influencing weather patterns and moderating temperatures. They also serve as a major source of food, providing seafood that is a significant part of the diet for many people around the world. Additionally, oceans are essential for global trade, as they facilitate the transportation of goods across continents. Furthermore, oceans are a rich source of minerals and energy resources, such as oil, gas and renewable energy from waves and tides. However, the health of our oceans is under threat due to pollution, overfishing and climate change, which can have devastating consequences for marine ecosystems and human societies.

(*a*) Why are oceans vital for regulating the Earth's climate ?

(*b*) List any three uses of oceans for humans.

(*c*) Mention the reasons responsible for deteriorating the health of our oceans.

36. Read the source given below and answer the questions that follow :

Community plays a vital role in the well-being and development of individuals and society as a whole. It provides a sense of belonging, support and shared identity. Within a community, people come together to share resources, knowledge and experiences, fostering a sense of mutual aid and cooperation. Communities offer a safety net for their members, providing assistance during times of need, such as natural disasters, economic hardships, or personal crises. Additionally, communities are essential for promoting social cohesion and reducing isolation. They create opportunities for social interaction, cultural exchange and collective action, which can lead to the development of strong social bonds and a sense of collective responsibility.

(*a*) How do communities offer a safety net to people ?

(*b*) Analyse the role of communities in the development of an individual and society as a whole.

(*c*) How do communities help in the development of social bonds ?

Preface

The **EXCELLENCE IN SOCIAL SCIENCE** series, thoughtfully crafted for classes 6 to 8, aligns with the latest NCERT content. Guided by the **National Education Policy (NEP) 2020** and the **National Curriculum Framework** for **School Education (NCF-SE) 2023**, this series aims to engage and inspire learners while fostering essential 21st-century skills, such as critical thinking, decision-making and problem-solving.

This series explores a variety of engaging themes aimed at fostering a comprehensive understanding of Social Sciences. These themes include **The Basics of the Geographical World Around Us**, offering insights into fundamental geography; **Tapestry of the Past**, exploring historical events beginning with India's rich history; **Our Cultural Heritage and Knowledge Traditions**, highlighting the diverse cultural and intellectual legacy; **Governance and Democracy**, explaining the structures and functioning of democratic systems; and **Economic Life Around Us**, examining the economic factors influencing daily life.

Salient features of the book :

- **Concepts** explained in simple, engaging language to ensure clarity and interest.
- **Relevant pictures** and **maps** to enhance comprehension.
- **"Do You Know"**, **"More to Know"** and **"Think and Answer"** sections to deepen understanding.
- **New words** with meanings and explanation (where necessary) at the end of each chapter to clarify important concepts.
- **Nutshell** provides chapter summaries for quick revision and reinforces the key points covered in each lesson.
- **Important NCERT solutions** are included for additional practice.
- **MCQs**, **Assertion-Reason Questions**, **Picture Study**, **Source-Based Questions** and **Map Skills** assess different cognitive skills and promote critical thinking.
- **Group Discussions**, **Role Plays, Poster Making** and other **Activities** foster experiential learning and enhance skills such as *Communication*, *Creativity and Collaboration*, promoting active learning & student engagement.
- **Digital learning tools** and **web-links** are provided as resources to encourage students to explore beyond the text and foster independent thinking.
- Two carefully designed **Practice Test Papers** encompass the five themes, covering all key aspects of the subject.

I have made every effort to ensure the accuracy of this book and welcome any feedback to help us improve its quality further.

—AUTHOR

National Curriculum Framework for School Education (NCF-SE) 2023

Goals and Competencies for Social Science at Middle Stage

CG-1 Comprehends and interprets sources related to different aspects of human life and makes meaningful interpretations	**C-1.1**	Collects and interprets multiple sources of information (primary and secondary) to understand the historical, cultural, geographical and socio-political aspects of human life
	C-1.2	Represents and analyses data related to various aspects of human life given in the form of text, tables, charts, diagrams and maps
CG-2 Explores the process of continuity and change in human civilisations through specific examples from their context and a few historical episodes	**C-2.1**	Explains and analyses major changes in the past and their impact on society
	C-2.2	Recognises elements of the continued prevalence of certain beliefs, relationships, practices and activities in human society, notwithstanding major changes in society
CG-3 Draws connections between the causes and effects of different social and historical events or episodes and connects them with the overall impact on human life	**C-3.1**	Analyses the effect of various changes in early human society from nomadism to settled life and early civilisation (such as the emergence of agriculture, changes in food habits, basic technologies like construction, transport, pottery, metallurgy) and changes in human habitation, family structures and relationships, the nature of work, people's sociocultural beliefs and concepts over time (*e.g.*, ahimsa and the fallout of major wars or invasions) that significantly impacted human societies
	C-3.2	Identifies reasons behind harmony and conflict among social groups and communities, in their region and in other parts of the world and their impact on human societies
CG-4 Understands the functioning of social, cultural and political institutions and their impact on society and the way individuals and collectives shape these institutions	**C-4.1**	Collects, organises and interprets information about various social, cultural, economic and political institutions in their vicinity and region and realises its significance for human society
	C-4.2	Assesses the influence of social, cultural and political institutions on an individual/group/community/society in general

CG-5 Understands various forms of inequality and prejudice in society—from those prevalent in a family to those at a community/regional/national level—and also the initiatives and efforts at various levels to address these issues	**C-5.1**	Identifies, explains and raises questions about different forms of inequality, prejudice and discrimination prevailing in one's own family, locality, region and national and global levels
	C-5.2	Identifies, explains and appreciates efforts (being) made at different levels through various (including social, cultural, economic and political) mechanisms and institutions and what individuals can do, to address these to ensure equity, inclusion and justice
CG-6 Understands the spatial distribution of resources (from local to global), their conservation, the interdependence between natural phenomena and human life and their environmental and other implications	**C-6.1**	Explains key natural phenomena such as climate, weather, ocean cycles, soil formation, the flow of rivers and how they are spatially distributed
	C-6.2	Identifies the distribution of resources such as water, agriculture, raw materials and services across geographies
	C-6.3	Analyses Indian perspectives on and efforts towards conservation and sustainability in society and advocates the importance of the same and what more needs to be done in these directions including in the context of global climate change
	C-6.4	Correlates the existence of different patterns of livelihoods with different types of landforms, availability of resources and climatic conditions and changes (in local, regional, national and global contexts)
CG-7 Appreciates the importance and meaning of being Indian (Bharatiya) by understanding (*a*) India's rich past and present including its glorious cultural unity in diversity, pluralism, heritage, traditions, literature, art, architecture, philosophy, medicine, science and other contributions to humanity and (*b*) other integrating factors despite the geographical diversity of India	**C-7.1**	Explains India's unity in diversity by recognising commonalities in its rich and diverse cultural elements, languages, art, philosophical ideas, values, clothing, cuisines, traditions, festivals, trade, commerce and health practices including ayurveda and yoga
	C-7.2	Discovers the topographical diversity of the Indian landmass–from the semi-arid zone in the west and the areas of heavy rains in the north-east to the long coastal areas in the south and the snow-clad mountains in the north, as well as the rich biodiversity of the country
	C-7.3	Appreciates India's tradition of inclusion across communities and social groups and its influence in vast parts of the world through its cultural elements

CG-8 Understands and appreciates the process of development of the Constitution of India and upholds its importance to promote democratic values in Indian society	**C-8.1** Understands the need for a constitution for any country during the last few centuries – especially in a country such as India – and its deeper objectives
	C-8.2 Explains the process of formation of the Indian Constitution and understands the ideas and ideals of the Indian national movement enshrined in it as well as those drawn from India's civilisational heritage
	C-8.3 Explains the working of the three tiers of local self-government and appreciates its significance in upholding democracy at the grassroot level
CG-9 Understands the processes of economic activities (production and consumption, trade and commerce)	**C-9.1** Explains the key elements of trade and commerce (commodity, production, consumption and capital) and its impact on individual life and society
CG-10 Understands and appreciates the contributions of India through history and in the present times, to the overall field of Social Science, including the different disciplines that constitute it	**C-10.1** Knows and explains the significant contributions of India to all matters (concepts, explanations, methods) studied within the curriculum, in an integrated manner along with the particular matter – illustratively, understands the strengths of India's democratic traditions through its history
CG-11 In the curricular goals CG-1 to CG-10, there is a basic and adequate understanding of the history, geography and culture of the locality, region and country	**NOTE :** *Competencies for this Curricular Goal have already been incorporated under CG-1 to CG-10*

BOOK OVERVIEW

Contents

Theme A — India and the World : Land and the People

1. Locating Places on the Earth ... 9–32
2. Oceans and Continents ... 33–47
3. Landforms and Life ... 48–66

Theme B — Tapestry of the Past

4. Timeline and Sources of History ... 67–83
5. India, That Is Bharat ... 84–93
6. The Beginnings of Indian Civilisation ... 94–111

Theme C — Our Cultural Heritage and Knowledge Traditions

7. India's Cultural Roots ... 112–136
8. Unity in Diversity, or 'Many in the One' ... 137–153

Theme D — Governance and Democracy

9. Family and Community ... 154–170
10. Grassroots Democracy — Part 1 : Governance ... 171–188
11. Grassroots Democracy — Part 2 : Local Government in Rural Areas ... 189–208
12. Grassroots Democracy — Part 3 : Local Government in Urban Areas ... 209–224

Theme E — Economic Life Around Us

13. The Value of Work ... 225–241
14. Economic Activities Around Us ... 242–259

- **Practice Test Papers***

Practice Test Paper—I ... 260–265
(Based on Chapters 1, 2, 4, 7, 9, 10 and 13)

Practice Test Paper—II ... 266–272
(Based on Chapters 3, 5, 6, 8, 11, 12 and 14)

**Chapters are choosen according to five themes covering each aspect of the subject.*

CHAPTER 1

Locating Places on the Earth

CG-1 : C-1.2

What's new to learn

- A Map and Its Components
- Mapping the Earth
- Understanding Time Zones

Riya had to attend her friend Tina's birthday at her home. Riya was very excited but also a little nervous because she had never been to her friend's place before and didn't know how to get there. She asked one of her friends, Shruti, to accompany her to Tina's home. Riya's mother gave her a map of the neighbourhood and showed her the way to Tina's home. She explained that Riya and Shruti would need to walk straight down their street towards the North, turn left at the big Mango tree and then turn right from the crossing after the Mango tree and again turn right from the next crossing. They will see a shopping store in the corner. From there, they would see their friend's home just 500 metres ahead on the right hand side.

Riya and Shruti listened carefully to her mother's instructions and studied the map. They both were a little nervous but Riya's mother assured them that they would reach Tina's home without any problem. Riya and Shruti started from their home towards the North and followed the instructions and directions given on the map precisely. Soon they reached Tina's home and they both felt a sense of relief and excitement. They joined the other children at the birthday party and went back home again following the directions given on the map. They both were proud of themselves for finding the way on their own. From that day on, Riya always carried a map with her wherever she went.

In this story, you see how maps and directions can help us in finding any area or place. Now, let's study maps and directions in detail.

A MAP AND ITS COMPONENTS

The word, 'Map' is derived from the Latin word 'mappa' which means 'sheet' or 'napkin'. It is so called because all the earlier maps were mostly either made or drawn on cloth, skin and parchments. If we draw the world or a part of it on a piece of paper, that drawing is called a map.

Thus, a map is a representation or a drawing of the Earth's surface or a part of it drawn on a flat surface according to a scale.

India : Physical

Types of Maps

Broadly, maps can be divided into three categories :

India : Political

(*i*) **Physical or Relief Maps :** Maps showing natural features of the Earth like mountains, plateaus, plains, rivers, oceans, etc. are called physical or relief maps.

(*ii*) **Political Maps :** Maps showing cities, towns and villages and various countries and states with their boundaries are called political maps. *For example,* a map of India showing its states is a political map.

(*iii*) **Thematic Maps :** Theme-based maps are called thematic maps. These maps are based on certain information, *for example,* climate, rainfall, population, railways, roadways, economy, etc.

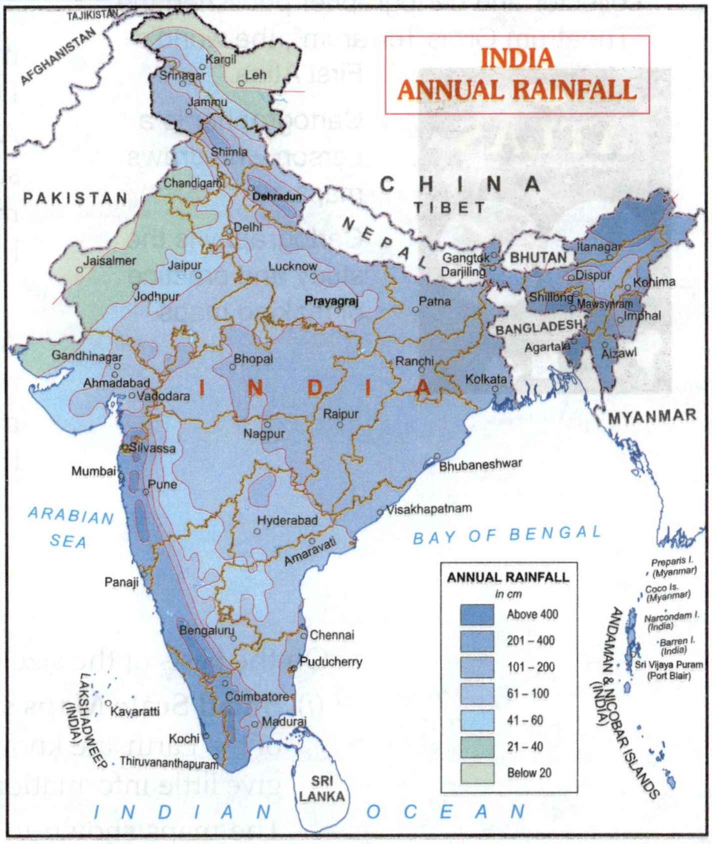

Thematic Map (Annual Rainfall : Map of India)

Check Your Progress — Understanding

1. "Mappa" is a ______________ word.
2. Rivers and oceans are shown in ______________ maps.
3. Theme-based maps are called ______________ maps.
4. A map that shows cities and countries is a ____________ map.

Components of a Map

There are four major components of a map. Without these components, we cannot study a map effectively. They provide us useful information about a map.

The four components are :

MORE TO KNOW

- A collection of maps of the world, countries and continents is called an Atlas.
- On 22 May, 1570, Abraham Ortelius, a Flemish book collector and cartographer published the "Theatrum Orbis Terrarum", the world's First Atlas.
- Cartographer is a person who draws maps.
- Cartography is the study and practice of making maps.

Gerardus Mercator

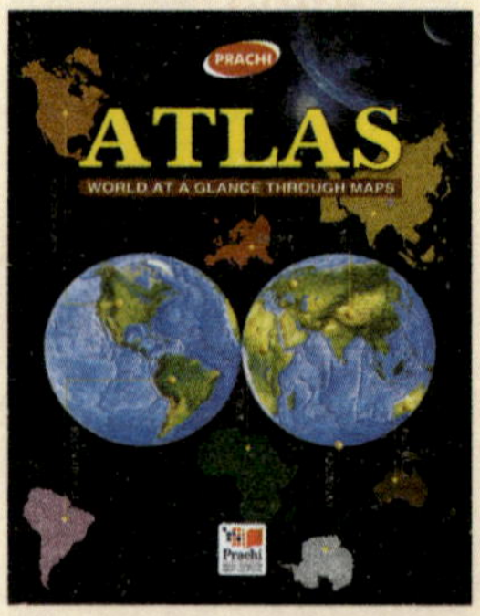

Atlas

Title

Title shows the name of a map. It tells the reader what the map is all about. All maps should have an effective and accurate title.

For example : If a map is titled "Rainfall Distribution in India", it means that the map shows the distribution of rainfall across different regions of India.

Scale

Scale is a ratio between a unit distance on the map to a proportionate distance on the ground. Distance on a map is shown with the help of a scale. All the maps are based on a scale. With the help of a scale, maps can be reduced or enlarged. The size of a map is compared to the real size of a place with the help of a scale.

For example : Suppose the distance between place A and place B is 100 km on the ground, but it is represented as 1 cm on map, *i.e.,* 100 km = 1 cm. This means 1 cm on the map corresponds to 100 km on the ground.

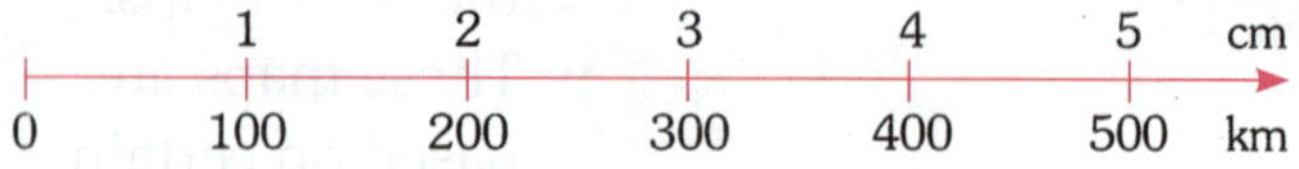

Scale : 1 cm = 100 km.

On the basis of the size of the scale, maps are classified into :

(*i*) **Small Scale Maps :** The maps that use a small scale to show large areas of the Earth, are known as the Small Scale Maps *e.g.,* 1 cm = 100 km. They give little information about large areas such as continents or countries. The maps shown in your atlas are based on a small scale. The map of India given in your book is an example of a Small Scale Map.

(*ii*) **Large Scale Maps :** The maps that are created by using large scales are called Large Scale Maps. In these maps, small areas are represented on a large size map. Its purpose is to show large amount of details about a small area *e.g.*, 1 cm = 100 metres.

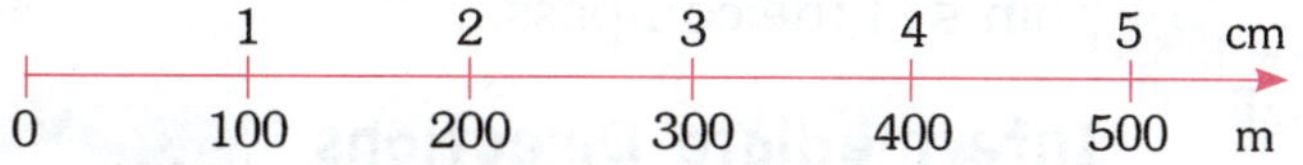

Scale : 1 cm = 100 m.

A village or a city map is an example of a Large Scale Map.

The differences between Small Scale Maps and Large Scale Maps can be summarised as under :

Small Scale Maps	Large Scale Maps
1. These maps represent large areas of the Earth (1 cm = 100 km).	1. These maps show small areas of the Earth (1 cm = 100 m).
2. They show a few details about a large area.	2. They show plenty of details about a small area.
3. A world map is a small scale map. All the maps shown on an atlas are small scale maps.	3. A road map, city map, etc. are examples of large scale maps.

Direction

Have you ever noticed an arrow with the alphabet 'N' marked on the right-hand side corner of a map ? It shows the north direction on a map. Most of the maps show direction with the help of an arrow with 'N' written on it. In some maps, you may also find a compass showing direction.

Map showing North Direction

Compass

Direction is actually a course along which someone or something moves. A compass is a device with a magnetic needle which tells us about the directions. Broadly, directions are of two types.

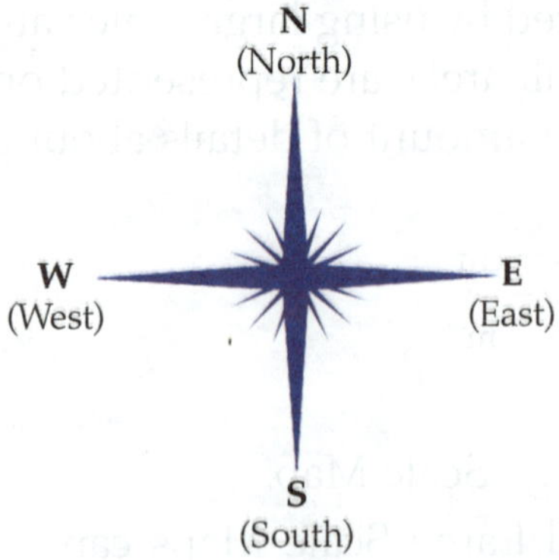

Cardinal directions

Cardinal Directions

North, East, West and South (NEWS) are the cardinal directions.

These are also called the four cardinal points of the compass.

Intermediate Directions

Directions that lie between two cardinal points are called intermediate directions. North-East, South-East, North-West and South-West are the intermediate directions.

All these directions tell us which way to go. They enable us to find out places accurately.

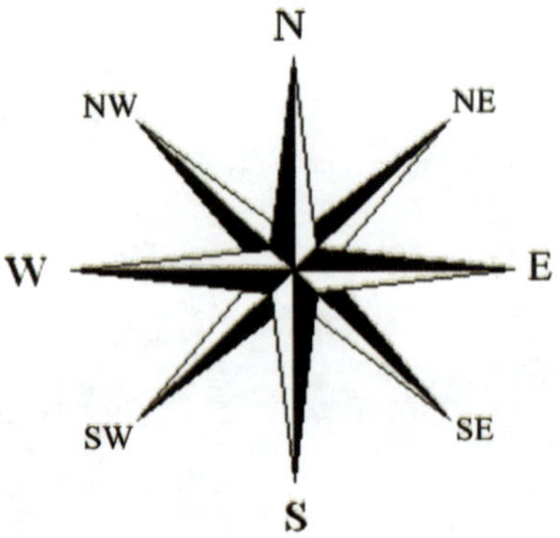

Intermediate directions

Conventional Symbols

Conventional symbols are universally accepted symbols that we use on maps to represent various features of the Earth's surface. These symbols provide plenty of information in a limited space. They make a map very simple and understandable.

Conventional symbols are also called map legends because they tell the story of a map. They are also called map keys as they unlock the meaning of various symbols.

There are three types of conventional symbols :

1. **Line Symbols :** road, railways, boundaries, etc.
2. **Point Symbols :** tanks, buildings, etc.
3. **Area Symbols :** settlements, cultivations, etc

Think & Answer

While going back home from your school, how many turns do you take ? In which directions do these turns lie ?

Think & Answer

Name any four features from the below mentioned table that lie in your surroundings.

SOME IMPORTANT CONVENTIONAL SYMBOLS

Features	Symbols
Roads metalled	
Roads unmetalled	
Cart-track; Pack-track and Pass, Footpath with bridge	
Streams : With track in bed; Undefined, Canal	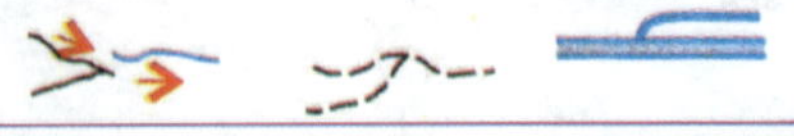
Dams : Masonry or rock-filled; Earthwork, Weir	
River bank : Dry with water channel; With island & rocks, Tidal river	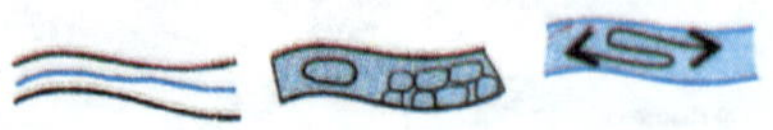
Submerged rocks; Shoal, Swamp, Reeds	

Features	Symbols
Wells : lined; unlined, Tubewell, Spring, Tanks : perennial; dry	
Embankment : Road or rail; Tank; Broken ground	2r
Railways : Broad gauge (double); Single with station, Under construction	RS
Railways : Other gauges (double); Single with distance stone, Under construction	20
Mineral line or tramway, Telegraph line; Klin cutting with tunnel	
Contours : With sub-features; Rocky slopes, Cliffs	100
Sand features : (1) Flat, (2) Sand-hills and dunes (surveyed), (3) Shifting dunes	(1) (2) (3)
Towns or Villages : Inhabited; Deserted, Fort	
Huts : Permanent; Temporary, Tower, Antiquities	Gaur
Temple, Chhatri, Church, Mosque, Idgah, Tomb, Graves	
Lighthouse, Lightship, Buoys–lighted; unlighted, Anchorage	
Mine, Grass, Scrub	
Palms : Palmyra; other Plantations; Conifers; Bamboos, Other trees	
Surveyed tree	
Boundary : International	
Boundary : State : Demarcated; Undemarcated	
Boundary : District, Sub-division : Tehsil or Taluk, Forest	
Boundary Pillars : Surveyed; Unlocated, Village trijunction	
Heights : Triangulated station; Point; Approximate	Δ 200 • 200 • 200
Bench-mark : Geodetic; Tertiary; Canal	• BM 63.2 • *BM 63.2* • *63*
Post Office, Telegraph Office, Combined Post and Telegraph Office, Police Station	*PO* *TO* *PTO* *PS*

DO YOU KNOW?

Reading/Learning

Differences between Globe and Map :

Globe	Map
1. Globe is spherical in shape.	1. Map is a flat representation of the Earth's surface.
2. Globe is three-dimensional.	2. Map is two-dimensional.
3. Globe accurately portrays the shape of continents and the distance between landmasses.	3. Map distorts shape and size of continents.

What are the globes and maps used for ?

We use globes and maps to know the locations of various places around the world.

A globe is better than a flat map. Give reasons why ?

A globe is more accurate than a flat map as it shows the true shape of the Earth's surface. It also represents accurate distance between landmasses.

Colour codes are also used in a map to show the following relief features :

Colour	Features
Brown	Land features like Mountains
Black	Road, Railways, Boundaries
Blue	Water
Red	Settlement, construction features
Green	Vegetation/Plains
Yellow	Plateau

Check Your Progress

Understanding

1. Name the three types of maps.
2. Draw a map of your school. Include the different structures like the staffroom, principal room, library, playground, etc. in your map. Use scale, directions and different colours for different structures.
3. Find out :

   (*a*) How many cm are there in 1 km ?

   (*b*) How many inches are there in 1 mile ?

   (*c*) How many metres are there in 1 km ?

MAPPING THE EARTH

Maps are useful when we have to study a part of the Earth like a country, a state or a city. What if you want to study the Earth as a whole ? You know that the Earth is spherical in shape while maps are flat. A flat map cannot show the Earth's curved surface without significant distortions. To study the Earth as a whole, man developed a small but exact model of the Earth to view it as a whole. This small model of the Earth is known as a globe.

A Globe

A **globe** is a true model or the miniature form of the Earth. It is a hollow sphere on which the whole world (land and ocean) is depicted. As its shape is similar to that of Earth, it shows the correct size and shape of different continents and oceans. It also shows various relief features like mountains, plateaus and plains. It is helpful in finding the shortest distance between two places. It tells the correct location and direction of different places with respect to each other. If you look at the globe carefully, you will find various horizontal and vertical lines.

Check Your Progress — Understanding

1. What is a globe ?
2. Take a globe and search for your country India.
3. Make a list of the objects that are similar to the Earth with reference to their shape.

Now, let us study some features of the globe :

(a) Understanding Coordinates

We have studied that to locate any place on the Earth, it is better to use a globe as its shape is quite similar to that of Earth. Now, to know the exact location of any place on Earth, we use the System of Coordinates. **A geographic coordinate system** is a three-dimensional system to find any global address on the Earth's surface. A global address of any place on the Earth is given as two numbers - a latitude number and a longitude number. These two numbers are called **coordinates.** The Longitude gives us the East-West position while the Latitude gives the North-South position of any place. In this way, we can determine the exact location of any place.

The Earth is a vast heavenly body. It consists of millions of natural and man-made features. It is very difficult to find out and locate these features without using any reference point. Understand what a reference point is with the help of the following example :

Suppose, today is your birthday and you invite your friends. They do not know the location of your home. You tell them that your home is near the D.A.V. School, just opposite the Prabhat Bakery. Here, you use D.A.V. School and Prabhat Bakery to explain the location of your home. Both these points are called the reference points. But such references are useful at local levels only. For national and international levels, we need to use some references that are internationally approved. The latitudes and longitudes are examples of such references. Now, let us study the latitudes and longitudes in some detail.

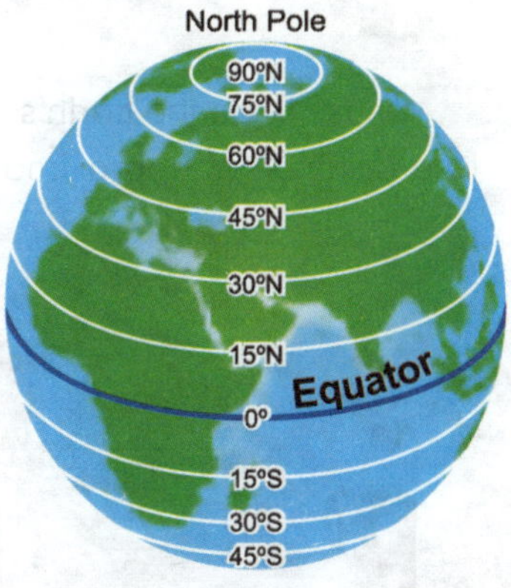

Latitudes

(b) Latitudes

A latitude is the angular distance of a point on the Earth's surface measured in degrees from an imaginary line named the equator which lies midway between the poles.

Usually, the distance is measured in kilometres or miles but the angular distance is measured and expressed in degrees. If you see the globe, you will find lines running from east to west. These imaginary lines are the latitudes.

Some Important Facts about Latitudes

- The latitudes are parallel to each other. All parallel circles from the equator upto the poles are called parallels of latitudes.
- These are imaginary lines that run east-west and are used to measure distance.
- The distance between the two parallels of latitudes is assumed to be 1°, that is equal to 111 km.
- The Equator is the most significant latitude. It was chosen as the reference line because it divides the globe into two equal halves. The northern half of the Earth is known as the Northern Hemisphere and the southern half is known as the Southern Hemisphere. The Equator represents the zero degree latitude. It is the largest latitude.

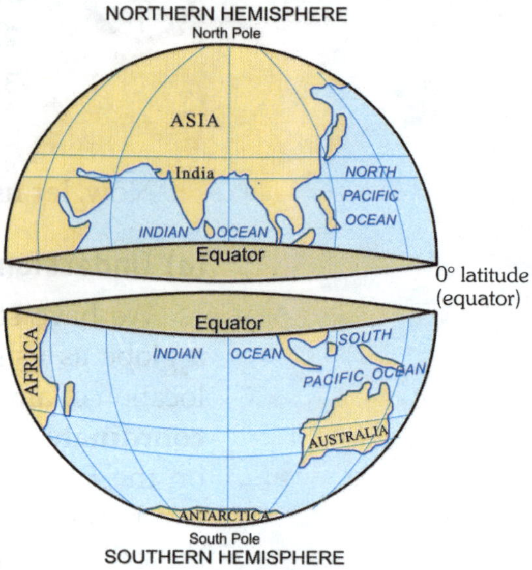

Northern Hemisphere and Southern Hemisphere

$$\frac{\text{Northern Hemisphere}\uparrow}{\text{Southern Hemisphere}\downarrow} \rightarrow 0° \text{ Latitude (Equator)}$$

- All parallels north of the equator are called 'north latitudes'. Similarly, all parallels to the south of the equator are called 'south latitudes'.
- Since the distance from the equator to the North or South pole is one-fourth of a circle round the Earth, it measures 1/4th of 360 degrees *i.e.,* 90°. So, 90 degrees north latitude (90°N) marks the North Pole and 90 degrees south latitude (90°S) marks the South Pole.
- The alphabet 'N' is used to indicate the North latitudes and 'S' is used to show the South latitudes.
- All parallels of latitudes are not equal in length. Their length decreases as one moves northward or southward *i.e.,* towards either of the poles.
- The distance between any two parallels of latitudes is always equal.

DO YOU KNOW?

The circumference of the Earth is approximately 40,000 km. Since the Earth is spherical in shape, it spans an angle of 360°.

- For 360°, the distance is 40,000 km (Earth's circumference).
- For 1°, the disance is $= \dfrac{40,000}{360} = 111.11$ kms

Thus, 1° on the Earth's surface corresponds to a distance of approximately 111 km.

Some Important Latitudes

(i) The Equator represents 0° latitude.

(ii) **The Tropic of Cancer :** 23½° North latitude in the Northern Hemisphere is called the Tropic of Cancer.

(iii) **The Tropic of Capricorn :** 23½° South latitude in the Southern Hemisphere is called the Tropic of Capricorn.

(iv) **Arctic Circle :** 66½° North latitude in the Northern Hemisphere is known as the Arctic circle.

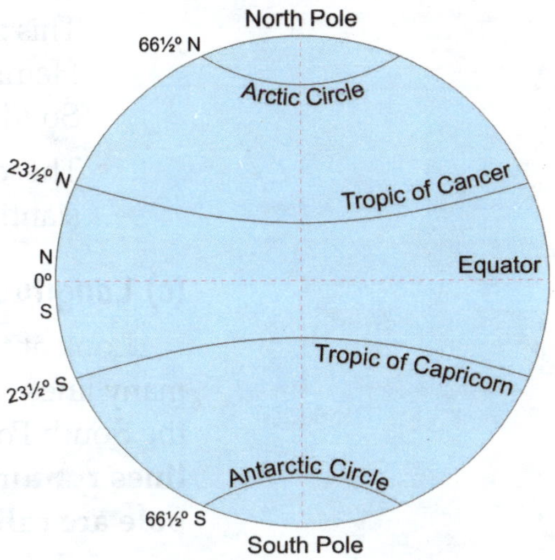

Important Latitudes

MORE TO KNOW

In India, the Tropic of Cancer passes through 8 states, namely Rajasthan, Gujarat, Madhya Pradesh, Chhattisgarh, Jharkhand, West Bengal, Tripura and Mizoram.

(v) **Antarctic Circle :** 66½° South latitude in the Southern Hemisphere is known as the Antarctic circle.

(vi) **North Pole :** 90°N in the Northern Hemisphere is called the North Pole.

(vii) **South Pole :** 90°S in the Southern Hemisphere is known as the South Pole.

Latitudes and Climate

All parts of the Earth do not receive equal amounts of heat from the Sun. Climate changes with change in latitude. The Earth is divided into three heat zones on the basis of heat received from the Sun.

These zones are :

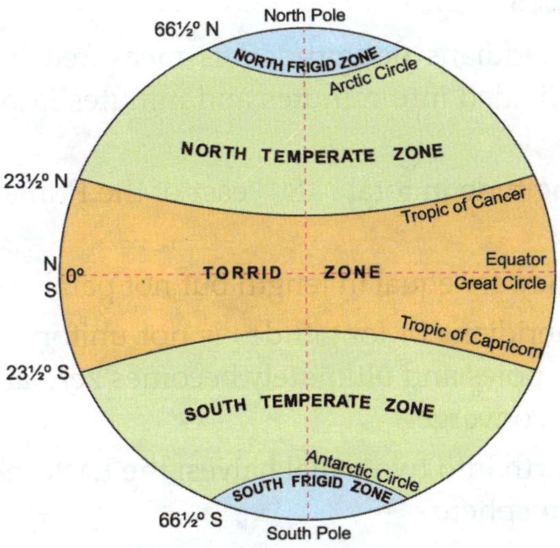

Heat Zones of the Earth

(i) Torrid Zone

- Torrid means hot. It is the hottest region of the Earth.
- It lies between the Tropic of Cancer and Tropic of Capricorn in both the hemispheres.
- The mid-day Sun is exactly overhead at least once a year on all latitudes of this region, so it receives maximum heat.

(ii) Temperate Zone

- It lies between the Tropic of Cancer and Arctic Circle in the Northern Hemisphere and between the Tropic of Capricorn and Antarctic Circle in the Southern Hemisphere.
- These regions have moderate temperatures as they receive slanting rays of Sun throughout the year. This is because the angle of the Sun's rays goes on decreasing towards the poles.

(iii) Frigid Zone

- This zone lies between the Arctic Circle and North Pole in the Northern Hemisphere and between the Antarctic Circle and South Pole in the Southern Hemisphere.
- These are the coldest regions of the Earth's surface as they receive very slanting rays of the Sun.

(c) Longitudes

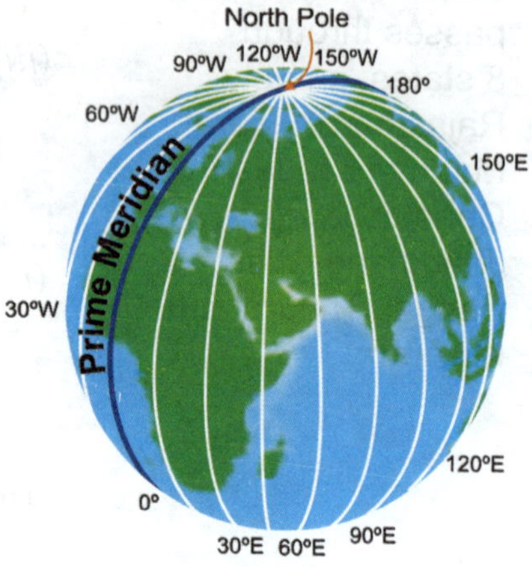

Longitudes

Look at the globe again. You will find many lines running from the North Pole to the South Pole. **The imaginary semi-circular lines running from the north pole to south pole are called the longitudes. These are also called the meridians of longitudes.**

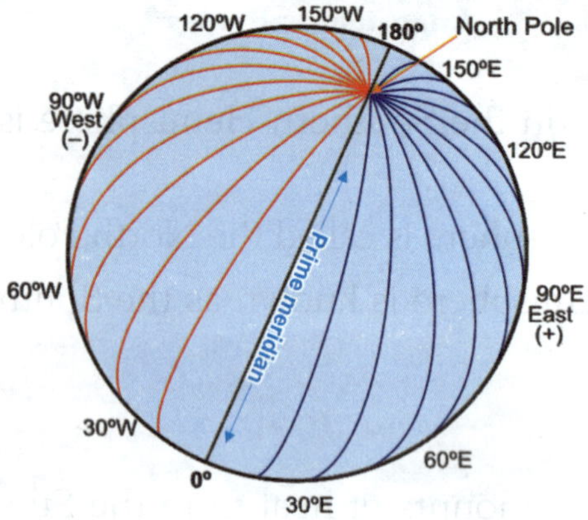

Longitudes with Prime Meridian

Unlike latitudes, all meridians are of equal length. Therefore, any meridian could have been chosen as the starting point for numbering longitudes. In 1884, an international agreement designated the meridian passing through the British Royal Astronomical Observatory at Greenwich, near London, as the starting point. This meridian is known as the Prime Meridian, with a value of 0° longitude. Longitudes are measured 180° eastward and 180° westward from the Prime Meridian.

Some Important Facts about Longitudes

- The distance between any two meridians (longitudes) is measured in degrees. The degrees are further divided into minutes and minutes into seconds.
- There are 360° of meridians of longitude in total : 180° east of the Prime Meridian and 180° west of it.
- The longitudes are semi-circles. They are equal in length but not parallel.
- The distance between any two meridians of longitudes is not uniform. It gradually decreases towards the poles and ultimately becomes zero at the poles, where all the meridians converge.
- The Prime Meridian divides the Earth into two equal halves: the Eastern Hemisphere and the Western Hemisphere.
- The alphabet E is used to indicate the Eastern Longitudes and W is used to show the Western Longitudes.
- The 180° East and the 180° West meridians of longitudes are the same line, forming a single meridian that is directly opposite to the Prime Meridian. It is referred to as the International Date Line.

Map of India with Latitudes and Longitudes

Grid

As we have already studied, the latitude number and the longitude number together make up the Coordinate system of the Earth. They help us in determining the exact location of any place on the Earth.

Now, look at the globe again. You will find various horizontal and vertical blue lines that represent the latitudes and longitudes respectively. The latitudes and longitudes intersect each other on the globe and form a grid system. **The grid lines (latitudes and longitudes) are a set of lines used to find the exact location of a place on a globe or a map.**

UNDERSTANDING TIME ZONES

The Sun is the most reliable time-keeper throughout the world. Time is measured based on the relationship between the Sun and the movement of the Earth. Since the Earth takes 24 hours to complete one full rotation (360°), it rotates through 15° in one hour or 1° in 4 minutes. The Earth rotates from west to east which causes local time to change as we move along the longitudes. For every 15° eastward, local time is advanced by 1 hour and for every 15° westward, local time is retarded by 1 hour. Thus, the places east of the Greenwich Meridian face the Sun earlier and gain time whereas, the places west of the Greenwich Meridian see the Sun later and lose time.

Local time at	Local time at	Local time at
New York is 7:40 am (4 hrs. 56 min. behind)	London (12 noon)	India is 5:30 pm (5 hrs. 30 min. ahead)
Lose time ← going Westwards	0° (Greenwich Meridian)	Gain time → going Eastwards

Local Time

The places situated on the same longitude will have the same time which is called the local time of all those places. Local time can be estimated by the shadow cast by the Sun, which is shortest at noon and longest at sunrise and sunset. *For example,* when the Prime Meridian has the Sun at the highest point in the sky, all the places along this meridian will have mid-day. That is, all the places on a given meridian of longitude have the same local time.

As the Earth keeps rotating, the places at different longitudes have different times. The Earth rotates from west to east. So, the people in the east see the Sun earlier. As the Earth rotates slowly, it takes 4 minutes to pass 1° of meridian.

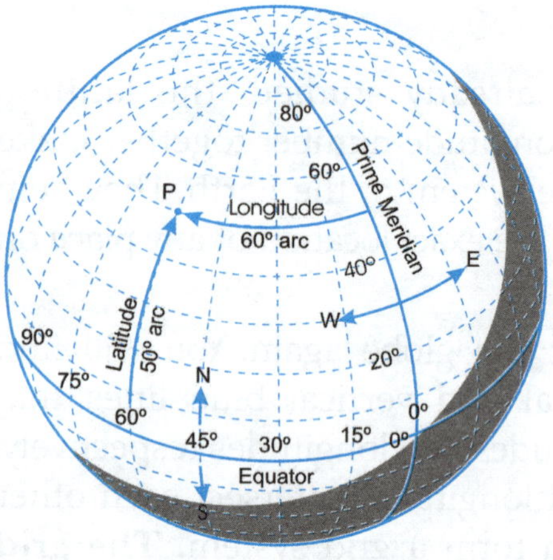

Longitude and Time

The Earth takes 24 hrs to complete one rotation, *i.e.,* 360°.

In 24 hrs the Earth rotates = 360°

$\therefore$ In 1 hr the Earth rotates = $\frac{360°}{24} = 15°$

The Earth rotates 15° in 1 hour (60 min)

$\therefore$ Time taken to pass 1° = $\frac{60°}{15} = 4$ minutes

Thus, the Earth rotates 1° in 4 minutes.

Since, the Earth takes 4 minutes to pass from one meridian to the other, it takes 24 hrs or 1440 minutes to complete one rotation.

Indian Standard Time (IST)

India lies between 68°7′E and 97°25′E longitudes. There are 29 longitudes that lie between the east and the west. We know that time changes with every longitude. If we calculate time from the Prime Meridian, then India would have 29 different timings. This would lead to utter confusion and chaos. To avoid this, it was necessary to adopt the local time of some central meridian of the country as the standard time for the whole country.

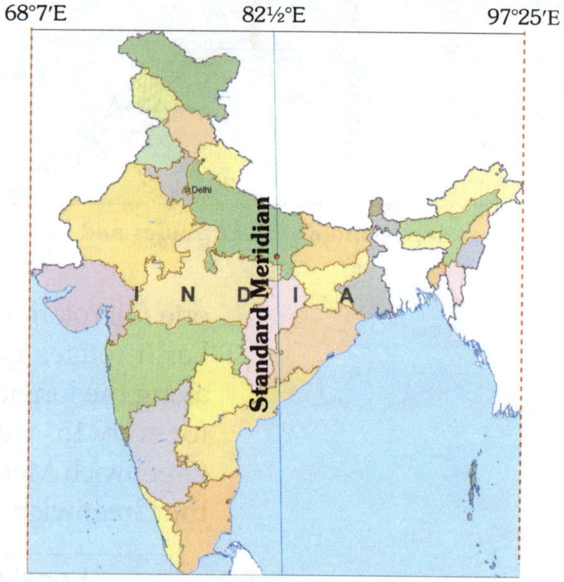

Indian Standard Meridian

MORE TO KNOW

What do you mean by A.M. and P.M. ?

A.M. stands for ante-meridian. Ante-meridian means before noon. Ante means before and meridian means Sun's position at noon.

Thus, the time after midnight and before noon is followed by A.M. *For example,* 6 O'clock in the morning is also written as 6 A.M.

P.M. stands for post meridian *i.e.,* after mid-day or noon.

Thus, the time after noon and before midnight is followed by P.M. *For example,* 5 O'clock in the evening is expressed as 5 P.M.

DO YOU KNOW?

It is 5:30 p.m. in India when it is 12:00 noon in London. This is because, Indian Standard Time is the local time of 82°30′E longitude. This longitude lies to the east of Greenwich (London) and the time here is 5 hours and 30 minutes ahead of Greenwich Mean Time (GMT).

The longitude of 82½°E or 82°30′E, passing through Mirzapur near Prayagraj (formerly Allahabad), is taken as the Standard Meridian, and the local time that prevails on that longitude is taken as the standard time for the whole country. This is called Indian Standard Time or IST.

Time Zones Around the World

Like India, most countries of the world adopt their standard time from the central meridian of their countries. For this, the whole world is divided into 24 standard time zones, each of which differs from the next by 15° in longitude or one hour in time. Time zones are regions of the Earth that have the same standard time. They help us to keep track of time in different places around the world. Each time zone represents 1 hour of the Earth's 24-hour day. The starting point for fixing time zones is the Prime Meridian. The time at the Prime Meridian is called the Greenwich Mean Time (GMT).

As, we travel East from the Prime Meridian, time increases. For every 15° longitude we move eastwards, we add one hour to the time. The Earth rotates 360° in 24 hours, so each 15° represents one hour. *For example,* if it is 12:00 noon at the Prime Meridian, it will be 1:00 PM at 15°E, 2:00 PM at 30°E and so on.

Time Zones of the World

On the other hand, as we move west from the Prime Meridian, time decreases. For every 15° longitude we move westwards, we subtract one hour from the time. *For example,* if it is 12:00 noon at the Prime Meridian, it will be 11:00 AM at 15°W, 10:00 AM at 30°W and so on.

Time zones help us know the time in any part of the world. This is important for travel, business and communication.

If you look at the world map, you will see that the lines dividing the time zones are not fully straight. This is because time zone boundaries often follow national or regional borders. Each country or region chooses it's own time zone to suit local needs. Time zone boundaries may also be adjusted to fit within certain political or administrative regions or to include major cities within a single time zone for convenience.

However, large countries like the USA, Canada and Russia, which have a great east-west stretch, have to adopt several time zones. Russia extends through almost 165° of longitude and is divided into 11 time zones. That is, in Russia there are 11 standard times. Both Canada and the USA have six time zones.

The line exactly opposite the Prime Meridian, at approximately 180° longitude is called the **International Date Line (IDL)**. The +12 and the –12 time zones touch each other at this line.

When we cross the International Date Line either by a ship or plane, the date changes. If we cross it from west to east, we go back one day. *For example,* date changes from Sunday to Saturday. But, if we cross it from east to west, we go forward one day *i.e.,* from Sunday to Monday. The International Date Line is also deviated at places to avoid dividing some countries into two different days.

By now, you must have understood how people in different places in the world experience the same moment of time differently based on their location with respect to the Prime Meridian.

Check Your Progress

Understanding

1. (*a*) 0° latitude represents the ____________.
   (*b*) The Earth takes ____________ to complete one rotation.
   (*c*) The hottest region of the Earth is the ____________ zone.
2. Take a map of India and show $82\frac{1}{2}°$ E longitude on it.
3. Calculate the local time of London when it is 5:30 pm in India.
4. Find out the latitudinal and longitudinal values of Delhi, Mumbai and USA.

NEW WORDS

- **Globe :** A three-dimensional true model of the Earth.
- **Map :** Representation of the Earth on a flat surface using a scale.
- **Scale :** Scale is a ratio between a unit distance on a map to a proportionate distance on the ground.
- **Direction :** A course along which someone or something moves.
- **Intermediate directions :** Directions that lie between two cardinal directions.
- **Indian Standard Meridian :** 82°30′ East longitude passing through Mirzapur near Prayagraj (formerly Allahabad) is considered as the Indian Standard Meridian.
- **Equator :** The imaginary line that divides the Earth into two equal halves.
- **Latitudes :** A latitude is the angular distance of a point on the Earth's surface measured in degrees from the Equator.
- **Longitudes :** Longitudes are imaginary semi-circular lines running from the North to the South Poles.
- **Grid :** A set of horizontal lines (Parallels of Latitude) and vertical lines (Meridians of Longitude).

NUTSHELL

- Map is a representation of the Earth on a flat surface or on a piece of paper with the help of a scale.
- Types of Maps : (*a*) Physical map (*b*) Political map (*c*) Thematic map.
- Components of Maps : (*a*) Title (*b*) Scale (*c*) Direction (*d*) Conventional symbols.
- A latitude is the angular distance of a point on the Earth's surface measured in degrees from an imaginary line named the equator which lies midway between the poles.
- The Equator is an imaginary line that divides the Earth into two equal halves, the Northern Hemisphere and the Southern Hemisphere. It represents 0° latitude.
- The imaginary semi-circular lines running from the north pole to the south pole are known as the longitudes.
- The Prime Meridian passes through the British Royal Astronomical Observatory at Greenwich, near London. Its value is 0° longitude and it divides the Earth into the Eastern Hemisphere and the Western Hemisphere.
- There are 360° of meridians of longitude in total, 180° east of the Prime Meridian and 180° west of it.
- The grid lines (latitudes and longitudes) are a set of lines used to find the exact location of a place on a globe or a map.
- The places situated on the same longitude have the same time which is called the Local Time of those places.
- The Indian Standard Meridian passes through 82°30′ E. Time for the whole of India is calculated by this meridian. It passes through Mirzapur near Prayagraj (formerly Allahabad).
- The whole world is divided into 24 standard time zones, each of which differs from the next by 15° in longitude or one hour in time.
- On moving towards East from the Prime Meridian, we gain time while on moving towards the West, we lose time.
- The line exactly opposite the Prime Meridian, at approximately 180° longitude is called the International Date Line (IDL).

IMPORTANT NCERT TEXTBOOK QUESTIONS (Solved)

Questions, activities and projects

1. Returning to page 10 and to Fig. 5.2 in Chapter 5 of this textbook, taking the scale to be 2.5 cm = 500 km, calculate the real distance from the estuary of the Narmada River to the estuary of the Ganga river. (*Hint : round off your measurement on the map to an easy number.*)

Ans. Suppose on the map, the distance from the estuary of the Narmada River to the estuary of the Ganga river is 10 cm.

Then, 2.5 cm = 500 km

∴ 10 cm = 10/2.5 × 500 = 2000 km.

Fig. 5.2. A physical map of the Indian Continent with some of it rivers

2. Why is it 5:30 pm in India when it is 12 pm or noon in London ?

Ans. London is located on the Prime Meridian (0° longitude) while India is located east of the Prime Meridian, at a longitude of 82.5° E. Thus, there is a difference of 82.5° between the Longitude of London and the Standard Meridian of India.

The Indian Standard Time (IST) is 5 hours and 30 minutes ahead of the local time at Greenwich (GMT).

In 24 hrs, the Earth rotates = 360°

∴ In 1 hr, the Earth rotates = 360°/24 = 15°

The Earth rotates 15° in 1 hour (60 min.)

∴ Time taken to pass 1° = 60°/15 = 4 minutes

∴ Time taken to pass 82.5° = 82.5° × 4 = 330 minutes or 5 hours 30 minutes.

3. Why do we need symbols and colours in the map ?

Ans. By using symbols, numerous details can be shown in the limited space available on a map. It makes it easy for the users to understand the map and the various features shown on the map like different kinds of buildings (post office, school, hospital, etc.), roads, railway lines and natural elements like river, pond or forest.

Colours help us to differentiate between different types of landforms as different colours are used on the map for different landforms like blue for water, brown for mountains, green for forests, etc. This makes it easier for us to understand the map more clearly and precisely.

4. Find out what you have in the eight directions from your home or school.

Ans. Students will do themselves.

5. What is the difference between local time and standard time ? Discuss it in groups, with each group writing an answer in 100 to 150 words. Compare the answers.

Ans. Local time is the time based on the position of the Sun in a specific location. It varies from place to place even within the same time zone, depending on the longitude and movement of the Sun across the sky. Different longitudes have different local time.

Standard time on the other hand, is a uniform time set for a region or a country based on the local time of a particular meridian passing through that region or country. It remains constant across a time zone and does not vary with longitudes. It is created to facilitate travel, communication and business across different regions.

6. Delhi's and Bengaluru's latitudes are 29°N and 13°N; their longitudes are almost the same, 77°E. How much will be the difference in local time between the two cities ?

Ans. As Delhi and Bengaluru have almost the same longitude, there will be no difference in their local time as local time depends on longitude and not latitude. Latitude affects the climate and length of daylight hours but does not affect the local time of a region.

7. Mark the following statements as true or false; explain your answers with a sentence or two.

Ans. → **All parallels of latitude have the same length.—False**

The length of latitudes decreases as we go from the equator towards the poles.

→ **The length of a meridian of longitude is half of that of the Equator.—True**

The length of a meridian of longitude is equal to half the length of the Equator as a meridian of longitude is a half circle while equator is a full circle.

→ **The South Pole has a latitude of 90°S.—True**

The South pole is the southernmost point on Earth situated at 90°S.

→ **In Assam, the local time and the IST are identical.—False**

The IST for India is calculated from 82½°E, while Assam lies further east of 82½°E. As the local time changes by 4 minutes every 1°, therefore, the local time of Assam and IST cannot be identical.

→ **Lines separating the time zones are identical with meridians of longitude.—False**

The lines dividing the time zones are not fully straight or identical with meridians of longitude. This is because they have to respect each country's standard time and, therefore, tend to follow international borders.

→ **The Equator is also a parallel of latitude.—True**

The equator is the most important parallel of Latitude situated at 0° that divides the Earth into the Northern Hemisphere and the Southern Hemisphere.

8. Solve the crossword below.

Across

1. Lets you squeeze a huge area into your map
4. A convenient sphere
5. The longest parallel of latitude
6. The place the Prime Meridian is attached to
8. So convenient to find your way
10. A measure of the distance from the Equator

Down

2. A measure of the distance from the Prime Meridian
3. These two together allow us to locate a place
6. What latitudes and longitudes together create
7. The time we all follow in India
9. These two are poles apart
11. An abbreviation for a line across which the day and date change

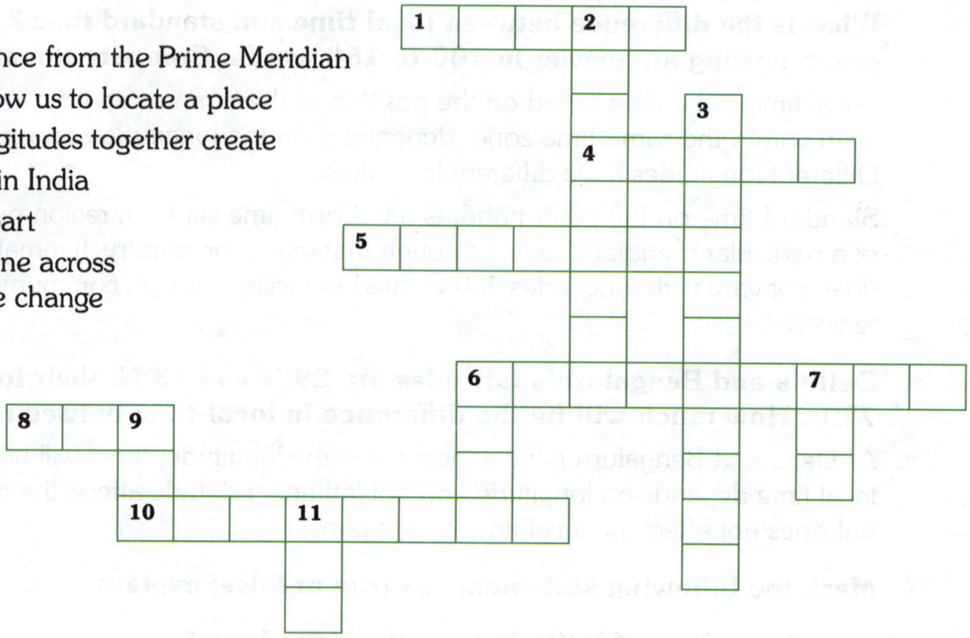

Ans.

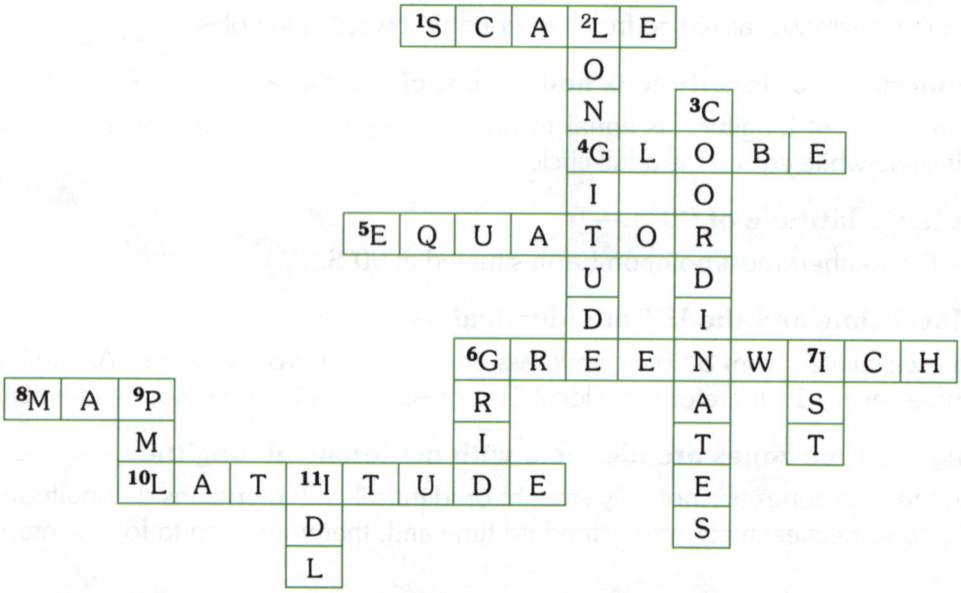

I. OBJECTIVE TYPE QUESTIONS

A. Choose the correct answer.

Conceptual Learning | Critical Thinking

1. *Which of the following maps shows countries, states, districts, etc. ?*
   (*a*) Physical Map (*b*) Political Map (*c*) Thematic Map (*d*) Sketch
2. *Directions that lie between two cardinal points are called* ________ *directions.*
   (*a*) cardinal directions (*b*) ordinal directions
   (*c*) intermediate directions (*d*) main directions

3. *The distance of Place A and Place B is 1000 km on the ground. But it is shown as 1 cm on the map. It means 7500 km of distance on the ground is equal to ________ cm of distance on the map.*
(*a*) 75 (*b*) 750 (*c*) 0.75 (*d*) 7.5

4. *Which one of the following items is a true model of the Earth ?*
(*a*) Map (*b*) Globe (*c*) Apple (*d*) Ball

5. *Net of latitudes and longitudes is also known as a*
(*a*) Grid (*b*) Sketch (*c*) Plan (*d*) None of these

6. *The Antarctic circle is located in the*
(*a*) Northern Hemisphere (*b*) Southern Hemisphere
(*c*) Eastern Hemisphere (*d*) Western Hemisphere

7. *Which of the following statements is false about the longitudes ?*
(*a*) These are semi-circular lines.
(*b*) The Greenwich Meridian is the most significant longitude.
(*c*) There are 180° of longitudes.
(*d*) All the longitudes converge at the North and the South Pole.

8. *How much time does the Earth take to pass one longitude ?*
(*a*) 4 minutes (*b*) 6 minutes (*c*) 7 minutes (*d*) 10 minutes

9. *Which of the following is called the Indian Standard Meridian ?*
(*a*) 23½°N (*b*) 66½°S (*c*) 66½°E (*d*) 82½°E

10. *Russia has ________ time zones.*
(*a*) 5 (*b*) 7 (*c*) 8 (*d*) 11

B. Mark the option that matches Column A with Column B.

Conceptual Learning | Problem Solving

Column A	Column B
1. Antarctic Circle	(*i*) 0° latitude
2. South Pole	(*ii*) 23½°N
3. Equator	(*iii*) 66½°S
4. Arctic Circle	(*iv*) 90°S
5. Tropic of Cancer	(*v*) 66½°N

(*a*) **1.**-(*iii*), **2.**-(*i*), **3.**-(*iv*), **4.**-(*v*), **5.**-(*ii*)
(*b*) **1.**-(*iii*), **2.**-(*iv*), **3.**-(*i*), **4.**-(*v*), **5.**-(*ii*)
(*c*) **1.**-(*v*), **2.**-(*i*), **3.**-(*iv*), **4.**-(*iii*), **5.**-(*ii*)
(*d*) **1.**-(*iii*), **2.**-(*iv*), **3.**-(*i*), **4.**-(*ii*), **5.**-(*v*)

C. State True or False

Knowledge Application

1. The globe is a flat representation of the Earth.
2. 66½°N latitude is also known as the Arctic circle.
3. The Greenwich Meridian is the 0° longitude.
4. Map is a true model of the Earth.
5. Yellow colour is used to show a settlement on the map.

D. Fill in the blanks with appropriate answers.

Knowledge Application | Critical Thinking

1.

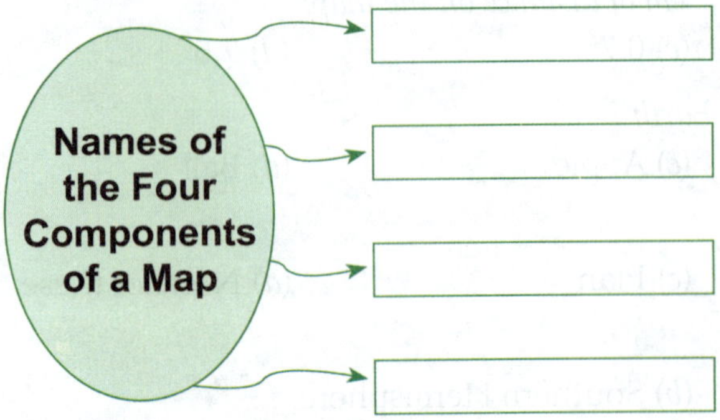

2.

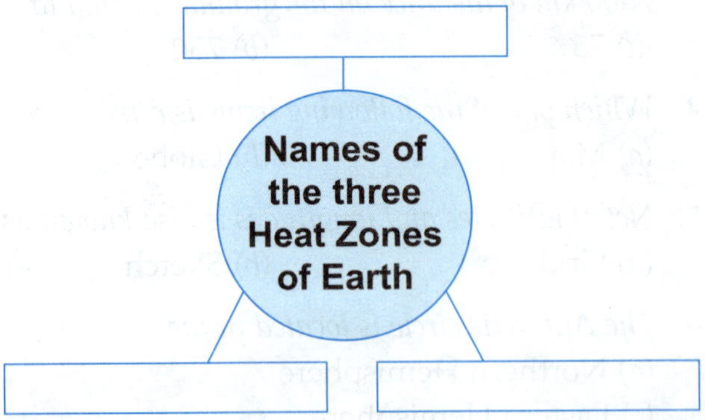

E. Assertion-Reason

Critical Thinking

For question numbers 1 to 4, two statements are given—one labelled Assertion (A) and the other labelled Reason (R). Select the correct answer to these questions from the codes (*a*), (*b*), (*c*) and (*d*) as given below :

(*a*) Both Assertion (A) and Reason (R) are true and Reason is the correct explanation of the Assertion.

(*b*) Both Assertion (A) and Reason (R) are true but Reason is not the correct explanation of the Assertion.

(*c*) Assertion (A) is true but Reason (R) is false.

(*d*) Assertion (A) is false but Reason (R) is true.

1. **Assertion (A)** : The globe is a three-dimensional true model of the Earth.
   Reason (R) : Map is a conversion of three-dimensional features of the Earth into two-dimensional showcases of the Earth.
2. **Assertion (A)** : North, South, East and West are the cardinal directions.
   Reason (R) : These are also called the four cardinal points of the compass.
3. **Assertion (A)** : Some countries have several time zones.
   Reason (R) : This is because their east-west stretch is very large.
4. **Assertion (A)** : The globe does not contain a grid.
   Reason (R) : Grid lines are used to find the exact location of a place.

II. SHORT ANSWER TYPE QUESTIONS

Conceptual Learning | Knowledge Application

1. What are the important components of a map ? Name the various types of maps.
2. Why are Conventional symbols called map keys ?
3. Write a note on the Greenwich Meridian.
4. What is IST ? Why have we taken one time zone for the whole of India ?
5. Write any two features of latitudes.

III. LONG ANSWER TYPE QUESTIONS

Knowledge Application | Critical Thinking

1. Explain the different types of maps.
2. Why are the conventional symbols important for a map ? Discuss the significance of a map.
3. Differentiate between the Torrid and Frigid zones.
4. Why is there a time difference of about 5 hours between India and London ?

IV. PICTURE STUDY

Conceptual Learning

Name the important latitudes marked as A, B and C. Also, write the degrees at which they are located.

1. Latitude A : ______________
   at (degree) : ______________
2. Latitude B : ______________
   at (degree) : ______________
3. Heat zone C : ______________
   at (degree) : ______________

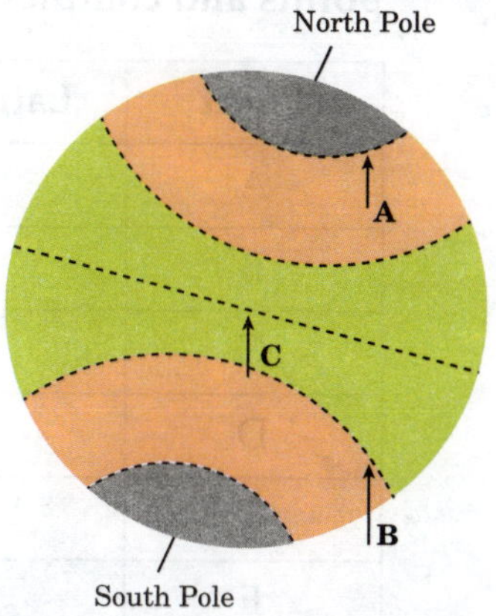

V. SOURCE BASED QUESTIONS

Conceptual Learning | Critical Thinking

Read the given paragraph and answer the following questions.

A map is a representation or a drawing of the Earth's surface or a part of it drawn on a flat surface according to a scale. Maps showing natural features of the Earth such as mountains, plateaus, plains, rivers, oceans, etc. are called (**X**) or relief maps. Maps showing cities, towns, states and countries of the world with their boundaries are called (**Y**) maps. Some maps focus on specific information, such as road maps, rainfall maps, maps showing distribution of forests, industries, etc. are known as thematic maps.

1. *Which of the following natural features a physical map does not show ?*
   (*a*) Mountains and Valleys (*b*) Plateaus and Plains
   (*c*) Rivers and Oceans (*d*) Rainfall and Climate
2. *The ratio between the actual distance on the ground and the distance shown on the map is termed as*
   (*a*) distance (*b*) direction (*c*) scale (*d*) dimension
3. *Which option correctly replaces X and Y in the paragraph ?*
   (*a*) X = Physical, Y = Thematic (*b*) X = Thematic, Y = Physical
   (*c*) X = Political, Y = Thematic (*d*) X = Physical, Y = Political
4. *A thematic map focuses on*
   (*a*) cities, towns, states and countries of the world with their boundaries.
   (*b*) roads, rainfall, distribution of forests, industries, etc.
   (*c*) mountains, plateaus, valleys, plains, rivers, oceans, etc.
   (*d*) all of these.

VI. ANALYSING INFORMATION

Problem Solving | Conceptual Learning

1. **Indian Standard Time (IST) is 5½ hours (5:30 Hours) ahead of time in London or Greenwich Mean Time (GMT)—Keeping this in mind, calculate the following time to complete the table given below.**

GMT	Time in India	IST	Time in London
8 AM		1.30 PM	
11.30 AM		5.30 PM	
6 PM		6 AM	

2. **Carefully observe the grid given on the right. Find out the latitude and longitude of the following points and complete the table.**

Point	Latitude	Longitude
A		
B		
C		
D		
E		
F		
G		
H		
I		
J		

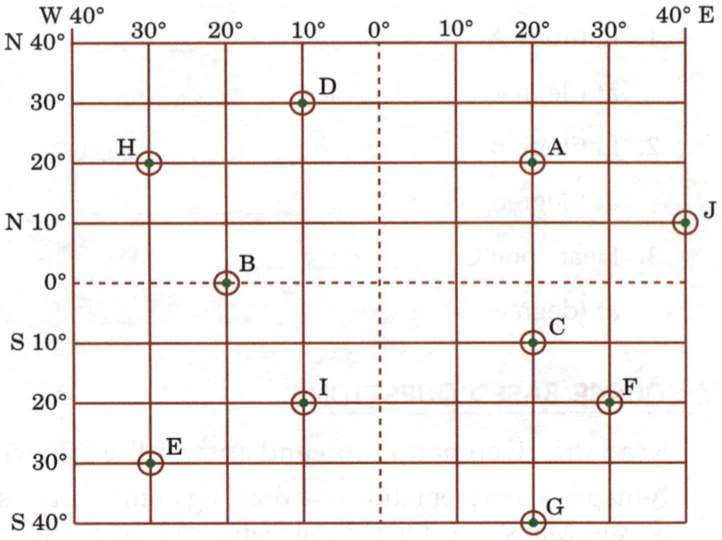

VII. PROJECT WORK

Experiential Learning | Creativity and Innovation

1. Draw the following conventional symbols :
   (*a*) Temple (*b*) International boundary (*c*) Lighthouse
   (*d*) Pack track (*e*) Post office (*f*) Fort
2. On an A-3 size sheet of paper, create a sketch of your school or locality using a scale, symbols and directions. Show it to your teacher and friends.

VIII. GLOBE READING

Multidisciplinary Approach | Experiential Learning | Collaboration

Identify the following with the help of a globe.

1. Equator, Tropic of Cancer, Tropic of Capricorn, Arctic Circle, Antarctic Circle, North Pole and South Pole.
2. Torrid Zone.
3. The longitudinal and latitudinal extent of your state.
4. The countries that together make the Indian subcontinent.
5. The northernmost latitude in degrees.
6. The southernmost latitude of the Indian mainland in degrees.
7. The states through which the Tropic of Cancer passes.
8. The place situated on the three seas.

WEB LINK

Digital Literacy

For further information log on to the following link :

- ***http://www.mapsofworld.com/Lat_Long/india_Lat_Long.html***

CHAPTER 2

Oceans and Continents

CG-1 : C-1.2; CG-6 : C-6.1, C-6.2

What's new to learn

- **The Distribution of Water and Land on the Earth**
- **Oceans**
- **Continents**

A little girl named Medha was very fond of adventures and travelling. She loved visiting and exploring different places. Her summer vacations were about to start and she began dreaming of visiting new places. She took out her globe and began watching it carefully. Soon, she started dreaming of flying over the vast Pacific Ocean. In the ocean, she saw dolphins jumping and colourful fish swimming. After some days, she landed on the shores of Asia where she saw tall mountains and vast plains. Next, she found herself in Africa where she saw lions on the shore and tall giraffes eating from trees. Next, her dreams carried her to South America where she saw rainforests and tall waterfalls. From there, she went to the cold waters of the Southern Ocean where she saw penguins and icebergs before reaching Antarctica. Finally, her dreams carried her to Australia, where she saw kangaroos hopping on the shore. In excitement, she started clapping and screaming with joy, when suddenly her eyes opened and she found her mother waking her up. She told her mother about her fascinating dream and her mother promised to take her to a new and exciting place during her vacations.

Like Medha, let us also now, dive into the world of oceans and continents.

THE DISTRIBUTION OF WATER AND LAND ON THE EARTH

Water is an essential resource of our life. We cannot think of our life without water. More than 71% of the Earth's surface is covered with water and only 29% is covered with land. Due to the presence of water, the Earth is often called the Water Planet or the Blue Planet. The Earth appears blue from space because of the presence of a large number of water bodies on it. Water bodies are the natural structures that contain water. All the water present on the Earth is found in oceans, seas, lakes, rivers, ponds, etc. These water bodies collectively form the hydrosphere. Water is a renewable resource.

Out of the total amount of water available on Earth, 97.3% is in the oceans. It is very salty and not fit for human use. About 2.68% of total water is in the form of ice-sheets, glaciers and underground water. Only 0.03% is available as fresh water for human use. That is why, despite being a Blue Planet, we face shortage of water.

DO YOU KNOW?

The amount of water present in different water bodies varies in terms of their volume. The table shows the distribution of water on the Earth's surface.

Water Bodies	Volume of Water (%)
Oceans	97.3
Ice caps	2.0
Groundwater	0.68
Fresh Water Lakes and Inland	0.009
Salt Lakes	0.009
Atmosphere	0.009
Rivers	0.0001
Total	**100.00**

OCEANS

Vast stretches of water are known as oceans. They form the major part of the hydrosphere or the part of the Earth covered with water. The average depth of oceans is about 4 km. The ocean water is not static. It keeps moving all the time. If you look at the world map, you will find that all the oceans are interconnected with one another. So, the surface of the ocean water level remains the same everywhere. This water level is taken as zero. Due to this equal level of water, the elevation of land is measured from the sea level. Ocean currents, waves and tides are the three movements of ocean water.

There are five major oceans in the world.

These are :

1. Pacific Ocean
2. Atlantic Ocean
3. Indian Ocean
4. Arctic Ocean
5. Southern/Antarctic Ocean

Ocean

Some Facts about Oceans

- The Pacific Ocean is the largest and deepest ocean in the world. It covers almost one-third area of the Earth. Mariana Trench (11,022 m), the deepest part of the Earth, lies in this ocean.
- The Atlantic Ocean is 'S' shaped. It is the second largest ocean and has a very long and indented coastline that provides a good location for sheltered harbours and ports. This coastline is the busiest trade and commerce route of the world
- The Indian Ocean is the third largest and is the only ocean in the world named after a country, India. This ocean is almost triangular in shape.

MORE TO KNOW

There are more mountains under the ocean than on land. These underwater mountains are called seamounts. The Mid-Ocean Ridge is the longest mountain range on Earth. It stretches over 65,000 kilometers (40,000 miles) and is mostly underwater.

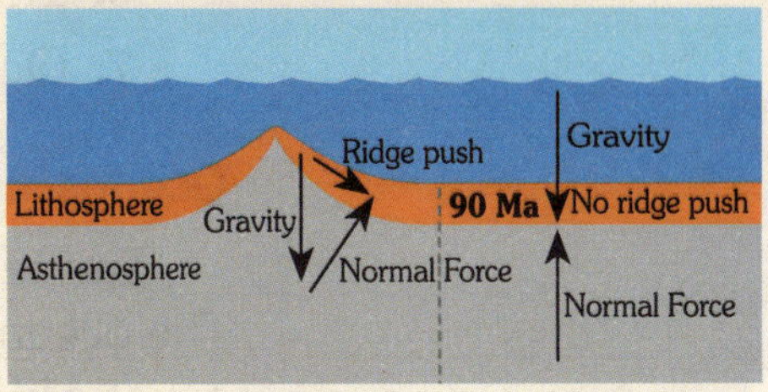

Mid-ocean ridge

- The Antarctic/Southern Ocean is the fourth largest ocean and has its northern limit with three oceans, *i.e.*, Indian Ocean, Atlantic Ocean and the Pacific Ocean.
- The Arctic Ocean is the smallest and connected to the Pacific Ocean by a narrow stretch of shallow water known as the Bering Strait. The Arctic Ocean surrounds the North Pole.

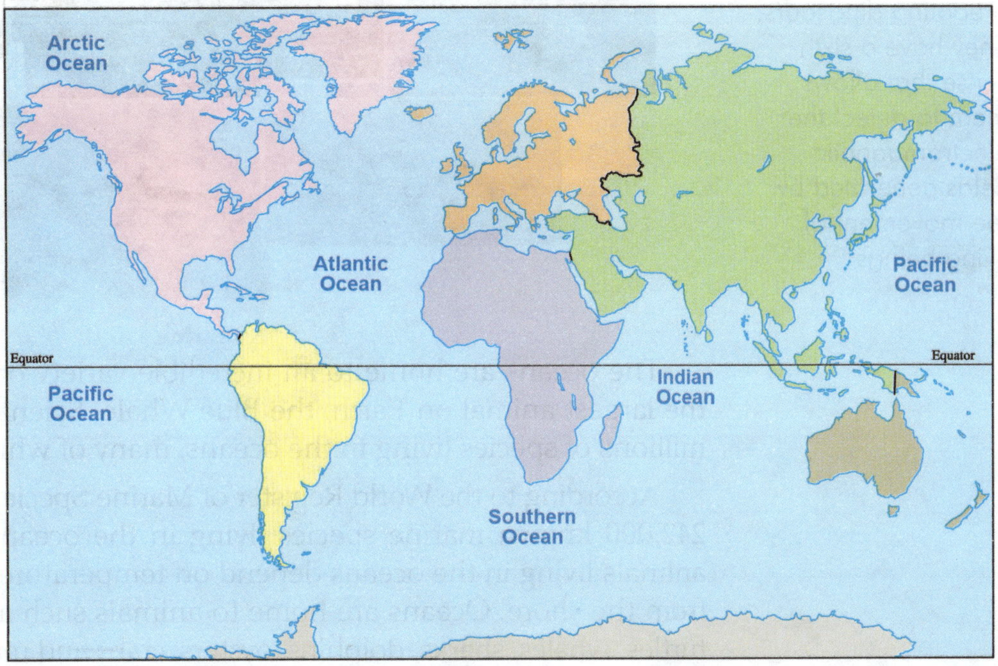

World : Oceans

Importance of Oceans

1. Oceans are the main source of moisture and water vapour in the atmosphere.
2. Oceans absorb heat from the Sun and distribute it around the globe through currents. This helps to regulate the climate of the Earth.
3. Oceans absorb a large amount of carbon dioxide from the atmosphere and thus, help to reduce the effects of global warming.
4. Oceans separate and connect one continent to another. Thus, they provide the cheapest means of transport.
5. Oceans act as the highways for trade and transport.
6. They provide shelter for marine flora and fauna.
7. Ocean water can be used to generate hydro-electricity.

Oceans and Life

The term marine comes from the Latin "mare", meaning "sea" or "ocean". The oceans have plenty of dissolved atmospheric gases, which are essential for aquatic life.

DO YOU KNOW?

Sharks have been around for over 400 million years, predating dinosaurs. They have a sixth sense that allows them to detect the electromagnetic fields generated by the movement of living beings.

Marine Life

The oceans are home to an incredible variety of life, from tiny plankton to the largest animal on Earth, the Blue Whale. Scientists estimate that there are millions of species living in the oceans, many of which are still undiscovered.

According to the World Register of Marine Species (WoRMS), there are about 242,000 known marine species living in the oceans. The types of plants and animals living in the oceans depend on temperature, ocean depth and distance from the shore. Oceans are home to animals such as seahorses, clownfish, sea turtles, whales, sharks, dolphins, oysters, crabs and many species of birds. Marine flora mainly include blue, green, red and brown algae, seaweeds and seagrass.

Oceans and Disasters

Disaster is a natural or man-made event which results in great damage or loss of life. The oceanic floor is constantly moving. The constant movement of tectonic plates sometimes leads to powerful and devastating natural disasters.

A Tsunami

The main types of ocean disasters are :

- **Tsunamis :** Tsunamis are large, powerful ocean waves usually caused by underwater earthquakes, volcanic eruptions, lava entering the sea or underwater landslides. When the seafloor suddenly moves, it displaces a huge volume of water, creating waves that can travel at speeds of up to 500 miles per hour. Tsunamis often grow to enormous heights and cause widespread floods and destruction.

A Hurricane

- **Hurricanes :** These are powerful storms driven by heat and moisture from the ocean. They occur over warm ocean waters and bring heavy rains, strong winds and storm surges that can cause severe damage to coastal areas. The storm surges lead to a rise in sea level and cause extensive floods.

Marine Pollution

- **Marine Pollution :** The pollution from land including plastics, chemicals and sewage that goes into the oceans harms wildlife, contaminates seafood and disrupts marine ecosystems.

Climate Change and Rising Sea Levels

- **Climate Change and Rising Sea Levels :** Human activities like burning fossil fuels, cutting down forests, etc. lead to global warming. This in turn, causes polar ice to melt and seawater to expand. The rise in sea levels leads to floods and soil erosion.

MORE TO KNOW

Some Famous Ocean Disasters

- One of the most devastating tsunamis in recent history was the 2004 Indian Ocean tsunami, caused by a massive undersea earthquake off the coast of Sumatra, Indonesia which killed over 230,000 people across 14 countries. Indonesia, Sri Lanka, India and Thailand were the hardest hit nations. Indira Point, the southernmost point of India got submerged under the sea in this Tsunami.
- Hurricane Katrina struck the Gulf Coast in 2005 and caused over 1,800 deaths and more than $125 billion in damage. There were massive floods and a need for disaster management was severely felt.

MORE TO KNOW

Disaster Management

- Disaster management comprises disaster prevention, mitigation measures, response and recovery from the dangerous situations. All of these aspects of disaster management depend on the nature of the hazard and the vulnerability of the community.

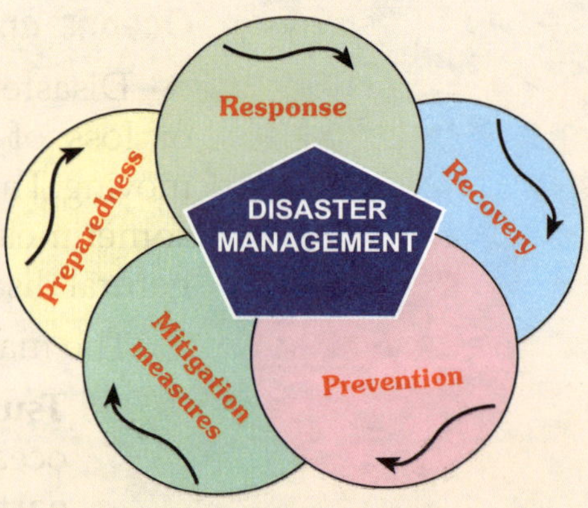

Disaster Management

Disaster Management Team of Government in Action

- The Government of India has enacted and notified the Disaster Management Act on December 26, 2005.
- The National Institute of Disaster Management (NIDM), Delhi is responsible for the training of Government officers, police, people's representatives and various development agencies.

Check Your Progress

Understanding

1. The Earth is called a water planet because ______________.
2. Water is a ______________ resource.
3. Oceans contain ______________ % of water present on the Earth's surface.
4. ______________ is the largest ocean in the world.
5. The Atlantic Ocean roughly resembles ______________ in shape.
6. The Indian Ocean is named after ______________.
7. The North Pole is surrounded by ______________.
8. ______________ is the busiest ocean route for trade and commerce.
9. The Disaster Management Act was notified on ______________.
10. NIDM refers to ______________.

Think & Answer

Discuss the usefulness of the hydrosphere in your life. Make a list of its uses and discuss them with your classmates and teachers. Also discuss small steps you can take to preserve water.

CONTINENTS

Continents are defined as the huge land masses that rise above the sea level. These were formed over millions of years, through the movement of tectonic plates. The outer part of the Earth is made up of tectonic plates that are always moving. The continents of the Earth once formed a single, giant landmass, called the Pangaea. Because of the movement of tectonic plates, the Pangaea slowly broke apart and the continents were formed. The continents are separated from one another by huge water bodies.

There are seven continents on the Earth namely—Asia, Africa, North America, South America, Antarctica, Europe and Australia. If you see the world map, you will find that the northern hemisphere has a greater part of the land mass. Asia, Europe and North America lie entirely in the Northern Hemisphere while Australia and Antarctica lie entirely in the Southern Hemisphere. The Northern Hemisphere is also called the Land Hemisphere.

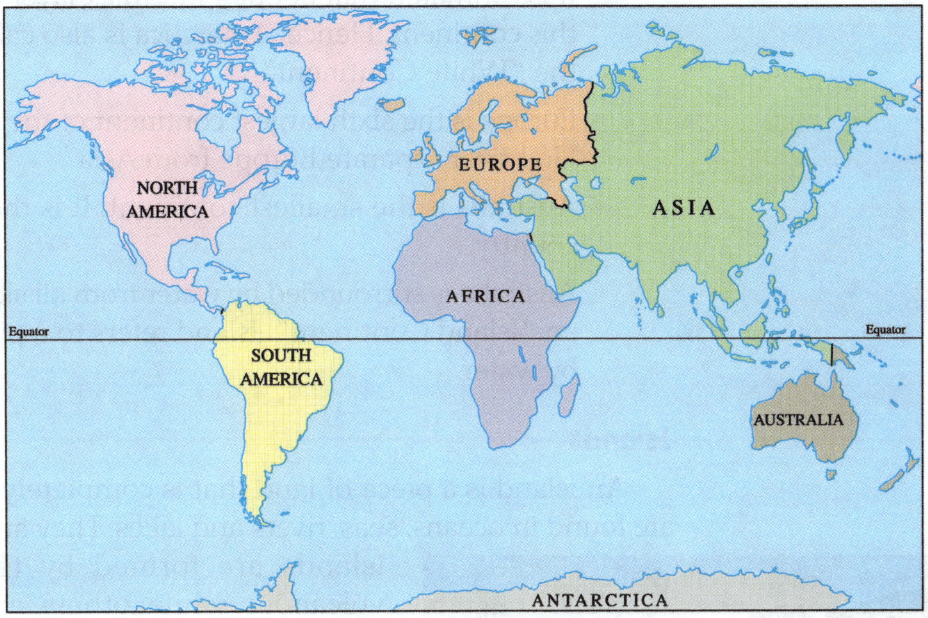

Seven Continents on the Earth

Some Facts about Continents

- Asia is the largest continent. It is home to half of the world's population and covers about 1/3rd of the total land area of the Earth's surface.
- On the western side of Asia are the Ural mountains and the Ural river. Both of these are considered as the natural boundary between Asia and Europe. The combined landmass of Europe and Asia is called Eurasia.
- Africa is the second largest continent of the world. It is also known as the "Dark Continent" because a greater part of this continent remained little known to the outside world until the last century.
- Africa is the only continent in the world that expands in all hemispheres *i.e.,* North, South, East and West Hemispheres.
- It is the only continent through which the Equator (0°N–S), Tropic of Cancer (23½°N), Tropic of Capricorn (23½°S) and the Greenwich Meridian pass.
- Africa is home to the world's longest river, the Nile, and the world's largest desert, the Sahara. The Sahara is the hottest and the driest desert in the world.
- North America is the third largest continent of the world. It is connected with South America by a narrow stretch of land called the Isthmus of Panama. Isthmus is a narrow strip of land connecting two large land masses.

MORE TO KNOW

India and many other countries have set up their research centres in Antarctica. Maitri and Dakshin Gangotri are the main research stations of India set up there.

- South America is the fourth largest continent and roughly triangular in shape. It is home to the world's largest river, the Amazon.
- Antarctica is the fifth largest continent of the world. It is the only uninhabited continent in the world. There is no permanent human settlement in Antarctica.
- It is estimated that about 4 km thick layer of ice is found permanently in this continent. Hence, Antarctica is also called the "Frozen Continent" or the "White Continent".
- Europe is the sixth largest continent of the world. The Ural mountain and Ural river separate Europe from Asia.
- Australia is the smallest continent. It is the only continent that is also a country.
- Australia is surrounded by water from all sides. That is why it is also called an "Island Continent". Island refers to a piece of land that is surrounded by water.

Islands

An island is a piece of land that is completely surrounded by water. Islands are found in oceans, seas, rivers and lakes. They are formed in many ways. Some islands are formed by the eruption of underwater volcanoes while others are formed by movement of tectonic plates. The accumulation of coral skeletons and other organic material can also form islands. Islands provide resources like fish, timber and fertile land for agriculture. They are also popular tourist destinations due to their beautiful landscapes, beaches and wildlife.

The Andaman Island

India has more than 1300 islands. Lakshadweep and Andaman and Nicobar are the main island groups of India. The Lakshadweep Islands are situated in the Arabian Sea. They are known as coral islands because they are formed on corals *i.e.,* the skeletons of polyps. Lakshadweep consists of a large number of coral islands.

The Andaman and Nicobar Islands lie in the Bay of Bengal. Most of these islands are volcanic in nature. Barren Island, part of the Andaman and Nicobar is the only active volcano of India.

Barren Island active volcano

MORE TO KNOW

Corals are the skeletons of tiny marine animals called polyps. When living polyps die, their skeletons remain. New polyps then grow on top of these skeletons. In this way, the structure grows higher and higher, eventually forming coral islands.

DO YOU KNOW?

Why are continents not considered islands ?

Continents are also surrounded by water, but because they are so large, they are not considered islands. *For example,* the smallest continent Australia is three times larger in size than Greenland, the largest island.

Beautiful landscape of islands.

Think & Answer

Think of the various uses of land for humans.

Check Your Progress

Understanding

Give one word answer for the following

1. The largest continent ____________
2. River between Asia and Europe ____________
3. The Dark Continent ____________
4. World's longest river ____________
5. World's largest desert ____________
6. The Frozen Continent ____________
7. The Island Continent ____________
8. The only active volcano of India ____________

NEW WORDS

- **Hydrosphere :** The part of the Earth covered with water is known as the hydrosphere.
- **Atmosphere :** The layer of gases that surround our planet is called the atmosphere.
- **Oceans :** Vast stretches of water.
- **Isthmus :** A narrow strip of land connecting two large land masses.
- **Continents :** Huge land masses that rise above sea level.
- **Eurasia :** Combined landmass of Europe and Asia.
- **Island :** A piece of land surrounded by water on all sides.
- **Disaster :** It is a natural or man-made event which results in great damage or loss of life.
- **Natural Disasters :** Disasters that occur naturally or are caused by nature.
- **Disaster Management :** A programme that comprises disaster prevention, mitigation measures, response and recovery from the dangerous situations.
- **Flood :** Overflow of large amounts of water.
- **Earthquake :** Sudden vibration in the Earth's crust

NUTSHELL

- More than 71% of the Earth's surface is covered with water and only 29% is covered with land.
- Due to the presence of water, the Earth is often called the Water Planet or the Blue Planet.
- Vast stretches of water are known as oceans.
- There are five major oceans in the world. These are : Pacific Ocean, Atlantic Ocean, Indian Ocean, Arctic Ocean and Southern/Antarctic Ocean.
- The Pacific Ocean is the largest and deepest ocean in the world.
- The Atlantic Ocean is 'S' shaped and provides a good location for sheltered harbours and ports.
- The Arctic Ocean is the smallest ocean.
- The constant movement of tectonic plates sometimes leads to powerful and devastating natural disasters.
- The continents are defined as huge land masses that rise above the sea level.
- The continents of the Earth once formed a single, giant landmass called the Pangaea.
- There are seven continents on the Earth namely—Asia, Africa, North America, South America, Antarctica, Europe and Australia.
- Asia is the largest continent while Australia is the smallest.
- An island is a piece of land that is completely surrounded by water.
- The Lakshadweep and the Andaman and Nicobar are the main island groups of India.

IMPORTANT NCERT TEXTBOOK QUESTIONS (Solved)

Questions, activities and projects

1. Explain the following terms :

(a) Continent **(b) Ocean** **(c) Island**

Ans. (a) **Continent :** A large continuous expanse of land is called a 'continent'. There are seven continents on the Earth namely—Asia, Africa, North America, South America, Antarctica, Europe and Australia. Asia, Europe and North America lie entirely in the Northern Hemisphere while Australia and Antarctica lie entirely in the Southern Hemisphere.

(b) **Ocean :** Vast stretches of water are known as oceans. There are five major oceans in the world. These are :

1. Pacific Ocean 2. Atlantic Ocean 3. Indian Ocean
4. Arctic Ocean 5. Southern/Antarctic Ocean

(c) **Island :** An island is a piece of land that is completely surrounded by water. Islands are found in oceans, seas, rivers and lakes. The Lakshadweep and the Andaman and Nicobar are the main island groups of India.

2. **Let us draw – Without looking at the maps in this chapter, draw the continents free hand on a sheet of paper and colour them. Then, compare your drawing with the map of oceans and continents in the chapter.**

Ans. Students will do themselves.

3. **Let us do – On the outline map of the world given below, label all the continents and oceans.**

Ans.

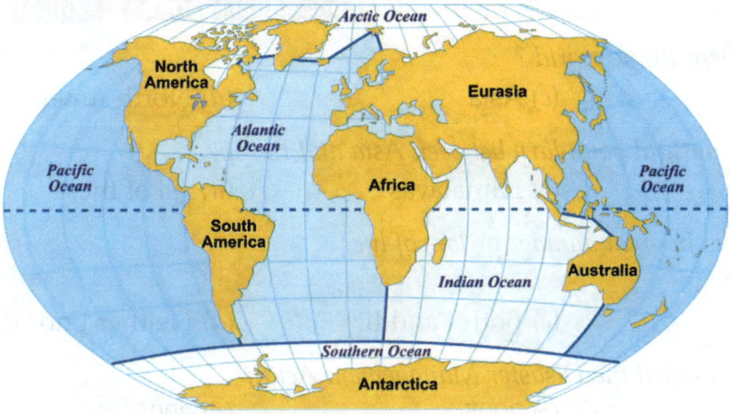

4. **Solve this crossword.**

Across

1. Abundantly produced by the oceans.
3. A large expanse of landmass.
6. A large continent of which India is a part.
8. A major source of pollution of the oceans.
10. The coldest continent.

Down

2. The largest island on Earth.
4. A huge destructive wave from the ocean.
5. The smallest continent.
7. The largest body of water on the Earth.
9. A landmass (but not a continent) surrounded by the sea or ocean.

Ans.

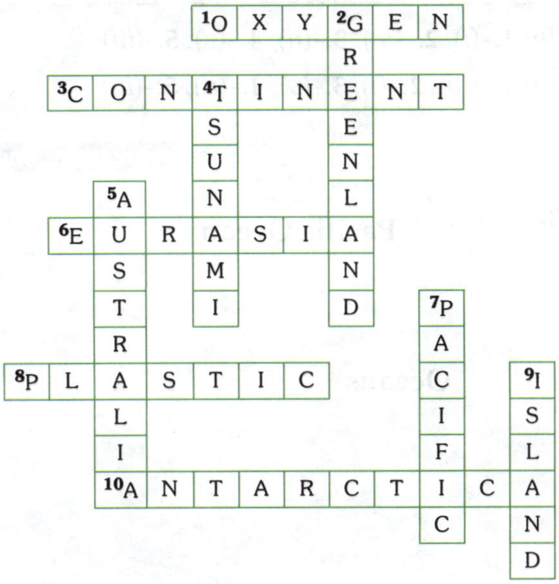

EXERCISES
As per NEP-2020 & NCF-2023

I. OBJECTIVE TYPE QUESTIONS

A. Choose the correct answer.
Conceptual Learning | Critical Thinking

1. *Which of the following is the largest continent in the world ?*
   (*a*) Australia (*b*) Europe (*c*) Asia (*d*) North America
2. *Which of the following mountains forms a natural boundary between Asia and Europe ?*
   (*a*) Ural (*b*) Atlas (*c*) Himalayas (*d*) All of these
3. *Disaster is a ________ event which results in great damage or loss of life.*
   I. natural II. man-made
   (*a*) Only I (*b*) Only II (*c*) Both I and II (*d*) Neither I nor II
4. *The Government of India has enacted and notified the Disaster Management Act in*
   (*a*) 2003 (*b*) 2004 (*c*) 2005 (*d*) 2006
5. *Which of the following got submerged under the sea water in 2004 during the Tsunami ?*
   (*a*) Port Blair (*b*) Indira Point (*c*) Nanda Devi (*d*) Palk Strait

B. Mark the option that matches Column A with Column B.
Conceptual Learning | Problem Solving

Column A	Column B
1. Australia	(*i*) Frozen continent
2. Antarctica	(*ii*) Dark continent
3. Asia	(*iii*) Roughly triangular in shape
4. Africa	(*iv*) Smallest continent
5. South America	(*v*) Largest continent

(*a*) **1.**-(*i*), **2.**-(*iii*), **3.**-(*iv*), **4.**-(*ii*), **5.**-(*v*)
(*b*) **1.**-(*i*), **2.**-(*iv*), **3.**-(*ii*), **4.**-(*v*), **5.**-(*iii*)
(*c*) **1.**-(*iv*), **2.**-(*i*), **3.**-(*ii*), **4.**-(*v*), **5.**-(*iii*)
(*d*) **1.**-(*iv*), **2.**-(*i*), **3.**-(*v*), **4.**-(*ii*), **5.**-(*iii*)

C. Fill in the blanks
Knowledge Application

1.
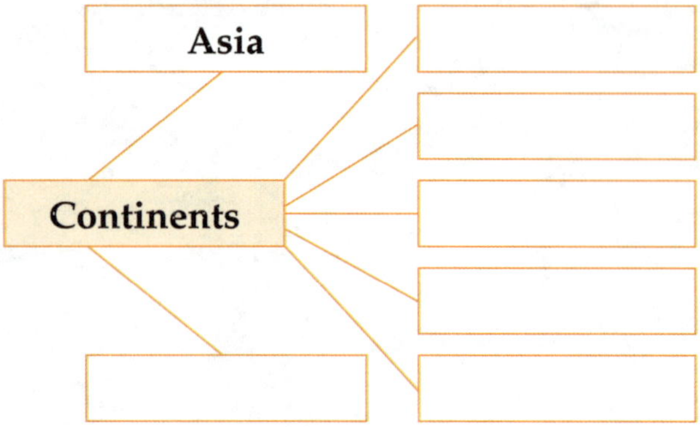

2.
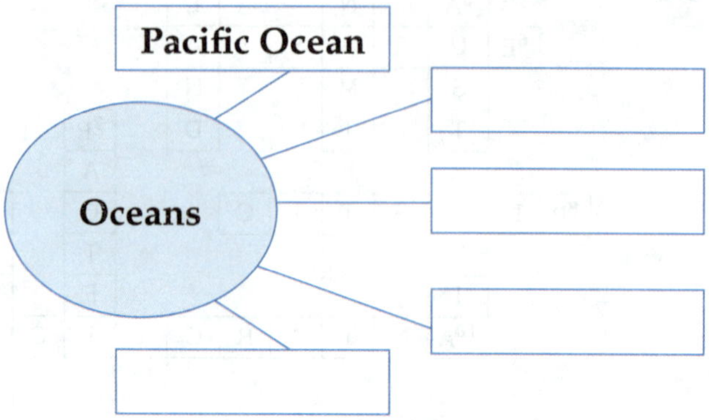

D. State True or False

Knowledge Application | Problem Solving

1. The Indian Ocean is named after India. ____________
2. Mariana Trench is the deepest point in the Atlantic Ocean. ____________
3. Andaman and Nicobar Islands lie in the Bay of Bengal. ____________
4. River Nile is found in Australia. ____________
5. The combined landmass of Europe and Asia is called Eurasia. ____________

E. Assertion-Reason

Critical Thinking

For question numbers 1 to 4, two statements are given—one labelled Assertion (A) and the other labelled Reason (R). Select the correct answer to these questions from the codes (*a*), (*b*), (*c*) and (*d*) as given below :

(*a*) Both Assertion (A) and Reason (R) are true and Reason is the correct explanation of the Assertion.
(*b*) Both Assertion (A) and Reason (R) are true but Reason is not the correct explanation of the Assertion.
(*c*) Assertion (A) is true but Reason (R) is false.
(*d*) Assertion (A) is false but Reason (R) is true.

1. **Assertion (A)** : The Earth is called a Blue Planet.
   Reason (R) : More than 71% of Earth is covered with water.
2. **Assertion (A)** : Europe is the Dark Continent.
   Reason (R) : Australia is the smallest continent.
3. **Assertion (A)** : The Atlantic Ocean is 'S' shaped.
   Reason (R) : The Arctic Ocean is the largest Ocean.
4. **Assertion (A)** : Lakshadweep islands are situated in the Arabian Sea.
   Reason (R) : They are known as coral islands because they are formed on corals i.e., the skeletons of polyps.

II. SHORT ANSWER TYPE QUESTIONS

Conceptual Learning | Knowledge Application

1. Why is the Earth called a Blue Planet ?
2. Mention any three features of the continent Asia.
3. Why do disasters occur in the oceans?
4. Write a note on marine life in the oceans.
5. Give reason why the surface of the ocean water level remains the same everywhere.

III. LONG ANSWER TYPE QUESTIONS

Knowledge Application | Critical Thinking

1. Explain why the Atlantic Ocean is the busiest trade and commerce route of the world.
2. Write a note on the importance of oceans.
3. Describe oceanic flora and fauna.
4. Discuss any two disasters of the oceans.
5. Describe the formation of islands.

IV. PICTURE STUDY

Problem Solving | Critical Thinking

The given picture shows a continent. Answer the following questions with respect to the picture.

1. Identify the continent.
2. Explain why this continent is called a 'Dark Continent'.
3. Name the hottest and the driest desert in the world that is located in this continent.

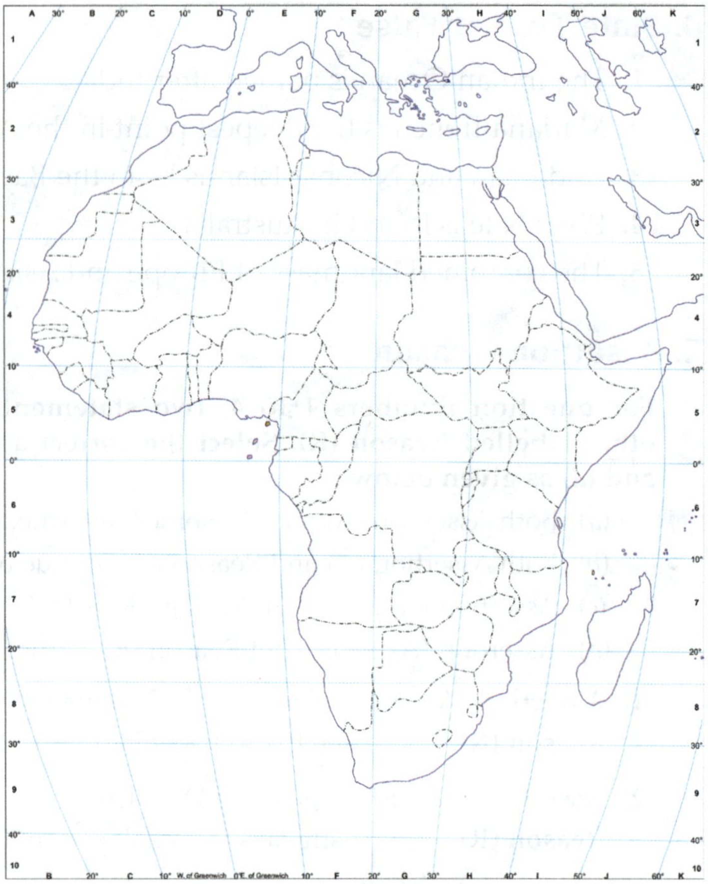

V. SOURCE BASED QUESTIONS

Problem Solving | Conceptual Learning | Critical Thinking

Topic : Two Main Divisions of the Earth's Surface

Continents—the large landmasses : The highest mountain peak on this Earth is Mount Everest. Its current official elevation is 8,848 metres above sea level. The elevation was measured and established by an Indian survey conducted in 1955. The border between Nepal and China runs across its summit points.

Ocean basins—the huge water bodies : Mariana Trench is the deepest Oceanic trench on the Earth. The deepest portion is at 11,034 metres. Mariana Trench is located in the Pacific Ocean. Mariana Trench is 69 km in width and 2550 km in length. Mariana Trench derives its name from the nearby Mariana Islands which is located at around 200 km from the Mariana Trench in the Pacific Ocean.

Choose the correct alternative for each question.

1. *The continent through which both the Tropic of Cancer and the Tropic of Capricorn pass is*
   (*a*) North America (*b*) Asia (*c*) Africa (*d*) Europe
2. *The percentage of oxygen in the air we breathe is*
   (*a*) 100 (*b*) 78 (*c*) 21 (*d*) 1
3. *The Pacific Ocean is the largest ocean, but the busiest ocean from the point of view of trade is*
   (*a*) Pacific Ocean (*b*) Indian Ocean (*c*) Arctic Ocean (*d*) Atlantic Ocean
4. *Depth of ocean or height of land is measured from*
   (*a*) Ocean floor (*b*) Mountain (*c*) Sky (*d*) Sea level

VI. MAP SKILL

Knowledge Application | Conceptual Learning

- Use the help box given below to label the different continents and oceans of the world.
  (Hint : Continents are the green boxes and oceans are the blue boxes on the globe.)

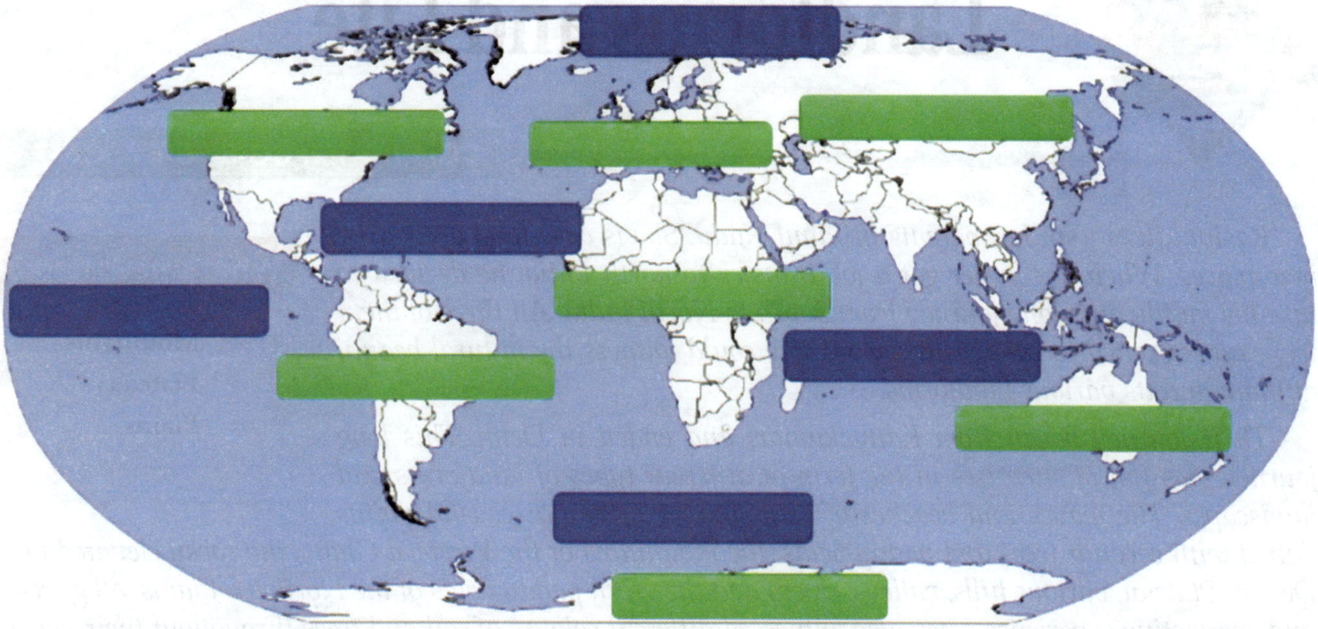

Atlantic Ocean	Asia	North America	Arctic Ocean
Africa	Pacific Ocean	Antarctica	Europe
Southern Ocean	Australia	Indian Ocean	South America

ACTIVITIES & PROJECTS

Multidisciplinary Approach | Experiential Learning | Collaboration

1. **Globe Reading :** Take a globe and identify all the oceans and continents you have read in this chapter. Search for the two main island groups of India, the Bay of Bengal and the Arabian Sea.
2. Write a paragraph on the steps that can be taken to conserve our oceans and marine life.

CHAPTER 3

Landforms and Life

CG-1 : C-1.2; CG-6 : C-6.4; CG-7 : C-7.2

What's new to learn

- Mountains
- Plateaus
- Plains

Rashmi lives with her parents in Tamil Nadu. She is very fond of visiting new places. When her father got a job transfer to north India, he decided to take his family on a long journey from South to North India. All three of them were super excited for their journey, as they could witness the natural beauty of India and its various landforms.

Their journey began from Kanyakumari and ended in Delhi. This long journey was full of surprises in the form of different types of landforms and landscapes. The waves and beaches of Kanyakumari, the flat coastal plains dotted with coconut trees and paddy fields, the mountains of the Western Ghats, the rocky elevated land of the Deccan Plateau, various hills, valleys, rivers and the green paddy fields of the Northern Plains, all gave a unique and everlasting experience. They also witnessed different colours of soil and trees throughout their journey.

MORE TO KNOW

The scientific study of landforms and their processes is known as Geomorphology.

DO YOU KNOW?

How does weathering differ from erosion ? Generally, people believe that both weathering and erosion are the same. But in reality, weathering includes only the disintegration of the rocks. Transportation of these small disintegrated materials is not a part of weathering. It is included in the process of erosion.

Like Rashmi, let us also learn about a few landforms in the present chapter.

The hard crust of the Earth on which we live is known as the lithosphere. The lithosphere is not a plain surface, but is made up of diverse landforms. A landform is a natural feature on the Earth's surface such as plains, mountains, valleys, plateaus, hills, etc. Different types of landforms are formed by various geological processes over millions of years like collision of tectonic plates, volcanic activity, erosion, weathering and other climatic conditions. Landforms are broadly divided into three categories—Mountains, Plateaus and Plains. Let us now study them is some detail.

MOUNTAINS

Mountains are the natural elevations of the Earth's surface. The term 'mountain' is usually applied to any region of land that is raised rather steeply above the surrounding terrain. Mountains are distinguishable from plateaus by their usually limited summit area. They are distinguishable from what are commonly called as hills by their generally higher elevation.

The elevation or altitude of a mountain can be defined as the height of the summit above sea level. Therefore, a mountain with an elevation of 4,000 m may rise to only 3,000 m above the surrounding land. Mountains are normally found in groups or ranges that consist of peaks, ridges and intermontane valleys. Apart from certain mountains that occur singly, the smallest unit is the range that comprises either a single complex ridge or a series of ridges which are generally alike in origin, age and form. Several closely related ranges in a parallel alignment or chain-like cluster are known as a mountain system, while an elongated series of such systems forms a mountain chain.

Characteristics of Mountains

- Mountains have broad bases and conical tops like a peak.
- Mountains have cold climate as compared to the plain areas.
- Mountains are the store houses of glaciers which are the main source of water for the rivers.
- The mountain ranges are usually found parallel to each other.

Types of Mountains

Broadly, the mountains can be divided into four types. They are :

(a) Young Fold Mountains

The mountains that have been formed recently are known as the young fold mountains. They are less than or equal to 100 million years old. They have tall and sharp peaks. The mountains like the Himalayas, the Alps, the Andes, and the Rockies are examples of young fold mountains.

Young Fold Mountains

(b) Old Fold Mountains

Old Fold Mountains

The mountains that were formed much earlier are known as the old fold mountains. They are not less than 100 to 500 million years old. They are shorter than the young fold mountains and have more rounded peaks. The rounded peaks are a result of erosion. The Urals, the Appalachians, the Tien Shan and the Aravallis are the best examples of old fold mountains.

Block Mountains

(c) Block Mountains

These mountains are formed as a result of tectonic activity. When the Earth's crust breaks into several blocks due to pressure, some blocks of rocks rise up while some drop down. The raised blocks of the Earth's surface are called the block mountains. Black Forest (Germany), Vosges Mountains (France), the Sierra Nevada (California) and the Salt Range (Pakistan) are examples of the block mountains.

Volcanic Mountains

(d) Volcanic Mountains

The volcanic mountains are formed due to the solidification of lava on the Earth's surface. Etna (Italy), Kilimanjaro (Africa), Cotopaxi (Andes), Korakatoa (Indonesia) and Fujiyama (Japan) are examples of the volcanic mountains.

The following table shows the important mountains of the world.

	Mountain	Continent
1.	Verkhoyansk	Asia
2.	Stanovoy	Asia
3.	Kolyma	Asia
4.	Sayan	Asia
5.	Altai	Asia
6.	Kunlun	Asia
7.	Himalayas	Asia
8.	Aravallis	Asia
9.	Vindhya	Asia
10.	Satpura	Asia
11.	Tien Shan	Asia
12.	Pamir	Asia

MORE TO KNOW

- **A Mountain Range :** It is a linear system of mountains and hills having a number of peaks, summits and valleys.
- **A Mountain Chain :** It has several long and narrow parallel mountain ranges.
- **A Mountain System :** A group of several mountain ranges is termed as a mountain system.
- **A Cordillera :** It refers to several mountain groups and systems. *For example,* the Western Cordillera in North America.

	Mountain	Continent
13.	Atlas	Africa
14.	Great Karoo	Africa
15.	Drakensberg	Africa
16.	Brooks	North America
17.	Alaska	North America
18.	Rocky	North America
19.	Appalachians	North America
20.	Andes	South America
21.	Alps	Europe
22.	Pyrenees	Europe
23.	Scandinavian	Europe
24.	Balkan	Europe
25.	Carpathian	Europe
26.	Cantabrian	Europe
27.	Apennines	Europe
28.	Urals	Europe
29.	Great Dividing Range	Australia
30.	Musgrave Range	Australia

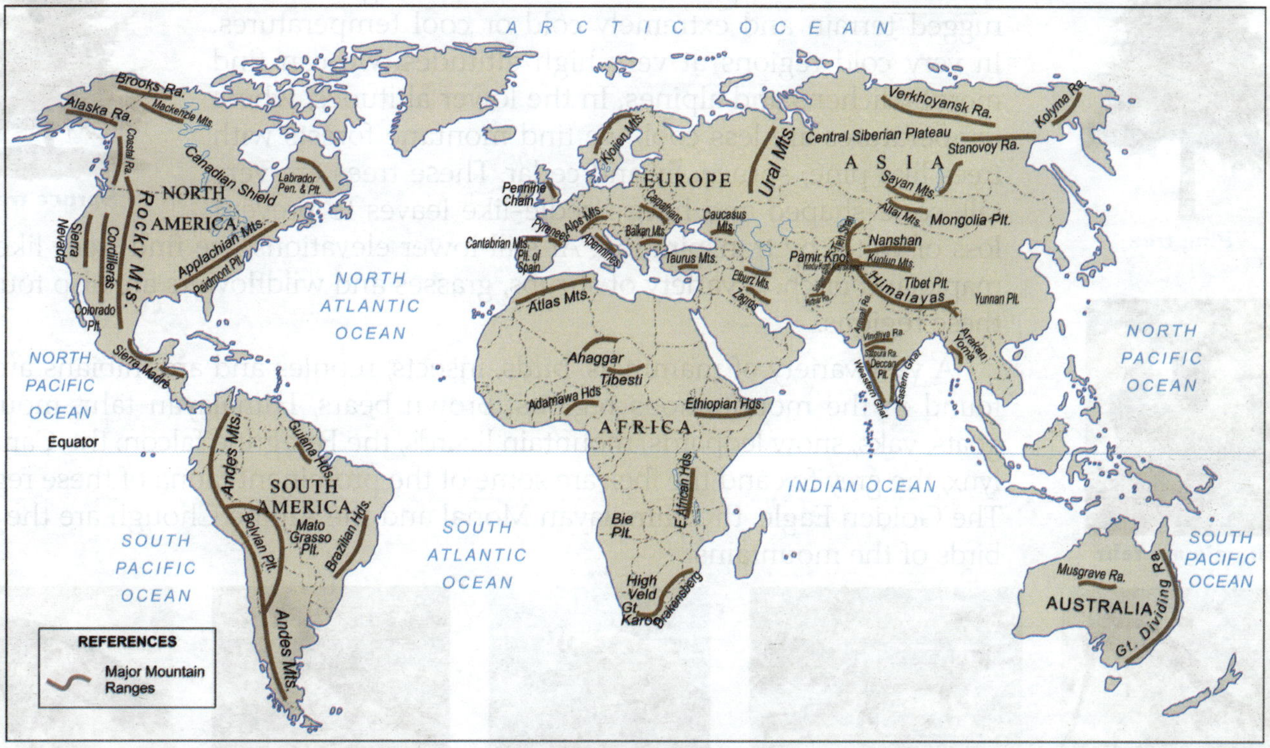

Major Mountains of the World

MORE TO KNOW

Climbing Routes to the Mount Everest

Mount Everest has two main climbing routes.
(*i*) The south-east ridge from Nepal.
(*ii*) The North-east ridge from Tibet.

Important Climbers

(*i*) Edmund Hillary of New Zealand and Tenzing Norgay Sherpa of India were the first men to climb the Mount Everest at 11:30 a.m. local time on 29th May, 1953.

Tenzing Norgay Sherpa

(*ii*) Junko Tabei of Japan was the first woman to reach the summit on 16th May, 1975. Bachendri Pal was the first Indian woman to scale Mt. Everest on 23rd May 1984. She reached the summit at 1:07 p.m. (IST). She was awarded the Padma Sri in the year 1984 and the Padma Bhusan in 2019.

(*iii*) On 8th May, 1978, Reinhold Mossner (Italy) and Peter Habeler (Austria) made the first ascent without supplementary oxygen.

(*iv*) Santosh Yadav, an Indian Indo-Tibetan Border Police Woman, reached Mt. Everest in the years 1992 and 1993.

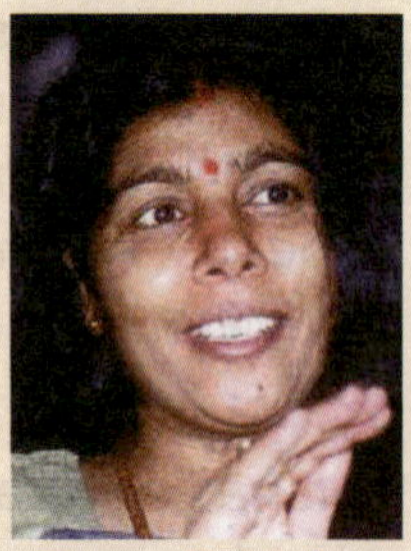

Santosh Yadav

(*v*) Arunima Sinha lost her leg in an accident when she was 31. With her determination, she climbed Mount Everest in 2013. She did not stop here, but went on to climb the highest peak of every continent. She was awarded Padma Sri in 2015.

Arunima Sinha

Mountain Environment

Pine tree

Spruce tree

Mountains are home to a variety of plant and animal species that are adapted to the situations of high altitudes, rugged terrain and extremely cold or cool temperatures. In very cold regions at very high altitudes, we can find mosses, lichens and alpines. In the lower altitudes, where temperatures are less cool, we find montane forests with trees like pine, spruce, fir and cedar. These trees are very tall, cone-shaped and have needle-like leaves to prevent loss of water by transpiration. At still lower elevations, we find trees like oak, maple and birch. A variety of shrubs, grasses and wildflowers are also found in these regions.

Himalayan tahr

A vast variety of mammals, birds, insects, reptiles and amphibians are also found in the mountainous regions. Brown bears, Himalayan tahr, mountain goats, yaks, snow leopards, mountain lizards, the Peregrine falcon, the Canadian lynx, the grey fox and the ibex are some of the prominent fauna of these regions. The Golden Eagle, the Himalayan Monal and the Alpine Chough are the main birds of the mountains.

Mountain lizard

Gray fox

Mountain goats

Peregrine falcon

Golden eagle

DO YOU KNOW?

Terrace farming or cultivation is a method of farming in which the land on a hill slope is converted into flat plots carved out in steps. The side of each plot is raised in order to retain water in the field. This method is best suited for rice cultivation.

Life in the Mountains

You have studied about the rugged terrain, sparse vegetation and extremely cold or cool temperatures of the mountains. By now, you can easily imagine how tough it would be to live in the mountains.

Life in the mountains is full of challenges in day-to-day life, but it also offers various opportunities due to its distinct landscape. The steep and rugged terrain of the mountains makes agriculture and transportation really difficult. People usually settle in the valleys in between the mountains. The houses have steep roofs so that snow and water slip off easily, and thick walls for insulation. Wood and stones are the most common materials for building houses. People practice terrace farming by creating flat steps on the steep slopes. The main crops grown are potatoes, barley, rice and corn. People also domesticate animals like cows, sheep, goats and yak for milk, meat and wool.

People in the mountains have a distinct traditional culture and celebrate various festivals dedicated to nature, the changing seasons, harvest of crops, etc. They have strong community bonds and live in close connection to each other.

Terrace farming

Houses with steep roofs

Hiking

Mountains are prone to natural disasters like extremely cold temperatures, heavy snowfall, avalanches, cloud bursts, earthquakes, floods and landslides. Challenges also come in the form of man-made disasters like deforestation, overgrazing and uncontrolled tourism.

Disaster caused by an earthquake

Cloud Burst

Landslides

Paragliding

In recent years, tourism has become the main occupation and source of income for the people living in the mountains. Thousands of tourists visit the mountains for hiking, skiing, paragliding and mountaineering. Some people come to visit the famous temples situated in the mountains. People also come to the mountains to witness the unique landscapes, breathe clean air, and experience snow, which are generally not found in the plains. They also feel peace, solace and an instant connection with nature.

Think & Answer

Imagine that you get an opportunity to live in the mountains for one year. You are totally new to that region. Write a note on the challenges you will face and the steps you will take to make your life comfortable there.

Significance of Mountains

- Mountains are a rich source of water for rivers.
- They provide different building materials like wood, mud and stones.
- They are the natural home to various wild animals and birds.
- The mountains are also famous as tourist destinations.
- The mountains are a great source of oxygen and they are indirectly helpful in bringing rain.
- Many precious stones like diamonds, rubies, etc. are found in the mountains.

Check Your Progress — Understanding

Fill in the blanks :

1. The Himalayas are the ____________ fold mountains.
2. ____________ and ____________ are the examples of old fold mountains.
3. ____________ is a block mountain.
4. ____________ process is responsible for the formation of block mountains.
5. ____________ farming is practised on the hilly slopes.
6. In recent years, ____________ has become the main source of income for people living in the mountains.

PLATEAUS

A plateau is an extensive land formation that rises sharply above the surrounding area on at least one side. It is also known as a tableland due to its table-like flat shape. Its elevation can reach from a few hundred to several thousand metres. A plateau can be formed by erosion or volcanic activity or by an upward movement of the Earth's crust.

Characteristics of Plateaus

- Plateaus are extensive in size and cover huge areas of land.
- They have flat or gently rolling surfaces, making them different from the surrounding lower land areas.
- Their height varies from a few hundred metres to a thousand metres.
- Plateaus generally have steep slopes on both sides. But, a few plateaus have steep slopes on one side and gentle slopes on the other.

Distribution of Plateaus

- Deccan Plateau in India
- East African Plateau in Kenya, Tanzania and Uganda
- Western Plateau of Australia
- Tibet Plateau of China

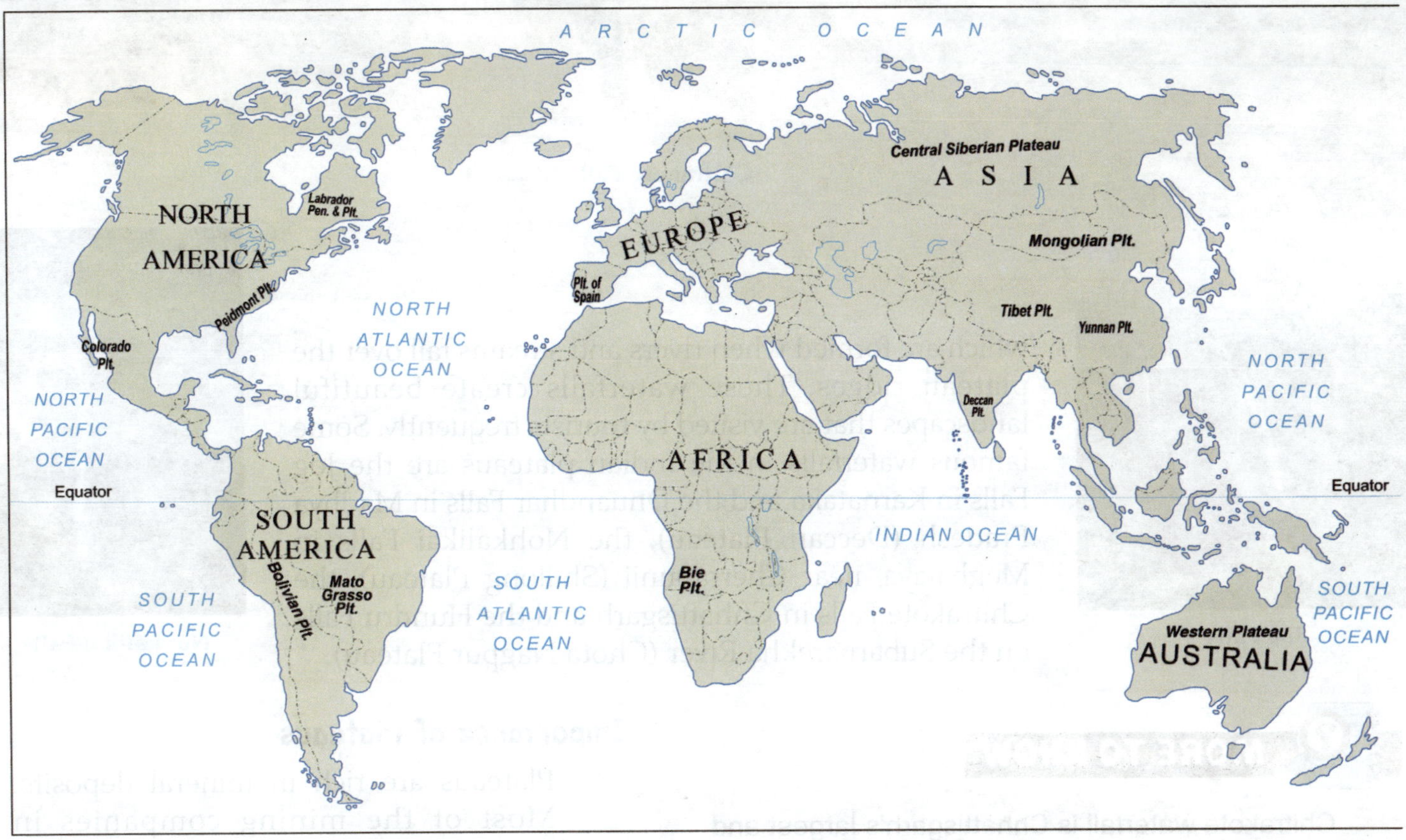

Different Plateaus of the World

- Central Siberian Plateau of Russia
- Mongolian Plateau of Mongolia
- Bie Plateau of Africa
- Plateau of Spain in Europe
- Colorado Plateau of North America
- Bolivian Plateau of South America

Life in the Plateaus

Plateaus have moderate to cool temperatures and lower humidity. Most of the plateaus have steep edges and flat tops. Their terrain is relatively flat as compared to the mountains and valleys. The flat tops are used for building houses and settlements. Plateaus also have fertile soils suitable for agriculture where crops such as wheat, barley, maize and potatoes are commonly grown. Terrace farming is also practised on plateaus with gentle slopes. Animals like donkeys and mules are domesticated for carrying goods and people.

Plateaus are rich in minerals like coal and iron ore and mining is an important economic activity of these regions. Tourism is another economic activity as people visit plateaus for their landscapes, hiking and camping. Plateaus also have waterfalls

MORE TO KNOW

- The Tibetan Plateau, located in Central Asia, is the highest and largest plateau in the world. It is also known as the "Roof of the World". It has an average altitude of 4,500 m and is nearly 2,500 km long from east to west.
- The East African Plateau is known for gold and diamond mines.
- The Deccan Plateau of India is famous for its rich black soil and extensive volcanic rock formations.
- The Colorado Plateau of the United States is famous for the Grand Canyon.

Chitrakote Falls

Jog Falls

which are formed when rivers and streams fall over the plateau ridges. These waterfalls create beautiful landscapes that are visited by tourists frequently. Some famous waterfalls in the Indian plateaus are the Jog Falls in Karnataka and the Dhuandhar Falls in Madhya Pradesh (Deccan Plateau), the Nohkalikai Falls in Meghalaya, near Cherrapunji (Shillong Plateau), the Chitrakote Falls in Chhattisgarh and the Hundru Falls on the Subarnarekha River (Chota Nagpur Plateau).

Nohkalikai Falls

MORE TO KNOW

- Chitrakote waterfall is Chhattisgarh's largest and most water-logged waterfall. The horseshoe-shaped waterfall creates a stunning sight and it is famous as the "Niagara of India".
- The Jog falls is formed by the Sharavathi River and is divided into four segments : Raja, Rani, Rover and Rocket. It is one of the highest waterfalls in India.
- Kunchikal Falls in Shimoga District Karnataka is the highest waterfall in India with a height of 1493 feet.
- The Nohkalikai Falls drop down 340 metres from the Cherrapunji Plateau.
- Dudhsagar falls, formed by the Narmada river is known as the 'Sea of milk',
- Ranchi, the capital city of Jharkhand is known as the city of waterfalls in India.

Dudhsagar falls

Importance of Plateaus

- Plateaus are rich in mineral deposits. Most of the mining companies in the world are located in the plateau regions. The plateaus are also called the 'storehouses of minerals'. *For example,* the Chota Nagpur Plateau in India is rich in coal, manganese and iron ore deposits.
- Plateaus are famous as tourist destinations. They have unique landscapes and waterfalls. The Deccan Plateau of India is a famous tourist destination.
- When rivers fall from high plateaus, they form waterfalls and hydroelectricity is generated with the falling water.
- Some plateaus are formed by volcanic activities. Such plateaus are a great source of black soil and are suitable for farming. Black soil is useful for cotton cultivation.
- Plateaus are also good for human settlement because of their flat surfaces and fertile soils.

Check Your Progress

Understanding

State True or false

1. Plateaus are flat on top.
2. Plateaus are colder than the mountains.
3. The Deccan Plateau is called "the roof of the world".
4. Terrace farming is practised on the plateaus.
5. Tourism is an important activity on the plateaus.

PLAINS

Plains are low-lying flat stretches of land. They generally do not change much in elevation. They are usually formed by rivers.

Characteristics of Plains

- Generally, plains are not more than 200 metres above the mean sea level.
- They are ideal for human settlement and building infrastructure like roads, cities, schools, hospitals, etc.
- The soils of plains are very fertile and most suitable for agriculture.
- Many plains have a network of extensive river systems that is important for irrigation, transportation, fishing, etc.
- Plains usually have a dense population owing to their fertile soil, easy access to water and flat terrain.

Formation of Plains

- The plains are usually formed by the deposition of silt and sediments brought by the rivers and their tributaries.
- The plains can be extremely flat or slightly rolling.
- Most of the plains are very fertile and useful for agricultural activities.

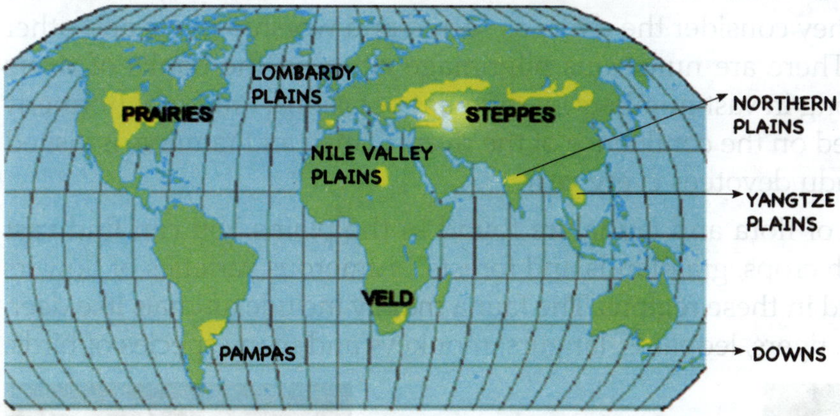

Plains of the World

Distribution of Plains

- Northern Plains of India
- Nile Valley Plains of Africa
- Yangtze Plains of China
- Prairies of North America
- Pampas of South America
- Downs Plains of Australia
- Lombardy Plains of Italy
- Veld in Africa.

Life in the Plains

Plains generally have a moderate climate. They are neither too cold nor too hot, which makes them comfortable for living. The favourable climate, abundance of water from rivers and lakes, fertile soils and flat terrain make the plains one of the most densely populated areas of the world.

Agriculture is the main occupation of people living in the plains. The fertile soils and vast stretches of fields yield abundant crops like wheat, rice, maize, barley, millets, vegetables and fruits. Fibre crops like jute, cotton and hemp are also grown. The vast river systems provide easy access to water for the fields. At many places, farmers grow multiple crops throughout the year. Cows, buffaloes, goats and sheep are also domesticated for milk, meat and wool. Fishing is also an important occupation of people living near rivers and lakes. People in the plains also work in various sectors such as education, healthcare, science and research, retail and industry.

People usually live in houses made of bricks,wood and cement. In cities, one can easily find apartments, multi-storey houses and skyscrapers.

Transportation is also easy and more accessible in the plains due to flat terrain. Plains have an extensive network of roadways, railways and airports. An efficient system of transportation facilitates trade and commerce to distant regions within the country. Waterways and pipelines are also well developed in the plains as compared to other regions. Waterways facilitate the movement of cargo, and boating is another important activity on rivers and lakes. These regions have a high level of industrial development, agricultural and mining activities and big markets where traders and buyers sell and buy agricultural produce and industrial products.

River Ganga

Taj Mahal

Tourism is also a source of livelihood for the people living in the plains. *For example,* Taj Mahal in Agra and the Buddhists Stupas of Uttar Pradesh and Agra are great tourist attractions in the world.

Sangam in Prayagraj

People in the plains follow distinct and a variety of cultural traditions. They celebrate different festivals related to harvest and other occasions. As rivers are a part of their life, they consider the rivers as sacred and worship rivers and other forces of nature. There are numerous pilgrimage cities on the banks of rivers where people throng in vast numbers on different occasions. Prayagraj (formerly Allahabad), situated on the confluence of the rivers Ganga and Yamuna, is visited by millions of Hindu devotees every year.

Tiger

A vast variety of flora and fauna are found in the plains. You can find vast fields covered with crops, grasslands and forests. Numerous varieties of flowers and trees are found in these regions. The fauna mainly include animals like deer, rabbits, elephants, tigers, leopards, langurs, monkeys and many species of birds.

Deer

Leopard

Elephant

Rabbit

DO YOU KNOW?

The Indo-Gangetic Plain also known as the North Indian River Plain situated in India is one of the most fertile and densely populated regions in the world. It stretches across the northern part of the country and extends into Pakistan and Bangladesh. It is named after the two major rivers that flow through it, the Indus and the Ganges. It also includes the Brahmaputra River basin in the eastern part. It covers a vast area of approximately 700,000 sq km, making it one of the largest plains in the world. It is famous for its fertile soil that makes the region one of the most productive farming areas in the world. This plain has a thick cover of fertile alluvium. The plain is watered by three major rivers : the Indus, the Ganges and the Brahmaputra. Rice, wheat, sugarcane, maize, gram, millets and a variety of fruits and vegetables are grown here. These plains are a great tourist attraction with a large number of monuments, ancient structures, gardens, temples and mosques.

Overpopulation, pollution, depletion of underground water levels, loss of agricultural land, flooding etc has led to a great extent of environmental degradation of these plains in recent times. The sewage and industrial waste from the cities situated in this region flows directly into the river Ganga and Brahmaputra and their tributaries. Air pollution is also affecting the region very badly. The motor vehicles emit dangerous gases in enormous quantities that cause health problems.

MORE TO KNOW

"Namami Gange Programme"

To save the river Ganga from pollution, the Ganga Action Plan was initiated several decades ago. The high concentration of population in the region has caused harm to various rivers and their tributaries. Now, the Ganga Action Plan has been replaced by a national plan for cleaning the rivers. To conserve the river Ganga, the "Namami Gange Programme" has been initiated, which has two main objectives : effective abatement of pollution, conservation and rejuvenation of National River Ganga.

Indo-Gangetic Plains

Importance of Plains

- The plains provide fertile soils. Therefore, they are useful for agricultural activities.
- The climate of plains is suitable for human settlement. Availability of water and flat land makes construction of houses easy.
- The plains are flat, which makes the construction of transport networks like roads, railways and airports easy.
- The plains include forests, grasslands and wetlands that support a variety of plant and animal species.

Think & Answer

Of the three landforms that you studied in this chapter, which one will you choose for making your house and why ? Give reasons to support your answer.

Check Your Progress

Understanding

State True or false

1. Plains have a low population.
2. Plains have many rivers and lakes.
3. Prairies are found in North America.
4. Agriculture is the main occupation of people living in the plains.
5. Plains do not have an efficient system of transportation.

NEW WORDS

- **Lithosphere :** The hard crust of the Earth on which we live.
- **Landforms :** Different forms of relief features are known as landforms.
- **Weathering :** It refers to the gradual disintegration of rocks by atmospheric agents like temperature, moisture, plants, etc.
- **Mountains :** The natural elevations of the Earth's surface.
- **Avalanche :** A very large amount of snow that slides quickly down the side of a mountain.
- **Plains :** Low-lying flat stretches of land.
- **Plateau :** The highlands having broad and flat surfaces and steep slopes.
- **Canyon :** I-shaped deep valleys.
- **Valleys :** An elongated narrow depression between two mountains, or hills which often has a river flowing through it.
- **Soil :** Upper thin layer of the lithosphere that consists of tiny sand particles.
- **Climate :** The sum total of the average atmospheric conditions, *i.e.*, temperature, rainfall, humidity, etc. that prevail in a region for a long period of time.
- **Intermontane :** Located between mountains or mountain ranges.
- **Elevation :** The height of a place above sea level.
- **Summit :** Top of a mountain.
- **Ridge :** A long, narrow piece of highland along the top of hills or mountains.

NUTSHELL

- The hard crust of the Earth on which we live is known as the lithosphere.
- Mountains are the natural elevations of the Earth's surface.
- Mountains can be divided into four types : Young Fold Mountains, Old Fold Mountains, Block Mountains and Volcanic Mountains.
- The steep and rugged terrain of the mountains makes agriculture and transportation really difficult.
- A plateau is an extensive land formation that rises sharply above the surrounding area on at least one side. It is also known as a tableland due to its table-like flat shape.
- A Plateau can be formed by erosion or volcanic activity or by an upward movement of the Earth's crust.
- Plateaus are rich in minerals like coal and iron ore.
- When rivers fall down from high plateaus, they form waterfalls.
- Plains are low-lying flat stretches of land. They are ideal for human settlement and building infrastructure like roads, cities, schools, hospitals, etc.
- Many plains have a network of extensive river systems that is important for irrigation, transportation, fishing, etc.
- Plains usually have a dense population owing to their fertile soil, easy access to water and flat terrain.
- The plains are usually formed by the deposition of silt and sediments brought by the rivers and their tributaries.
- Agriculture is the main occupation of people living in the plains.

IMPORTANT NCERT TEXTBOOK QUESTIONS (Solved)

Questions, activities and projects

1. In what type of landform is your town/village/city located ? Which features mentioned in this chapter do you see around you ?

Ans. I live in Delhi which is a plain. Delhi is located in the Northern Plains. It has vast stretches of flat and fertile land situated on the floodplains of the river Yamuna.

The river provides water for drinking, farming and industry.

The flat land facilitates the construction of buildings, schools, hospitals, malls, etc. Delhi is well connected to other parts of the country by a huge network of roadways, railways and airways.

Delhi also has many parks and gardens with a great variety of flora.

It also has many historical monuments like the Red Fort, India Gate and Qutb Minar and famous religious places like the Akshardham Temple, the Birla temple and the Lotus Temple.

2. Let us go back to our initial trip from Chhota Nagpur to Prayagraj and Almora. Describe the three landforms you came across on the way.

Ans. On my initial trip from Chhota Nagpur to Prayagraj and Almora, I mainly came across three major landforms. They are :

1. Chhota Nagpur : This is a plateau.

The main features of a plateau are :

- It is extensive in size and covers huge areas of land.
- It has flat or gently rolling surfaces, making it different from the surrounding lower land areas.
- The height of a plateau varies from a few hundred metres to a thousand metres.
- A plateau generally has steep slopes on both sides.
- The flat tops are used for building houses and settlements.
- Plateaus are rich in minerals like coal and iron ore and mining is an important economic activity of these regions.
- Tourism is another economic activity as people visit plateaus for their landscapes, hiking and camping.
- Plateaus also have waterfalls which are formed when rivers and streams fall over the plateau ridges.

2. Prayagraj : This is a plain.

The main features of plains are :

- Plains are low-lying flat stretches of land.
- They are ideal for human settlement and building infrastructure like roads, cities, schools, hospitals, etc.
- The soils of plains are very fertile and most suitable for agriculture.
- Many plains have a network of extensive river systems that is important for irrigation, transportation, fishing, etc.
- Plains usually have a dense population owing to their fertile soil, easy access to water and flat terrain.
- The plains are usually formed by the deposition of silt and sediments brought by the rivers and their tributaries.
- Prayagraj is on the confluence of three rivers—The Ganga, Yamuna and Saraswati and is visited by millions of Hindu devotees every year.

3. Almora : This is a mountainous region.
The main features of mountainous regions are :

- Mountains have broad bases and conical tops like a peak.
- Mountains have a cold climate as compared to the plain areas.
- Mountains are the store houses of glaciers which are the main source of water for the rivers.
- Mountains are home to a variety of plant and animal species that are adapted to the situations of high altitudes, rugged terrain and extremely cold or cool temperatures.
- The houses have steep roofs so that snow and water slip off easily, and thick walls for insulation.
- Mountains are prone to natural disasters like extremely cold temperatures, heavy snowfall, avalanches, cloud bursts, earthquakes, floods and landslides.

3. List a few famous pilgrimage spots in India along with the landforms in which they are found.

Ans. A few famous pilgrimage spots in India along with the landforms in which they are found are :

Pilgrimage spot	Landform
• Amaranth	Mountains
• Vaishno Devi	Mountains
• Rishikesh and Haridwar	Foothills of the Himalayas
• Varanasi	Plains
• Mathura and Vrindavan	Plains
• Jagannath Puri	Coastal Plains
• Shirdi	Plains
• Tirupati	Hills

4. State whether true or false :

→ The Himalayas are young mountains with rounded tops.—**False**
→ Plateaus usually rise sharply at least on one side.—**True**
→ Mountains and hills belong to the same type of landform.—**True**
→ Mountains, plateaus and rivers in India have the same types of flora and fauna.—**False**
→ Ganga is a tributary to the Yamuna.—**False**
→ Deserts have unique flora and fauna.—**True**
→ Melting snow feeds rivers.—**True**
→ Sediments from rivers deposited in the plains makes the land fertile.—**True**
→ All deserts are hot.—**False**

5. Match words in pairs :

Mount Everest	Africa
Rafting	Roof of the world
Camels	Rice fields
Plateaus	Desert
Gangetic Plains	River
Waterway	Ganga
Mount Kilimanjaro	Tributary
Yamuna	Climbing

Ans.

Mount Everest	Climbing
Rafting	River
Camels	Desert
Plateaus	Roof of the world
Gangetic Plains	Rice fields
Waterway	Ganga
Mount Kilimanjaro	Africa
Yamuna	Tributary

EXERCISES As per NEP-2020 & NCF-2023

I. OBJECTIVE TYPE QUESTIONS

A. Choose the correct answer.

Conceptual Learning | Critical Thinking

1. *The hard crust of the Earth on which we live is known as the*
   (*a*) Atmosphere (*b*) Lithosphere (*c*) Biosphere (*d*) Hydrosphere
2. *Which of the following is not a volcanic mountain ?*
   (*a*) Kilimanjaro (*b*) Krakatoa (*c*) Andes (*d*) Fujiyama
3. *Consider the following statements about mountains —*
   I. Mountains have a broad base and a conical top.
   II. They have cold climate as compared to the plains.
   III. They have a flat surface that makes the construction of the transport network easy.
   IV. They are a storehouse of glaciers which are the main source of water for rivers.
   Which statement does not explain the characteristics of mountains ?
   (*a*) I and II (*b*) Only III (*c*) III and IV (*d*) Only IV
4. *The Dhuandhar Falls are an example of*
   (*a*) A waterfall (*b*) A plateau (*c*) A lake (*d*) A mountain
5. *Animals found on the plains include*
   (*a*) Tigers (*b*) Langurs (*c*) Rabbits (*d*) All of these

B. Mark the option that matches Column A with Column B.

Conceptual Learning | Problem Solving

Column A	Column B
1. Alps	(*i*) North America
2. Prairies	(*ii*) Young Fold Mountain
3. Indo-Gangetic Plains	(*iii*) Africa
4. Nile Valley Plains	(*iv*) India

(*a*) **1.**-(*ii*), **2.**-(*i*), **3.**-(*iv*), **4.**-(*iii*) (*b*) **1.**-(*iv*), **2.**-(*ii*), **3.**-(*i*), **4.**-(*iii*)
(*c*) **1.**-(*i*), **2.**-(*iv*), **3.**-(*ii*), **4.**-(*iii*) (*d*) **1.**-(*iii*), **2.**-(*iv*), **3.**-(*i*), **4.**-(*ii*)

C. State True or False

Knowledge Application | Problem Solving

1. The Himalayas are an example of a mountain range.
2. Plains are usually found at high elevations, similar to mountains.
3. Rivers that flow through plains can create fertile valleys ideal for farming.
4. The Deccan Plateau in India is known for its rich deposits of minerals and black soil.
5. The Indo-Gangetic Plain is known for its fertile soil and is one of the most densely populated regions in the world.

D. Assertion-Reason

Critical Thinking

For question numbers 1 to 4, two statements are given—one labelled Assertion (A) and the other labelled Reason (R). Select the correct answer to these questions from the codes (*a*), (*b*), (*c*) and (*d*) as given below :

(*a*) Both Assertion (A) and Reason (R) are true and Reason is the correct explanation of the Assertion.

(*b*) Both Assertion (A) and Reason (R) are true but Reason is not the correct explanation of the Assertion.

(*c*) Assertion (A) is true but Reason (R) is false.

(*d*) Assertion (A) is false but Reason (R) is true.

1. **Assertion (A)** : Different types of landforms are formed by various geological processes over millions of years.
   Reason (R) : Landforms are the same throughout the world.
2. **Assertion (A)** : The mountains do not attract tourists for many reasons.
   Reason (R) : Mountains have cold temperatures and rugged terrain.
3. **Assertion (A)** : The plains of Ganga and Brahmaputra are sparsely populated.
   Reason (R) : These plains have fertile, alluvial soil.
4. **Assertion (A)** : Plateaus generally have steep slopes on both sides.
   Reason (R) : Plateaus do not have mineral deposits.

II. SHORT ANSWER TYPE QUESTIONS

Conceptual Learning | Knowledge Application

1. Mountains play an important role in our life. How ?
2. Mention the importance of plateaus.
3. Write a short note on life in the plains.
4. Discuss the different types of mountains.

III. LONG ANSWER TYPE QUESTIONS

Knowledge Application | Critical Thinking

1. Explain why plains are densely populated as compared to the mountains.
2. Describe the importance of plateaus and mountains for human beings.

IV. DISTINGUISH BETWEEN THE FOLLOWING

Conceptual Learning **Understanding**

1. Mountains and Plains
2. Young Fold Mountains and Old Fold Mountains
3. Block Mountains and Volcanic Mountains
4. Plains and Plateaus

V. PICTURE STUDY

Knowledge Application **Critical Thinking**

In the given picture, you can see two landforms that you studied in this chapter. Answer the following questions with respect to the picture.

1. Name the two landforms.
2. List two features of each of the two landforms.
3. Give two examples of each of the two landforms.
4. State two ways you can prevent pollution in both the landforms. Why is it important to conserve resources ?

VI. SOURCE BASED QUESTIONS

Analysing **Conceptual Learning** **Understanding**

Read the given paragraph and answer the following questions.

Plains are extremely flat and low-lying lands found on the Earth's surface. Generally, they are not more than 200 metres above the mean sea level. Plains can be formed by the deposition of sediments bought by the rivers and their tributaries. These regions are suitable for agriculture due to their fertile soil and easy accessibility.

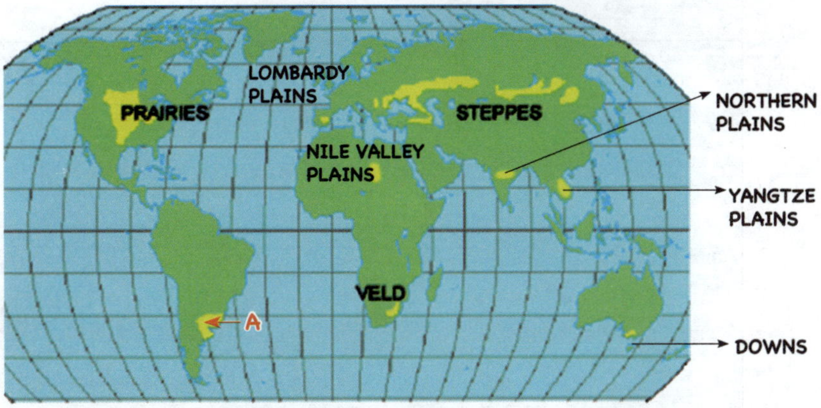

Plains of the World

1. *Which of these plains is marked as* **'A'** *on the world map ?*
   (*a*) Pampas Plains (*b*) Indo-Gangetic Plains
   (*c*) Downs Plains (*d*) Lombardy Plains
2. *How would you describe plains based on the above paragraph ?*
   (*a*) Hilly and mountainous regions. (*b*) Volcanic regions with active lava flows.
   (*c*) Extensive flat lands with low elevation. (*d*) Deep ocean trenches and canyons.
3. *Which of these plains are found in North America ?*
   (*a*) Pampas (*b*) Prairies (*c*) Velds (*d*) Downs
4. *What geological processes can lead to the formation of plains ?*
   (*a*) Volcanic eruptions and earthquakes. (*b*) Deposition of silt and sediments.
   (*c*) Melting of glaciers and ice sheets. (*d*) Uplifting of land through tectonic forces.

5. *Which of these key characteristics makes plains suitable for agriculture ?*
   (*a*) They have hilly terrain and arid climate.
   (*b*) They have abundant rainfall and frequent floods.
   (*c*) They have fertile soil and are easy to access.
   (*d*) They have steep slopes, ideal for terrace farming.

VII. MAP SKILL

Knowledge Application | Experiential Learning

On the given outline map of the world, mark the following :

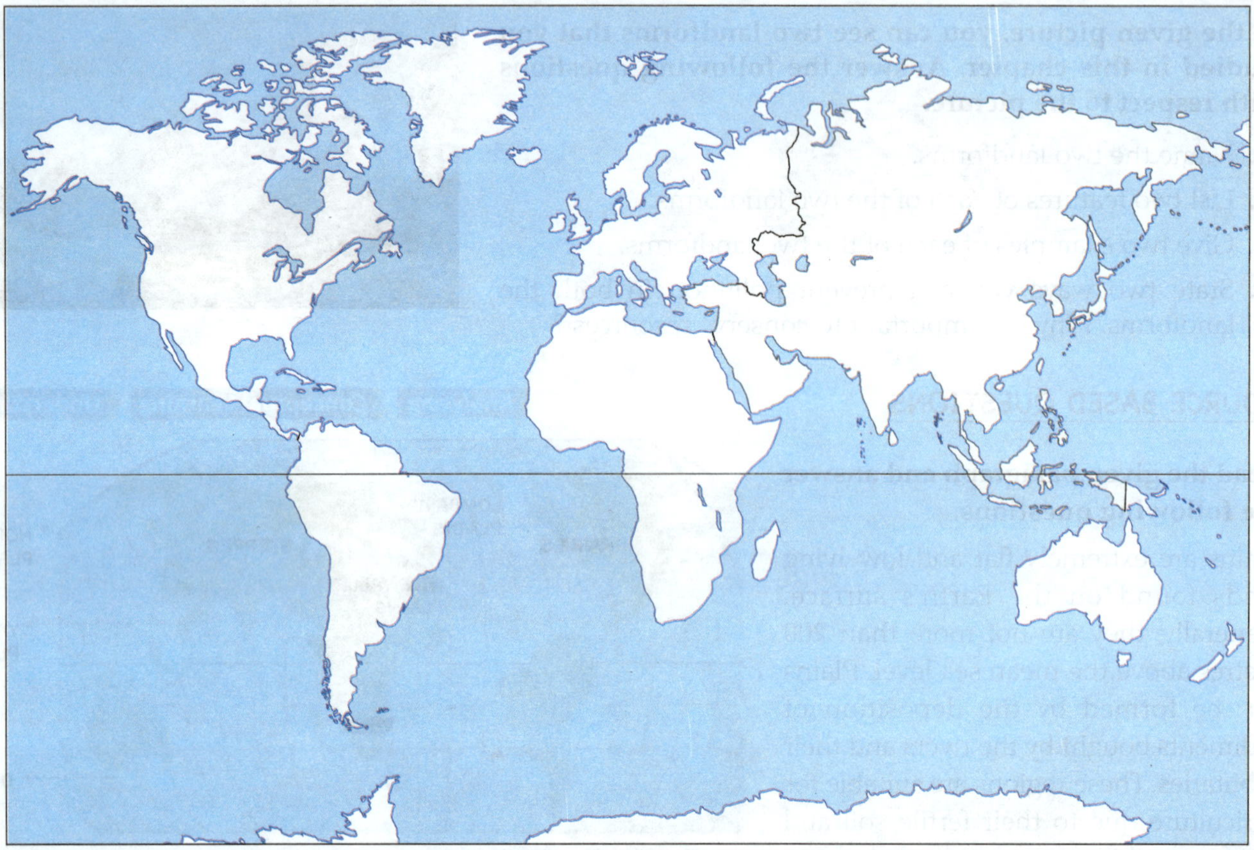

1. **Mountains :** Himalayas, Alps, Andes, Rocky, Kilimanjaro, Black Forest, Urals, Appalachians, Aravallis.
2. **Plains :** Northern Plains, Nile Valley, Prairies, Downs, Pampas.
3. **Plateaus :** Deccan, Tibet, Mongolian, Colorado, Plateau of Spain.

ACTIVITIES & PROJECTS

Multidisciplinary Approach | Creativity and Innovation

1. Work in groups to make clay models of different landforms like mountains, plains, plateaus and organise a quiz competition in the class for locating important landforms on the world map.
2. Collect pictures of the different landforms you have learnt and make a collage. You can collect pictures from different magazines, newspapers or the internet.
3. You must have all gone to different places either by a car, taxi, bus, train or plane. You must have seen different types of landforms on the way. Recollect your experiences and share them with your class.
4. You studied about three landforms and the economic activities of people in these landforms. Write a note on the co-relation of different types of livelihood activities with different types of landforms.

Theme B—Tapestry of the Past

CHAPTER 4

Timeline and Sources of History

CG-1 : C-1.1, C-1.2; CG-2 : C-2.1, C-2.2; CG-3 : C-3.1

What's new to learn

- How do We Learn about the Past ?
- How is Time Measured in History ?
- What are the Sources of History ?
- The Beginnings of Human History

What is History ?

History is the study of past events. It involves the study of societies, cultures, people, events and problems that existed in the past and that have shaped the present and would also influence the future. With the help of various sources, historians collect information, observe and analyse them and come to conclusions regarding our past and its effect on the present and future. History covers political, social, economic, religious, scientific, cultural, intellectual as well as technological aspects of human society.

HOW DO WE LEARN ABOUT THE PAST ?

Who are the people who study history and bring the past before us ? There are a number of people who help us in finding out about the past.

Some of these are :

A historical document

An inscription

A Geologist

An Anthropologist

- **Historians :** These are people who are specialists in the field of history. They conduct research, observe and analyse the resources, and finally interpret the historical events. They generally focus their research on a particular theme, time frame or region. They present their findings to the world through articles in newspapers, journals and books.
- **Archaeologists :** They work at particular sites and conduct excavations. They interpret history through the physical remains found in the excavations like fossils, artefacts, pottery, tools, ornaments, beads, figures and figurines, toys, burnt grains, ruins of buildings and houses, bricks, bones and teeth of men and animals, etc.

An Archaeologist

- **Epigraphists :** These are specialists in the study of inscriptions. They study the words that are written or inscribed on hard materials like stone, metals or clay.
- **Genealogists :** These people use historical records to study family history and lineages. They trace family trees and try to understand the social and cultural life of our ancestors.
- **Geologists :** They study the history of the Earth, its nature, materials and processes. They also study human impact on the Earth and its resources, formation of physical features of the Earth like rocks, hills, mountains, oceans, rivers, seas, soils, etc.
- **Palaeontologists :** They study the history of life on Earth through the study of fossils. Fossils are the remains of plants, animals, fungi, bacteria, etc. which are atleast 10,000 years old and are preserved in rocks or soil.
- **Anthropologists :** They study human societies and cultures both from the past and the present. They try to interpret and understand the social and cultural aspects of different periods.

A Palaeontologist

HOW IS TIME MEASURED IN HISTORY ?

If somebody asks your date of birth, what would you say ? Suppose, you say, 15 (Date)/ 04 (Month)/2015 (Year) , then, do you know how these days, months and years are counted ?

In the study of history also, we notice dates, years, decades, centuries, etc. *For example,* 273 BC or AD 711. What does BC or AD mean ? How is it calculated ?

These dates or years are counted from the assumed date of birth of Jesus Christ who was the founder of Christianity.

BC (BCE)

BC stands for 'Before Christ.' All dates before the birth of Jesus Christ are expressed in BC. They are counted backwards. *For example,* 273 BC means 273 years before the birth of Christ.

BCE stands for 'Before Common Era.' BCE is also used instead of BC, but since Christian Era is now used in most countries of the world, we use BC.

AD (CE)

AD stands for two Latin words, 'Anno Domini,' that means in the year of the Lord (*i.e.,* Christ.)

CE is also used in place of AD. It stands for 'Common Era'.

All dates or years after the birth of Jesus Christ are expressed in AD. These years are counted forwards. *For example,* 2011 can also be written as AD 2011 *i.e.,* 2011 years after the birth of Jesus Christ.

Jesus Christ

> **MORE TO KNOW**
>
> Vikram Samvat is an ancient Hindu calendar system that is widely used in India and Nepal. It is a lunisolar calendar, which means that it follows both the lunar and solar cycles. It was started in 57 B.C. by King Vikramaditya of Ujjain after he gained victory over the Sakas. The year count of the Vikram Samvat calendar is usually 57 years ahead of the Gregorian calendar. The calendar is based on the Moon's movement and has 354 days a year, with 12 months divided into two phases. The year begins in the month of Vaishak, which usually falls in February or March and ends in Chaitra, which falls in March or April. It is still used by many communities to mark festivals and plan agricultural activities, religious events, auspicious occasions, festivals, etc.
>
> It is the official calendar of Nepal and is used for all administrative purposes.

At present, the commonly used calendar to measure and calculate time is the Gregorian Calendar. But, in this calendar, there is no 'year zero'. The year 1 CE follows immediately the year 1 BCE.

To find out the difference between two dates that are either both in BC or both in AD, we subtract the smaller date from the bigger one.

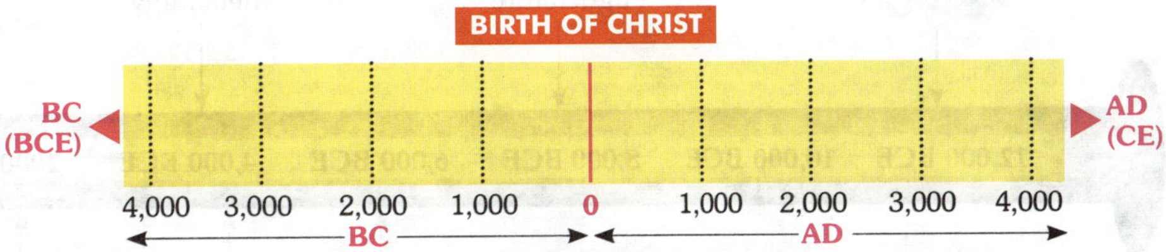

Timeline

For example, the time difference between 2,000 BC and 500 BC = 2,000 BC – 500 BC = 1,500 years. Similar is the case with AD.

On the other hand, to calculate the time difference between two dates where one is in BC and the other is in AD, we add the two dates and subtract 1 to adjust the 0 year. *For example,* for calculating the time difference between 500 BC and AD 1,500 we first add *i.e.,* 500 years + 1,500 years = 2,000 years and now subtract 1, so, 2000 – 1 = 1999 years.

BP

Sometimes, BP *i.e.,* Before Present is also used to denote past events.

For the convenience of our study, we assume 2,000 AD/CE as the present age.

In India, we began to use the terms BC and AD about 200 years ago under the influence of the Britishers. Earlier we calculated dates according to the Vikram Samvat.

Timeline

A timeline is a representation of events in a chronological order. It helps us to determine the order in which the events occurred and the time intervals between them. The events on a timeline are listed according to the order in which they occurred from the earliest to the most recent. A timeline also contains summaries of the events mentioned so as to provide some context to the readers. It may be linear, vertical or horizontal and may also contain visual elements like lines, arrows, icons or images for better understanding.

In history, a timeline helps the historians as well as students to understand the chronology of historical events like the rule of dynasties, the rise and fall of civilizations and empires, important wars, discoveries and inventions.

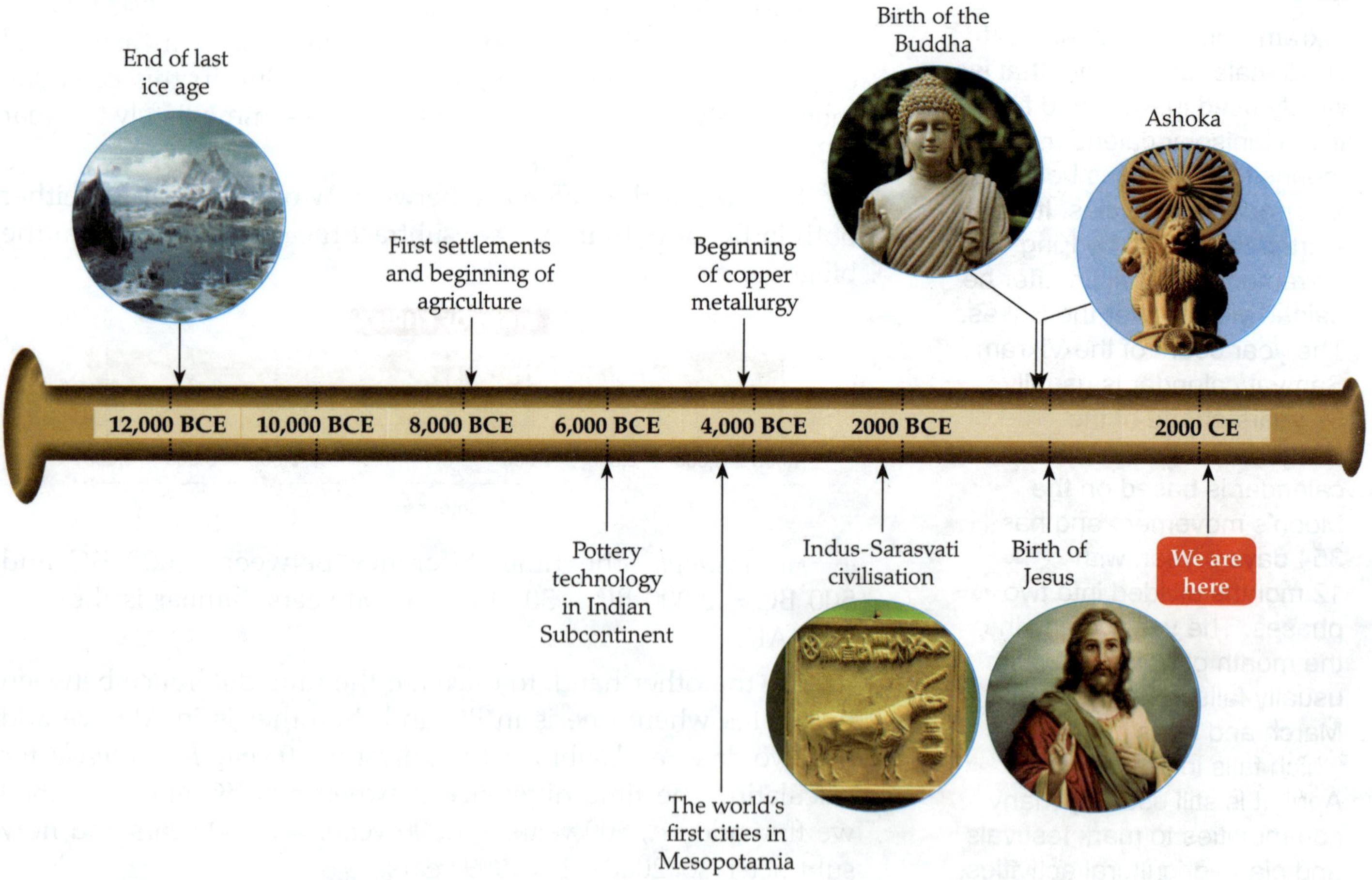

Important Terms Associated with Time

- **Year :** A period of 365 or 366 days, in the Gregorian calendar, divided into 12 calendar months, beginning from January 1 and ending on December 31.

- **Decade :** A period of 10 years, *for example,* the 1990s represents the period from 1990–1999. They share the same tens digit.
- **Century :** A period of 100 years. It is generally used to state a date. *For example,* the 19th century is the period from 1801-1900. At present, we are in the 21st century that runs from 2001 to 2100.
- **Millennium :** A period of 1,000 years or the time when a period of 1000 years ends. *For example,* at present we are in the third millennium which began in 2001 CE and will end in 3000 CE.

Check Your Progress — Understanding

A. State whether True or false

1. History is the study of past events.
2. An archaeologist traces family trees and lineages.
3. Fossils are the remains of dead plants, animals, fungi, etc.
4. Jesus Christ was the founder of Christianity.
5. A timeline does not contain visual images or summaries.

B. Talk to an elder person in your family like your grandfather or grandmother. Ask them about the important events of their life and note down the dates on which the events occurred. Now, prepare a timeline based on the information you have gathered by using symbols, arrows, summary, etc.

WHAT ARE THE SOURCES OF HISTORY ?

Clues and evidence on the basis of which we write history are known as sources. Historians use different types of sources to learn about the past. The sources they choose, depend upon the period of their study and the nature of their investigation.

The sources of history are collected and interpreted by historians, archaeologists, genealogists, anthropologists, epigraphists etc, about whom you have studied earlier in this chapter. While gathering information about any particular event, place or person, they take great care and refer to as many sources as possible related to that event, place or person. It may happen that sometimes the information from different sources relates to each other while at other times, the sources give contradictory information. In case of the latter, it is upto the historians to decide which source to trust and which to not.

Sanchi Stupa, Madhya Pradesh

Some of the main sources of history are as follows :

- **Remains of Buildings or Monuments :** Any structure, building or site that is of historical, archaeological or artistic interest and is not less than 100 years old is considered an "Ancient Monument" in India.

Coins of Samudragupta's Reign

It may either be buried, as in the case of Harappa and Mohenjo-daro, or it may still be standing like the Red Fort in Delhi, the Taj Mahal in Agra, etc. Monuments may be in the form of temples, forts, palaces, stupas, monasteries, mausolea, etc. They provide useful information about the development of art and architecture, as well as the social and economic life of the people of the times when they were constructed.

- **Coins :** The study of coins is known as 'Numismatics'. Coins tell us about kings, the extent of their empires, dates, languages that were in use, trade, art, religion and literary skills of a particular time. *For example,* the coins of Samudragupta show that he was an efficient Veena player.
- **Other Objects :** Archaeologists find out, explore and unearth tools, weapons, pots, pans and ornaments by digging under the surface of the Earth. These objects may be made of stone, bone, baked clay or metal. Archaeologists also look for the bones of animals, fish and birds to determine the food of early man. The plant remains such as seeds of grains or wood are rarely available. They are mostly found in charred form.

Stone tools

Weapons

Pots

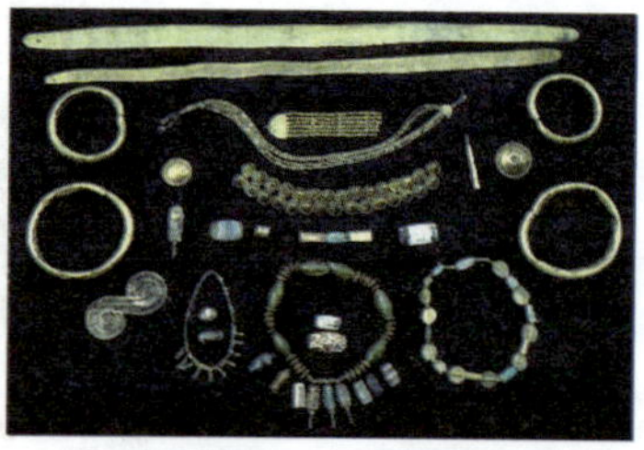

Ornaments

- **Manuscripts (*Literary Sources*) :** The books that were written by hand long ago are called manuscripts (It comes from the Latin word 'manu' meaning hand). Usually, two types of materials were used for writing manuscripts—palm leaves and a specially prepared bark of a tree known as the birch that grows in the Himalayas. These manuscripts are in the form of epics, poems and plays. They were written in Sanskrit, Prakrit (language of ordinary people) and Tamil. Although many manuscripts have been destroyed by the insects, some of them are still preserved in temples and monasteries. They give us information on the lives of kings, religious beliefs and practices, science, medicine, etc.

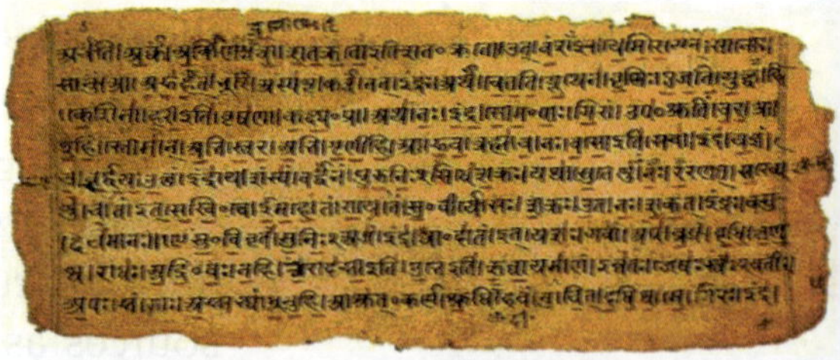

A manuscript

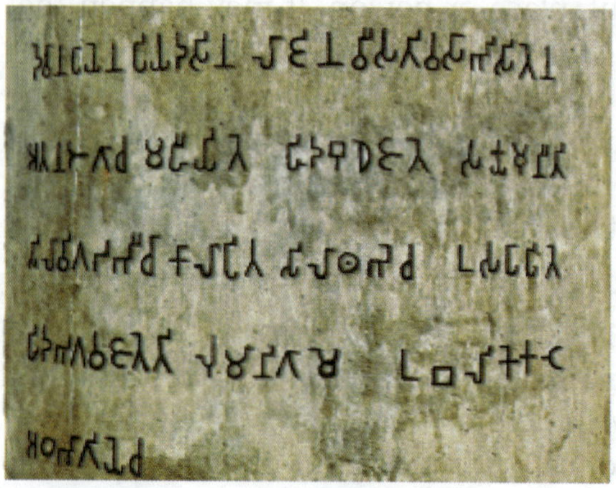

Ashokan Pillar Inscription in Brahmi Script at Lumbini

- **Inscriptions :** These are writings on relatively hard surfaces like stone and metals or can be on paper also (anything can be inscribed). They generally conveyed the king's orders, their deeds, their preachings, etc. *For example,* the inscriptions of Asoka. Kings often kept records of victories in battles as inscriptions. Some inscriptions also contain the records of ordinary men and women. The study of inscriptions is known as Epigraphy. Decipherment is the process of reading and understanding the script used in inscriptions. Scripts consist of signs or letters.

In the last 50 years, scientific studies have increasingly contributed to our understanding and reconstruction of the past. Through various technologies, new insights have been provided that help to reconstruct a more accurate, precise and detailed picture of the past. Scientific studies go beyond the traditional methods of interpreting history and give new insights into the life of our ancestors and their societies. They have enhanced our understanding of different historical events and human evolution. *For example,* Radiocarbon dating is a scientific method that is used to determine the age of organic materials, such as wood, bones and seeds, up to about 50,000 years old. This technique helps us in a better understanding of the chronology of historical events. Satellite Imagery helps to identify and monitor archaeological sites from space. Genetic Analysis helps to understand the movement of people and genetic diversity. Historians also take help of newspapers and historical journals to study the history of the last two or three centuries. They also refer to electronic media like the internet and television to study about the last few decades.

Think & Answer

Suppose you are an archaeologist and you have to conduct excavations at a site. Write a note on the techniques you will use to find out the sources of history. Also, mention the challenges you faced in your work.

Check Your Progress — Understanding

Fill in the blanks

1. The Red Fort is in ______________.
2. The study of coins is known as ______________.
3. The books that were written by hand long ago are called ______________.
4. The study of inscriptions is known as ______________.
5. Satellite Imagery helps to identify and monitor archaeological sites from ______________.

THE BEGINNINGS OF HUMAN HISTORY

The first *Homo sapiens* (modern humans) appeared on the Earth around 300,000 years ago in Africa. This marked the beginning of human history. Around 60,000 to 70,000 years ago, the Homo sapiens started to migrate out of Africa and spread to various parts of the world like Asia, Europe and America. This gradually led to the distribution of human population around the world and the development of various cultures and civilizations.

Early man was a hunter-gatherer

Early man was a hunter-gatherer. He hunted animals and gathered fruits, nuts and plant roots for food. He led a nomadic life mostly in search of food, shelter and resources. He mostly lived in groups to provide support and help to each other. He lived in natural shelters like caves and rock shelters or built simple huts with the materials available in the forests. He wore animal skin to protect himself from extreme cold. He was the first to make tools from bone, wood and stone. The main tools were hand axes, arrowheads, blades, knives, needles and spears. He used these tools for hunting, cutting and making huts.

Discovery and use of Fire

Discovery of fire was one of the greatest achievements of early man. Fire was used to cook food, for protection against wild animals and as a means to provide warmth. Early man also communicated with each other through gestures, sounds and simple languages that are lost now. Communication helped him during hunting and during migration to new places. In course of time, he also learnt to make simple ornaments like pendants from animal teeth and stone or shell beads. He exchanged these ornaments with people from other groups.

Cave painting

Numerous cave paintings have been discovered from all over the world that reflect the daily life, beliefs and practices of early man. Mostly the cave paintings and carvings depict hunting scenes, animals and humans. It is believed that early man also had some beliefs about nature and afterlife.

The First Crops

Millions of years ago, there was a time when the temperature of the Earth was extremely cold and most of the Earth's surface was covered with thick sheets of ice and glaciers. This period was known as the **Ice Age.** During this time, large parts of North America, Europe and Asia were covered with ice. Large volumes of water was trapped in the ice. People and animals adapted to these harsh conditions of climate by developing new tools, shelter and clothing. Some species migrated to warmer regions in search of food. The last Ice Age known as the **Pleistocene Ice Age**, lasted from over 100,000 years ago and ended around 12,000 years ago.

An Early village

Around this time, the climate of the world became relatively warm. With an increase in temperatures, the ice in glaciers melted and there was now abundant water in the rivers. Grasslands developed naturally in many areas of the world. Several grain bearing grasses including wheat, barley and rice grew naturally in different parts of the subcontinent. People observed these changes and started to grow crops and became farmers. Wheat and barley were the first cereals to be grown. Later on, people started cultivating more food crops like rice and lentils as well as cotton, jute, etc. They used simple tools such as hoes and crude plough and harvested the crops with sickles made of flint. People now became food producers from food gatherers. Their lives changed for the better. As they had to look after the crops they grew, people now began to give up their nomadic lives and started to settle down. They built mud houses with thatched roofs and began to live in groups in small villages. They mostly chose to settle near rivers as they could get fertile soil as well as plenty of water for agriculture and everyday use.

Domestication of animals

People also started to domesticate animals like sheep, goats, cattle, pigs, camels, horses and donkeys. This solved the problem of food for early man to a great extent. Dogs helped people in saving their lives from dangerous wild animals. Animals like cows, goats, sheep, camels provided fresh milk. They also got meat from goats, sheep, etc. Thus, the animals that were reared, could be used as a 'store' of food. Now, humans did not have to go on dangerous hunting trips in search of food.

Domesticated animals also helped the early man in agricultural work. Bullocks, donkeys, horses and camels were used for riding and ploughing the field. These animals provided manure to increase the fertility of the soil.

The animals also helped in solving the problem of clothing. They provided wool and skin which people used as clothes. The animals also multiplied naturally. Thus, domestication made human lives much easier and safer than the lives of early hunter-gatherers.

The settlement of people in groups led to the formation of the earliest communities. As you have read earlier, these communities settled near rivers like the Indus, Nile and Euphrates. People gradually built permanent houses, developed new tools for agriculture, began to store surplus food and also developed new crafts to fulfil their other needs. They worked together to cultivate land, raise animals and protect each other. The lands, forests, grasslands, water and their usage were regarded as the wealth of the entire community. They were shared and used by all men together. Rich and poor lived in harmony and worked for each other's welfare.

DO YOU KNOW?

Which form of settlement is called a village ?

The basic feature of a village is that most people who live there are engaged in food production.

This period also witnessed the development of complex social structures. There were some men who were regarded as leaders by the community because of their inherent qualities like bravery, wisdom and ability to lead. These leaders came to be known as "chieftains". They could be old and experienced men or young brave warriors. They took decisions on behalf of the community, resolved disputes and managed the distribution of food and resources. They also protected people from wild animals and conflicts with other communities. Old women were respected for their wisdom and experience.

With the growth in population, gradually the small villages or hamlets grew in size. To meet their needs, people developed networks of communication and also traded with each other. They exchanged products like food, tools and raw materials. They also shared knowledge and developed cultural practices. They developed new technology for making advanced tools, pottery, ornaments and clay objects. This was also the time when humans first used metals. Copper was the first metal to be used by humans for making tools and ornaments around 8,000 BCE. Iron was discovered around 3,000 BCE. The use of iron marked significant advancements in agriculture, warfare and construction as the tools and weapons made of iron were more strong and durable.

All these developments and advancements in the life of early man led to the formation of more complex societies and civilizations about which you will study in chapter 6.

MORE TO KNOW

What is domestication ?

It is the process in which people grow plants and look after animals.

Why do the tamed plants that are tended by people generally become different from wild plants ?

This is because people select only those plants and animals that are not prone to disease. They select plants that yield large size grain and have strong stalks that could bear the weight of the ripe grain. Seeds from selected plants are preserved and sown to ensure that new plants would be of the same quality. Animals that are relatively gentle are selected for domestication. The earliest plants that were domesticated were wheat and barley and the earliest animals domesticated were sheep and goat.

Check Your Progress

Understanding

State whether True or False

1. Early man was a hunter-gatherer.
2. Early man made his tools himself.
3. People did not settle near river valleys.
4. Resources were in the hands of only a few people.
5. Copper was the first metal to be used by humans.

NEW WORDS

- **Lithosphere :** The hard crust of the Earth on which we live.
- **Historian :** A person who studies and writes about the past.
- **Archaeologist :** A person who works at particular sites and conducts excavations.
- **Epigraphist :** A person who is a specialist in the study of inscriptions.
- **Genealogist :** A person who uses historical records to study family history and lineages.
- **Geologists :** A person who studies the history of the Earth, its nature, materials and processes.
- **Palaeontologist :** A person who studies the history of life on Earth through the study of fossils.
- **Anthropologist :** A person who studies human societies and cultures both from the past and the present.
- **Fossils :** Impressions of footprints or parts of plants or animals that are found preserved within layers of soil or rocks.

- **Era :** A distinct period of time.
- **Gregorian calendar :** The calendar now used the world over; it has 12 months adding up to 365 days and a leap year every four years. However, century years — *for example,* 1800, 1900, 2000 — are leap years only if they are multiples of 400; so in the three centenary years above, only 2000 is a leap year.
- **Timeline :** A timeline is a representation of events in a chronological order.
- **Numismatics :** The study of coins.
- **Auspicious :** Favourable or bringing luck
- **Archaeology :** The study of human history and prehistory through the excavation of sites and the analysis of artefacts and other physical remains.
- **Inscription :** A thing inscribed, as on a monument or in a book.
- **Manuscript :** A book or document written by hand generally on palm leaves or on bark of a birch tree.
- **Source :** Historians used the word 'source' to refer to information found from manuscripts, inscriptions and archaeology.
- **Source of history :** A place, person, text or an object from which we gather information about some past event or period.
- **Ice-Age :** The time when the temperature of the Earth was extremely cold and most of the Earth's surface was covered with thick sheets of ice and glaciers.
- **Welfare :** Health, prosperity and well-being.
- **Domestication :** Act of taming and keeping animals as pets and growing plants.
- **Farmers :** Persons who grow crops or manage farms.
- **Herders :** Persons who look after a herd of livestock.
- **Hamlet :** A small settlement or small village.

NUTSHELL

- History is the study of past events.
- History covers political, social , economic, religious, scientific, cultural, intellectual as well as technological aspects of human society.
- BC stands for 'Before Christ.' All dates before the birth of Christ are expressed in BC. They are counted backwards.
- AD stands for two Latin words, 'Anno Domini,' that means 'in the year of the Lord' (*i.e., Christ*). All dates or years after the birth of Jesus Christ are expressed in AD. These years are counted forwards.
- A timeline is a representation of events in a chronological order.
- Clues and evidence on the basis of which we write history are known as sources.
- Any structure, building or site that is of historical, archaeological or artistic interest and is not less than 100 years old is considered an "Ancient Monument" in India.
- The study of coins is known as 'Numismatics'.
- The books that were written by hand long ago are called manuscripts.
- Inscriptions are writings on relatively hard surfaces *e.g.,* stone, metal or paper.
- In the last 50 years, scientific methods like radiocarbon dating, satellite imagery, genetic analysis, etc. have increasingly contributed to our understanding and reconstruction of the past.
- The first **Homo Sapiens** (*modern humans*) appeared on the Earth around 300,000 years ago in Africa.
- Early man was a hunter-gatherer.

- The Ice Age was the time when the temperature of the Earth was extremely cold and most of the Earth's surface was covered with thick sheets of ice and glaciers.
- The last Ice Age, known as the **Pleistocene Ice Age**, lasted from over 100,000 years ago and ended around 12,000 years ago.
- Wheat and barley were the first cereals to be grown.
- Early man domesticated animals like sheep, goats, cattle, pigs, camels, horses and donkeys.
- The settlement of people in groups led to the formation of the earliest communities.
- Chieftains were regarded as leaders by the community because of their inherent qualities like bravery, wisdom and ability to lead.
- Copper was the first metal to be used by humans for making tools and ornaments around 8,000 BCE.
- Iron was discovered around 3,000 BCE.

IMPORTANT NCERT TEXTBOOK QUESTIONS (Solved)

Questions, activities and projects

1. As a project, write the history of your family *(or village if you live in one)*, using sources of history at your disposal. Ask your teacher to guide you.

Ans. Students will do themselves. They can use sources of history like old photographs, diaries, ID cards, letters and other family related documents.

2. Can we compare historians to detectives ? Give reasons for your answers.

Ans. Yes, we can surely compare historians to detectives as they both perform nearly the same tasks to obtain their objectives. The reasons for this comparison are :

- **Investigation :** Both the historians and detectives investigate the events. While historians investigate the events using a variety of sources, the detectives investigate the crime scenes.
- **Collection of evidence :** Historians collect evidence like pottery, sculptures, writings, manuscripts, etc. to prove their points while detectives collect evidence like fingerprints, DNA samples, statements of witnesses, etc. from the crime scenes.
- **Analysis and Interpretation :** Historians analyse the different sources of history, arrange them chronologically and interpret the events based on the analysis. Detectives also carry out analysis on the basis of the evidence collected and try to understand the sequence in which the crime was committed.
- **Critical Thinking and Formation of Theories :** Historians use their ability to think critically to assess the reliability of various sources and evidences and form theories on this basis. Detectives also use critical thinking to examine the various aspects of cases and give emphasis to the minutest of details.
- **Conclusion :** Historians finally come to a conclusion about events of history and present their findings in journals, articles, books, etc. to inform the public about it. Detectives present their final conclusions in reports and courts and aim to bring justice for the victims and punishments for the accused.

3. **A few exercises with dates :**

* **Place these dates chronologically on the timeline : 323 CE, 323 BCE, 100 CE, 100 BCE, 1900 BCE, 1090 CE, 2024 CE.**

Ans. 1900 BCE, 323 BCE, 100 BCE, 100 CE, 323 CE, 1090 CE, 2024 CE

* **If King Chandragupta was born in 320 CE, which century did he belong to ? And how many years was that after the Buddha's birth ?**

Ans. 320 CE is the 4th century as the 1st century runs from 1-100 CE and so on. So, 320 CE will lie in 300-400 CE. So, King Chandragupta belonged to the 4th century.

King Chandragupta's birth year is 320 CE

Gautama Buddha's birth year is 560 BCE

So the number of years from 560 BCE to 320 CE will be : $320 + 560 - 1 = 879$ years.

* **Rani of Jhansi was born in 1828. Which century did she belong to ? How many years was that before India's Independence ?**

Ans. Birth year of Rani of Jhansi is 1828 CE, this falls in 19th century (1801-1900 CE)

India gained independence in 1947

So, the number of years in between Rani of Jhansi 's birth and Indian Independence :

$1947 - 1828 = 119$ years.

* **Turn '12,000 years ago' into a date.**

Ans. Present year is 2024 CE

So, 12,000 years ago the date was $2024 - 12{,}000 = -9976$ or 9976 BC

4. **Plan a visit to a nearby museum : the visit should be prepared with some prior research on the kind of exhibits the museum holds. Keep notes during the visit. Write a brief report afterwards, highlighting what was unexpected / interesting / fun about the visit and the exhibits.**

Ans. Students will do themselves.

5. **Invite to your school an archaeologist or a historian and ask them to speak on the history of your region and why it's important to know it.**

Ans. Students will do themselves.

I. OBJECTIVE TYPE QUESTIONS

A. Choose the correct answer.

Conceptual Learning | Critical Thinking

1. *Which of the following aspects does history cover ?*

   (*a*) Political (*b*) Social

   (*c*) Scientific (*d*) All of these

2. *People who are specialists in the study of inscriptions are called*

   (*a*) Geologists (*b*) Archaeologists

   (*c*) Epigraphists (*d*) Genealogists

3. *In BC, years are counted*
   (*a*) Backwards (*b*) Forward
   (*c*) Both Backward and Forward (*d*) None of these

4. *Manuscripts were written in*
   (*a*) Sanskrit (*b*) Prakrit (*c*) Tamil (*d*) All of these

5. *Which of the following is NOT a feature of Early Man ?*
   (*a*) Early man was a hunter-gatherer.
   (*b*) He led a nomadic life mostly in search of food, shelter and resources.
   (*c*) He lived in well developed cities.
   (*d*) He was the first to make tools from bone, wood and stone.

B. Mark the option that matches Column A with Column B.

Conceptual Learning | Problem Solving

Column A	Column B
1. Year	(*i*) A period of 100 years
2. Decade	(*ii*) A period of 1,000 years
3. Century	(*iii*) A period of 365 or 366 days
4. Millenium	(*iv*) A period of 10 years

(*a*) **1.**-(*iii*), **2.**-(*iv*), **3.**-(*i*), **4.**-(*ii*) (*b*) **1.**-(*iii*), **2.**-(*ii*), **3.**-(*iv*), **4.**-(*i*)
(*c*) **1.**-(*iii*), **2.**-(*iv*), **3.**-(*ii*), **4.**-(*ii*) (*d*) **1.**-(*i*), **2.**-(*ii*), **3.**-(*iii*), **4.**-(*iv*)

C. Fill in the blanks

Knowledge Application

1.

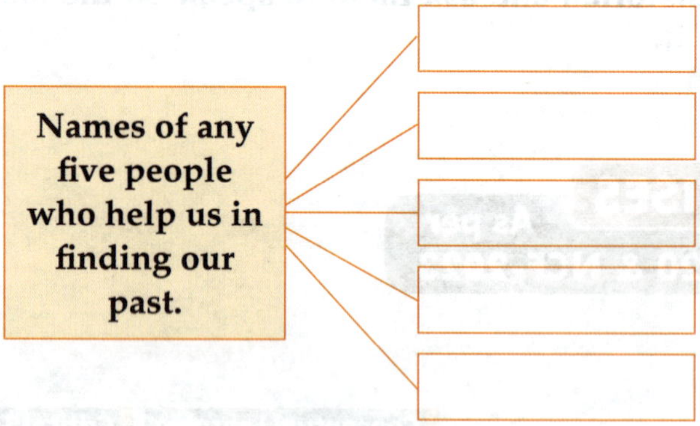

2.

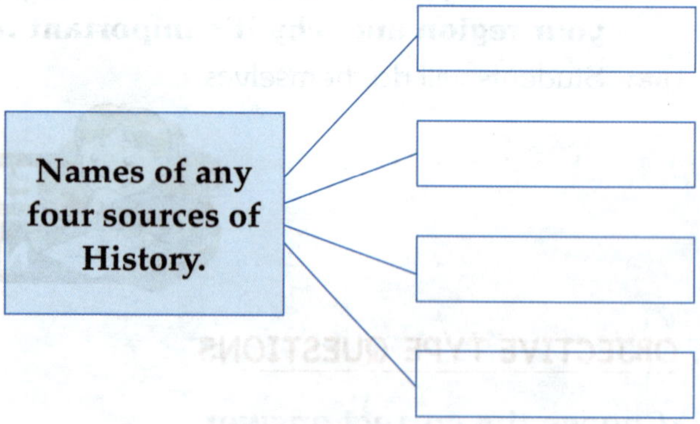

D. State True or False

Knowledge Application | Problem Solving

1. Hunter-gatherers were the people who hunted and gathered their food.
2. Manuscripts are the handwritten materials which reflect our rich past.
3. Specially handwritten books on birch bark are called inscriptions.
4. Archaeologists are the persons who explore and excavate the sites to know about our past heritage.
5. Gold was the first metal to be used by Early Man.

E. Assertion-Reason

Critical Thinking

For question numbers 1 to 4, two statements are given—one labelled Assertion (A) and the other labelled Reason (R). Select the correct answer to these questions from the codes (*a*), (*b*), (*c*) and (*d*) as given below :

(*a*) Both Assertion (A) and Reason (R) are true and Reason is the correct explanation of the Assertion.

(*b*) Both Assertion (A) and Reason (R) are true but Reason is not the correct explanation of the Assertion.

(*c*) Assertion (A) is true but Reason (R) is false.

(*d*) Assertion (A) is false but Reason (R) is true.

1. **Assertion (A)** : People settled on the banks of rivers.
   Reason (R) : They got plenty of water to fulfill their needs.
2. **Assertion (A)** : The earliest crops grown were sugarcane and banana.
   Reason (R) : Early man also domesticated animals.
3. **Assertion (A)** : Literary sources include manuscripts.
   Reason (R) : Inscriptions are writings on hard surfaces.
4. **Assertion (A)** : Scientific studies have enhanced our understanding of different historical events and human evolution.
   Reason (R) : The study of Social Science does not involve scientific studies.

II. SHORT ANSWER TYPE QUESTIONS

Conceptual Learning | Knowledge Application

1. Write a note on the life of hunter-gatherers.
2. How did people begin growing crops such as wheat and barley ?
3. "Animals played a key role in the life of Early man". Do you agree with this statement ? Why ?
4. Discuss the role of Chieftains in communities.

III. LONG ANSWER TYPE QUESTIONS

Knowledge Application | Critical Thinking

1. Write a note on the role of historians and archaeologists in finding about the past.
2. Explain how a timeline helps historians and students.
3. Describe any three sources of history.
4. Discuss how the life of Early man changed after the last Ice Age.

IV. DISTINGUISH BETWEEN THE FOLLOWING

Conceptual Learning | Understanding

1. Genealogist and Geologist
2. BC and AD
3. Manuscripts and inscriptions.

V. PICTURE STUDY

Knowledge Application **Critical Thinking**

Study the following pictures that includes images of various sources of history.

(i)

(ii)

(iii)

(iv)

1. Identify the various sources of history.
2. Make a separate list for each category such as archaeological sources, manuscripts and inscriptions.

VI. SOURCE BASED QUESTIONS

Analysing **Conceptual Learning** **Understanding**

- **Read the given paragraph and answer the questions that follow :**

Remains of Buildings or Monuments

Any structure, building or site that is of historical, archaeological or artistic interest and is not less than 100 years old is considered an "Ancient Monument" in India. It may either be buried, as in the case of Harappa and Mohenjo-daro, or it may still be standing like the Red Fort in Delhi, the Taj Mahal in Agra, etc. Monuments may be in the form of temples, forts, palaces, stupas, monasteries, mausolea, etc. They provide useful information about the development of art and architecture as well as the social and economic life of the people of the times when they were constructed.

1. *Which of the following options correctly tells the name and location of the monument shown in the picture given in the source (paragraph) ?*

   (*a*) Kesaria Stupa, Bihar (*b*) Mahabodhi Stupa, Bodh Gaya

   (*c*) Sanchi Stupa, Madhya Pradesh (*d*) Dhamek Stupa, Sarnath

2. *An ancient monument is considered as any structure, building or site that is :*

   (*a*) Historical (*b*) Archaeological

   (*c*) Not less than 100 years old (*d*) It includes all of these

3. *Consider the following statements regarding ancient monuments :*

   I. An ancient monument may be found buried under the ground.

   II. It may still be standing like the Red Fort in Delhi, the Taj Mahal in Agra, etc.

   III. It may be in the form of temples, forts, palaces, stupas, monasteries, etc.

   Which of the above statements is correct with reference to ancient monuments ?

   (*a*) Only I and II (*b*) Only II and III

   (*c*) Only I and III (*d*) All I, II and III

ACTIVITIES & PROJECTS

Multidisciplinary Approach | Creativity and Innovation

1. Sow some cereals in a pot and observe the growth of plants. Show different stages of its growth with the help of a chart.
2. Make some posters on the life of Early Man. Show them in your class and hold discussions on their way of living.
3. **Knowledge to be gained :** To explain the significance of historical places and monuments.

   Activity : Design a collage of historical places and monuments. The project will include images, geographical information and historical significance. Display the collage in your class and explain the significance of the historical places and monuments you studied for your activity.

   You will need :
   - Access to research materials (internet, library)
   - Art supplies (coloured pencils, crayons, markers)
   - Copies of pictures of historical places and monuments (as per your choice)
   - Map of region (as per your choice)
4. **Find out information and relevant pictures and make a scrapbook on the following topics :**
   - Archaeological sources of Ancient Indian history.
   - Literary sources of Ancient Indian history.

ROLE PLAY

Collaboration | Communication

- Work in pairs as archaeologists. Suppose you have found many objects while digging a site. Prepare a report on the objects found at the site and what conclusions can you draw from them.

WEB LINK

Digital Literacy

For further information log on to the following link :

- *http://www.webindia123.com/history/source.html*

CHAPTER 5

India, That Is Bharat

CG-1 : C-1.1, C-1.2; CG-7 : C-7.3

India is known throughout the world for its cultural heritage and diversity. India, as we call it today, was quite different from the present day political boundaries. The region referred to as "India" or "Bharat" included a much broader geographical area than today. India was also called by various names by different people which reflects the cultural and linguistic influences of the people that lived here. Throughout ancient history, many groups of people migrated and settled in India. In the present chapter, we will study the different names of India as it was called by the Indians and the foreigners. We get knowledge of these different names mainly from literary sources of history like ancient texts, accounts of foreign travellers and pilgrims and from inscriptions.

What's new to learn

- **How Indians Named India**
- **How Foreigners Named India**

HOW INDIANS NAMED INDIA

The various names used for India in the ancient Indian texts are as follows :

- **Sapta Sindhava** : The oldest Veda, Rigveda, mentions the name "Sapta Sindhava" which means "Land of the Seven Rivers" in Sanskrit. It refers to the region in the northwestern part of the Indian subcontinent. The word "Sindhava" comes from the word "Sindhu" which refers to the river Indus.

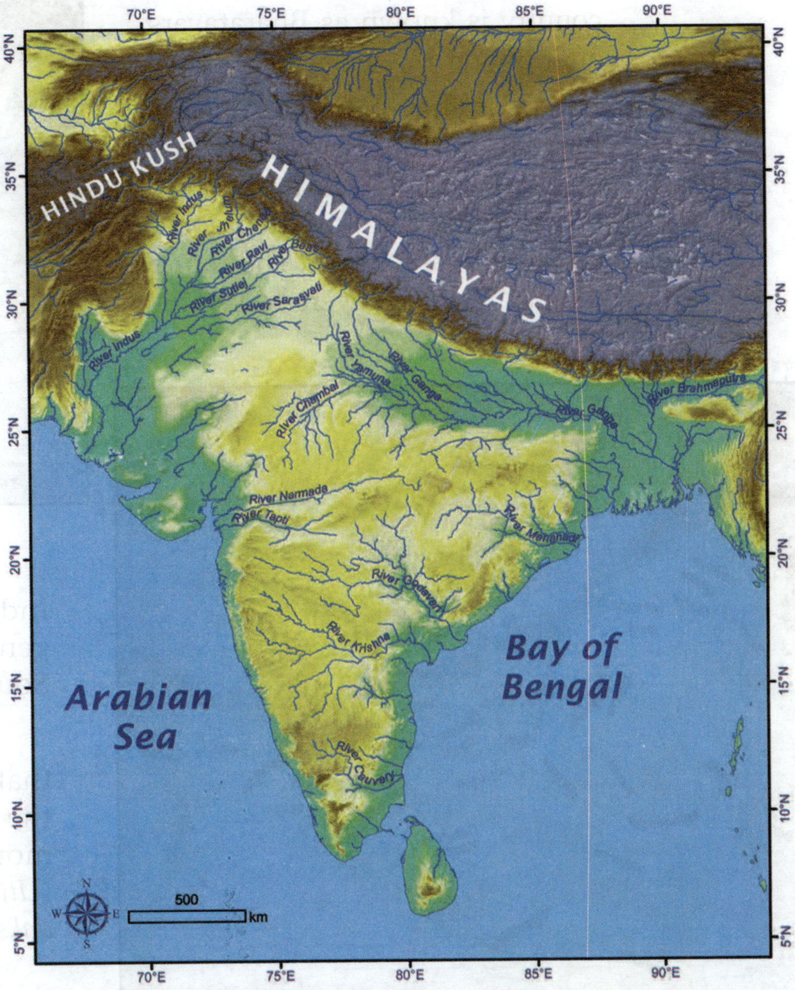

A physical map of the Indian Subcontinent, with some of its rivers.

The Rig Veda describes the Sapta Sindhava as a fertile and prosperous region that was drained by the rivers Indus and its five tributaries and the river Saraswati.

- **Bharata** : The term Bharata is first mentioned in the Rig Veda. It was used to describe a tribe or a group of people who lived in the northwest.
- **Bharatavarsha** : This term first appears in the Mahabharata, a famous ancient Indian epic poem. It was composed by Ved Vyasa from a few centuries BCE onward. According to this text, the term "Bharata" is from the king Bharat, who was the son of King Dushyant and Shakuntala and "vars" means a division of Earth. Thus, the term Bharatavarsha means the

DO YOU KNOW?

The Puranas

There are 18 Puranas that are supposed to have been compiled by Vyasa. The word 'Purana' means old. Puranas were originally orally narrated and later written down. They contain stories about Gods and Goddesses such as Shiva, Vishnu, Durga, Parvati, etc. and how they should be worshipped. They also describe the creation of the world, the solar system, the Earth, the family tree of Gods and Rishis and the royal families.

The Puranas were written in simple Sanskrit verse and were meant to educate the common people. They were recited by priests in temples.

country of the Bharatas and with passage of time, the term was used for the whole of India.

The Puranas like Vishnu Purana, Vayu Purana, Skanda Purana, Agni Purana, Brahmanda Purana, etc. also mention that this country is known as Bharatavars after Bharat.

According to the Bhagavata Purana, "He (Bharat) had the best qualities and it was because of him that this land by the people is called Bharatavars". The name 'Bharat' is used even today for

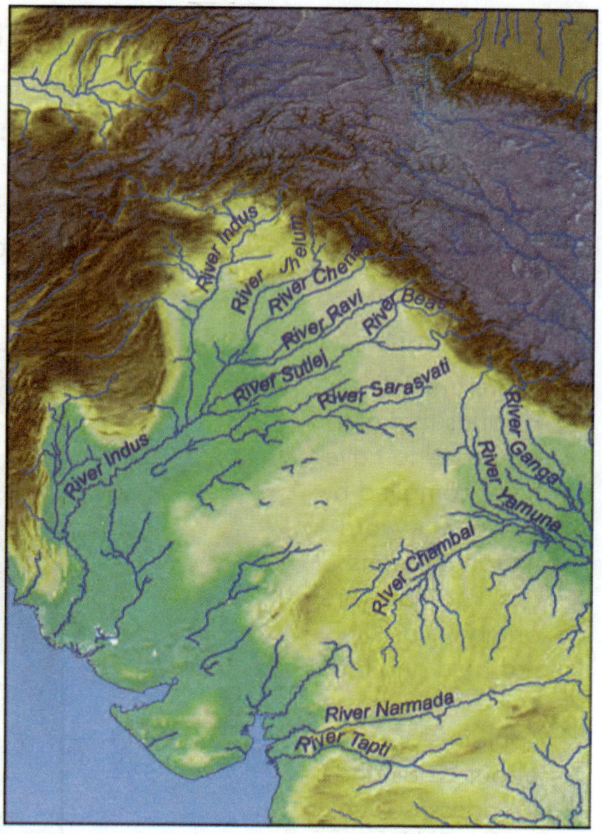

The northwest region of the Indian Subcontinent

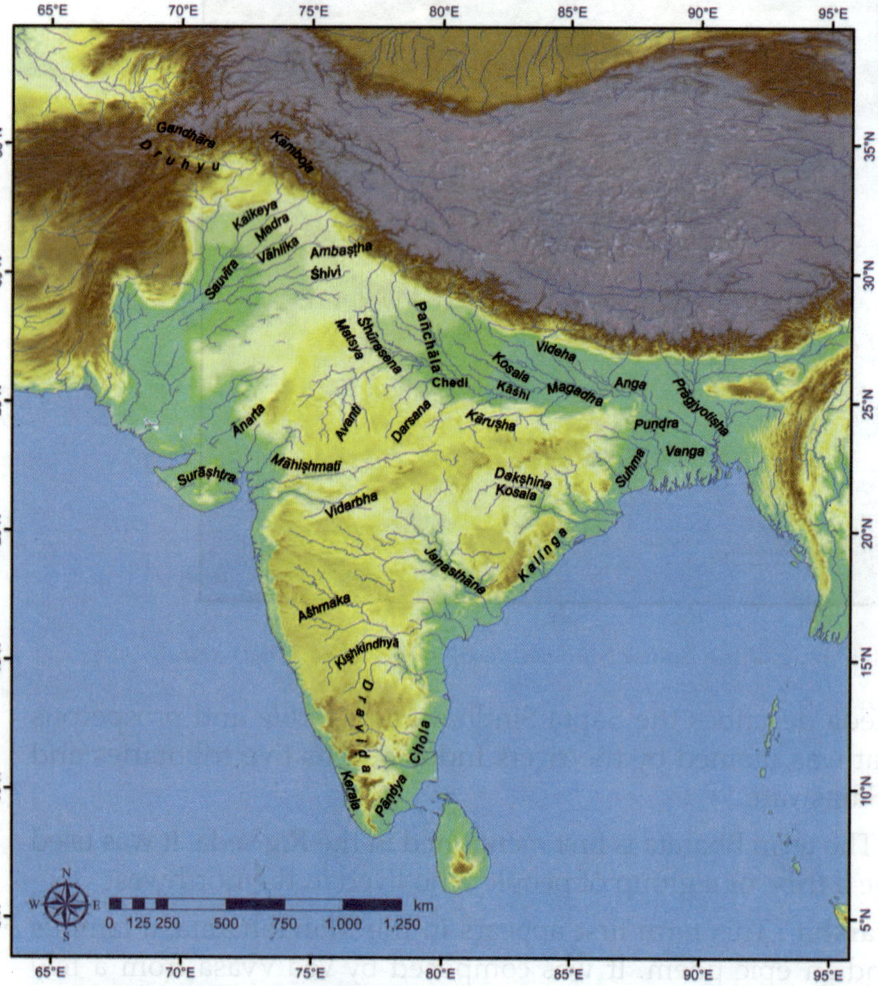

Map of a few regions listed in the Mahabharata. (Many of them are also mentioned in the text as kingdoms.) You do not need to remember those regions, but notice how they cover the entire geography of the Subcontinent.

India. While in North India, it is generally spoken as 'Bharat', in the South, it is referred to as' Bharatam'.

The Vishnu Purana mentions that "the country that lies north of the ocean and south of the snowy mountains is called Bharatam". (*Uttaram yat samudrasya himadrescaiva daksinam varsam tad bharatam nama).*

The Mahabharata also mentions the names of several other regions of India like Indraprastha (present-day Delhi), Panchala (parts of present-day Uttar Pradesh), Matsya (present-day Rajasthan), Videha (present-day Bihar and parts of Nepal), Kerala (present day Kerala), Kashmira (present day Kashmir), Pragjyotisha (roughly today's Assam), Avanti (area around present-day Madhya Pradesh), Dakshinapatha (regions of present-day Maharashtra, Karnataka, Andhra Pradesh and Tamil Nadu) and many more.

- **Jambudvipa** : This name for India appears in the Mahabharata as well as some Buddhist and Jain texts. The term *"Jambu"* refers to the Indian blackberry (*Jamun*) tree which is found in this region in abundance and *"Dvipa"* means an island or continent in Sanskrit. Thus, *Jambudvipa* means the "island of the fruit of the *jamun* tree" which is the Indian subcontinent.

  The term *"Jambudvipa"* is also mentioned in one of the inscriptions of the Mauryan Emperor Ashoka, where it means the whole of India, including present day Bangladesh, Pakistan and some parts of Afghanistan.

- **Aryavarta** : Some of the early ancient Indian texts like the Vedas and the Manusmriti also mention the name *Aryavarta*. The term is derived from the Sanskrit words *"Arya"* (noble) and *"Varta"* (land), which means "the land of the Noble Ones". It corresponded to the northern and central parts of India where the Aryans settled during the Vedic Age.

MORE TO KNOW

The earliest epigraphical evidence of the use of Bharatvars is found in the Hathigumpha inscription of King Kharavela of Kalinga (1st cent. BC) where it applies to the region of the Ganges, west of Magadha.

Check Your Progress

Understanding

Fill in the blanks

1. The oldest Veda is the ____________.
2. The word "Sindhu" refers to the river ____________.
3. The term Bharata is first mentioned in the ____________.
4. The son of King Dushyant and Shakuntala was ____________.
5. Matsya corresponds to present-day ____________.

HOW FOREIGNERS NAMED INDIA

The various names by which the foreigners called India are as follows :

- **Hidu or Hindu or Hindustan :** The Persians were the first foreigners to mention the name of India. The Persian emperor Darius-I gained control over the Indus valley in about 516 BC. You have already studied that the river Indus was called *Sindhu*. The Persians too, adopted this name and called the lower Indus basin as "Hindu" which was the Persian equivalent of *Sindhu*. The name "Hindu" was prevalent as far as Egypt.

  From the 1st century BC, the suffix -stan was added to Hindu, which formed the name **Hindustan**.

MORE TO KNOW

Article 1 of the Indian Constitution states "India, that is Bharat, shall be a Union of States." Thus, our Constitution recognises both "India" and "Bharat" as the official names of our country.

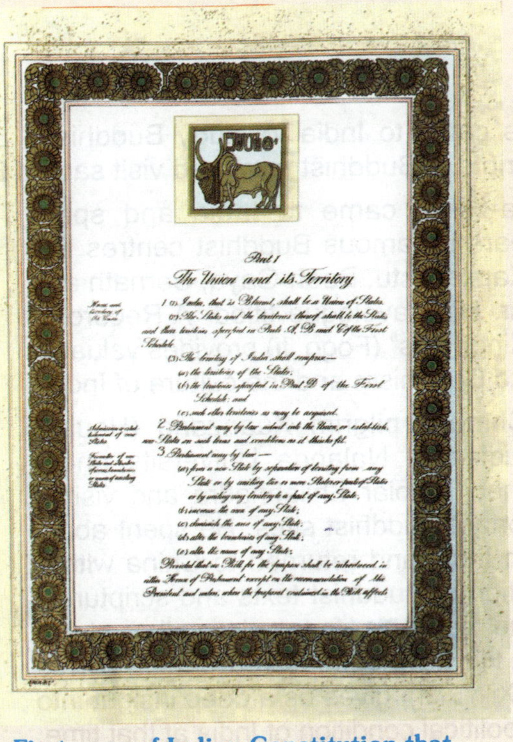

Part I

The Union and its Territory

1. (1) India, that is Bharat, shall be a Union of States.

(2) The States and the territories thereof shall be the States and their territories specified in Parts A, B and C of the First Schedule.

(3) The territory of India shall comprise—

(a) the territories of the States;

(b) the territories specified in Part D of the First Schedule; and

(c) such other territories as may be acquired.

2. Parliament may by law admit into the Union, or establish, new States on such terms and conditions as it thinks fit.

3. Parliament may by law—

(a) form a new State by separation of territory from any State or by uniting two or more States or parts of States or by uniting any territory to a part of any State;

(b) increase the area of any State;

(c) diminish the area of any State;

(d) alter the boundaries of any State;

(e) alter the name of any State:

Provided that no Bill for the purpose shall be introduced in either House of Parliament except on the recommendation of the President and unless, where the proposal contained in the Bill affects

First page of Indian Constitution that states 'India, that is Bharat'

One of the inscriptions of Emperor Shapur-I refers to Sindh as HIndustan. The term "Hindustan" was used by the British also along with "India".

- **Indoi or Indike** : The Greeks came in contact with the Indus region during the invasion of Alexander, the Great in the 4th century BC. They adopted the name "Hindu" from the Persians and dropped the initial letter "I" from this name as the letter did not exist in the Greek language. Thus the word "Hindu" became *"Indoi"* or *"Indike"*.

  The name *"Indoi"* became the basis for the latter Latin name "India".

- **Tianzhu or Yindu or Shendu :** The Chinese also interacted with India and referred to it with various names. One of the most common names that the Chinese used for India is *"Tianzhu"*. This name was widely used in Chinese historical records, Buddhist texts and the accounts of Chinese pilgrims who visited India.

  "Tianzhu" is also derived from the word *"Sindhu"* and was used to glorify India as a "heavenly centre" because India was the land of the Buddha.

  The Chinese also referred to India as *"Yindu"* which was derived from the ancient word *"Hind"*. This term was more commonly used during the Tang dynasty.

  The early Chinese historical texts also refer to India as *"Shendu"* which is supposed to be a translation of *"Sindhu"*. This term was more in use during the Han dynasty.

  Some Chinese texts also refer to India as *"Jambudvipa"* or the land where Buddhism flourished.

MORE TO KNOW

In ancient times, Chinese pilgrims came to India to study Buddhism, understand Buddhist philosophy, obtain original manuscripts of Buddhist texts and visit sacred Buddhist places.

The Chinese pilgrim Faxian (Fa-Hien) came to India and spent several years in famous Buddhist centres like Lumbini, Kapilavastu, Bodh Gaya, Sarnath and Kushinagar. His travelogue titled "A Record of Buddhist Kingdoms" (Fogo Ji) provides valuable insights into Buddhism and the culture of India.

Faxian

Another Chinese pilgrim Xuanzang (Hsuan-Tsang) studied at Nalanda University under the renowned scholar Shilabhadra and visited many important Buddhist sites. He spent about 17 years in India and returned to China with a vast collection of Buddhist texts and scriptures. He spent the rest of his life translating these texts to Chinese. His travelogue, "Great Tang Records on the Western Regions" (Da Tang Xi Yu Ji), gives us a deep insight into the geography, culture, religion and political condition of India at that time.

Xuanzang

- **Gyagar and Phagyul :** The Tibetans referred to India as *Gyagar* and *Phagyul*. It is supposed that the word "*Gyagar*" comes from the Indian Sanskrit word "*vihara*" which means a Buddhist monastery.

  The term "*Phagyul*" means the "land of the Aryas" *i.e.*, India.
- **India :** The British referred to our nation as "India" which was derived from the Sanskrit word "*Sindhu*", one of the names of the Indus river.

  As you have read earlier, the Greeks used the term "*Indoi*" which became the basis for the name "India".

Check Your Progress

Understanding

State True or False

1. The Persians were the first foreigners to mention the name of India.
2. Alexander was a Persian king.
3. The river Indus was also called *Sindhu*.
4. Chinese pilgrims never came to India.
5. The Tibetans referred to India as *Phagyul*.

NEW WORDS

- **Heritage :** The traditions, qualities and culture of a country that have existed for a long time.
- **Linguistic :** Connected with language or the study of language.
- **Epic :** A long poem, about the actions of great men and women or about a nation's history, typically one derived from ancient oral tradition.
- **Puranas :** Sacred Sanskrit writings on Hindu mythology and folktales of ancient times.
- **Pilgrim :** A person who travels a long way to visit a religious place.
- **Tributary :** A small river that flows into a larger river
- **Tribe :** A social division in a traditional society consisting of a group of families.
- **Inscription :** Words that are written or cut on something.
- **Constitution :** A document that spells out the basic principles and laws of a nation. The Indian Constitution came into force in 1950.
- **Monastery :** A building where monks and nuns live.

NUTSHELL

- India was called by various names by different people which reflect the cultural and linguistic influences of the people that lived here.
- The various names of India as mentioned in different ancient Indian texts are : Sapta Sindhava, Bharata, Bharatavarsha, Jambudvipa and Aryavarta.
- The word "Sindhava" comes from the word "Sindhu" which refers to the river Indus.
- The term Bharata is first mentioned in the Rig Veda.

- The term Bharatavarsha first appears in the Mahabharata, a famous ancient Indian epic poem.
- The name Jambudvipa for India appears in the Mahabharata as well as some Buddhist and Jain texts.
- The Vedas and the Manusmriti mention the name Aryavarta for India.
- The different names by which the foreigners called India are Hidu or Hindu or Hindustan, Indoi or Indike, Tianzhu or Yindu or Shendu, Gyagar and Phagyul and India.
- The Persians were the first foreigners to mention the name of India.
- The Greeks came in contact with the Indus region during the invasion of Alexander the Great in the 4th century BC.
- The name "Tianzhu"was widely used in Chinese historical records, Buddhist texts and the accounts of Chinese pilgrims who visited India.
- The British referred to our nation as "India" which was derived from the sanskrit word "Sindhu", one of the names of the Indus river.

IMPORTANT NCERT TEXTBOOK QUESTIONS (Solved)

Questions, activities and projects

1. Discuss what could be the meaning of the quotation at the start of the chapter.

"In India at a very early time the spiritual and cultural unity was made complete and became the very stuff of the life of all this great surge of humanity between the Himalayas and the two seas."—Sri Aurobindo

Ans. The quotation can have the following meanings :

- It emphasises upon the spiritual and cultural unity of India from the very early times and this unity became an inseparable part of the lives of its people.
- The quote also refers to the geographical expanse of India. It says that the boundaries of India extend from the great Himalayas to the two seas (Arabian Sea and Bay of Bengal).
- Despite differences in religions, culture, traditions, beliefs, languages, etc. India has an underlying unity that reflects in our daily lives, art, culture, music, architecture, etc.

2. True or False ?

→ The Rig Veda describes the entire geography of India.—**False**

→ The Vishnu Purana describes the entire Subcontinent.—**True**

→ In Ashoka's time, 'Jambudvipa' included what is today India, parts of Afghanistan, Bangladesh and Pakistan.—**True**

→ The Mahabharata lists many regions, including Kashmir, Kutch and Kerala.—**True**

→ The term 'Hindustan' first appeared in a Greek inscription more than 2,000 years ago.—**False**

→ In ancient Persian, the word 'Hindu' refers to the Hindu religion.—**False**

→ 'Bharata' is a name given to India by foreign travellers.—**False**

3. **If you were born some 2,000 years ago and had the chance to name our country, what name or names might you have chosen and why? Use your imagination!**

Ans. I would choose one of the following names :

(*a*) **Bharatavarsha :** The name extends to the whole of India.

(*b*) **Aryavarta :** It means the "Land of nobles".

(*c*) **Sapta Sindhu :** The name highlights the importance of rivers in the life of people.

(*d*) **Vishwaguru :** The name emphasises that India is a beacon of knowledge and wisdom for the entire world.

4. **Why did people travel to India from various parts of the world in ancient times? What could be their motivations in undertaking such long journeys? (*Hint : There could be at least four or five motivations*)**

Ans. People travelled to India in ancient times for the following reasons :

(*a*) **Education and Knowledge :** Various scholars travelled to India to study in ancient universities like the Nalanda and Takshila where subjects like mathematics, astronomy, philosophy, etc. were taught.

(*b*) **Trade and Commerce :** Indian spices, silk, gemstones and cotton were famous all over the world. Traders from the Middle East, Europe and Southeast Asia travelled to India to trade in these commodities.

(*c*) **Spiritual and Religious Pilgrimage :** Pilgrims from all over the world came to India to visit sacred places like Varanasi, Sarnath, Bodh Gaya, Mathura, Ayodhya, etc.

(*d*) **Cultural exchange :** People also travelled to learn about Indian music, dances, folkart, sculpture and architecture.

(*e*) **Political missions :** Rulers often sent their ambassadors to India for political motives, strengthening alliances and peace treaties.

I. OBJECTIVE TYPE QUESTIONS

A. Choose the correct answer.

Conceptual Learning | Critical Thinking

1. *The literary sources include*

(*a*) Ancient texts
(*b*) Accounts of foreign travellers
(*c*) Accounts of pilgrims
(*d*) All of these

2. *Sapta Sindhava refers to the region of the ________ part of the Indian subcontinent.*

(*a*) Northeastern
(*b*) Northwestern
(*c*) Southeastern
(*d*) Southwestern

3. *The term Bharata is first mentioned in the*

(*a*) Upanishads
(*b*) Puranas
(*c*) Rig Veda
(*d*) Accounts of Greek travellers

4. *The name for India most widely used in Chinese historical records, Buddhist texts and the accounts of Chinese pilgrims is*

(*a*) Tianzhu
(*b*) Yindu
(*c*) Shendu
(*d*) Jambudvipa

B. Mark the option that matches Column A with Column B.

Conceptual Learning | Problem Solving

Column A	Column B
1. Bharatavarsha	(*i*) Manusmriti
2. Aryavarta	(*ii*) Tibetans
3. Indoi	(*iii*) Mahabharata
4. Gyagar	(*iv*) Greek

(*a*) **1.**-(*ii*), **2.**-(*i*), **3.**-(*ii*), **4.**-(*iv*)
(*b*) **1.**-(*i*), **2.**-(*iii*), **3.**-(*iv*), **4.**-(*ii*)
(*c*) **1.**-(*i*), **2.**-(*ii*), **3.**-(*iii*), **4.**-(*iv*)
(*d*) **1.**-(*iii*), **2.**-(*i*), **3.**-(*iv*), **4.**-(*ii*)

C. Fill in the blanks

Knowledge Application

1. **Names given to India by the Chinese travellers.**

2. **Names given to India by Greeks**

D. State True or False

Knowledge Application | Problem Solving

1. Throughout ancient history, many groups of people migrated and settled in India.
2. The Sapta Sindhava was drained by the river Ganga and its tributaries.
3. Videha corresponds to present day Kerala.
4. "Dvipa" means an island or continent in Sanskrit.
5. The name "Indoi" became the basis for the latter Latin name "India".

E. Assertion-Reason

Critical Thinking

For question numbers 1 to 4, two statements are given—one labelled Assertion (A) and the other labelled Reason (R). Select the correct answer to these questions from the codes (*a*), (*b*), (*c*) and (*d*) as given below :

(*a*) Both Assertion (A) and Reason (R) are true and Reason is the correct explanation of the Assertion.
(*b*) Both Assertion (A) and Reason (R) are true but Reason is not the correct explanation of the Assertion.
(*c*) Assertion (A) is true but Reason (R) is false.
(*d*) Assertion (A) is false but Reason (R) is true.

1. Assertion (A) : India was called by various names by people who came here.
Reason (R) : This reflects the cultural and linguistic influences of the people that lived here.

2. Assertion (A) : The Rig Veda describes the Sapta Sindhava as a fertile and prosperous region.
Reason (R) : The region had no source of water.

3. **Assertion (A)** : The term "Jambu" refers to the Indian blackberry (Jamun) tree.
Reason (R) : Aryavarta corresponded to the northern and central parts of India where the Aryans settled during the Vedic Age.

4. **Assertion (A)** : The name "Indoi" was used by the Tibetans to refer to India.
Reason (R) : The name "Indoi" became the basis for the latter Latin name "India".

II. SHORT ANSWER TYPE QUESTIONS

Conceptual Learning | Knowledge Application

1. Write a note on the Sapta Sindhava.
2. What does the Mahabharata tell us about "Bharata"?
3. Write in short about the origin of the term "Jambudvipa".
4. Name the different foreign powers that came to India.

III. LONG ANSWER TYPE QUESTIONS

Knowledge Application | Critical Thinking

1. Describe the information we get about ancient India from the Mahabharata.
2. Discuss the different names that the Chinese gave to India.

IV. SOURCE BASED QUESTIONS

Analysing | Conceptual Learning | Understanding

Read the given paragraph and answer the following questions.

The ancient texts and historical records have referred to India by different names. The Rigveda, one of the oldest texts of India, mentions the land as "Bharata." Mahabharata, a famous ancient Indian epic poem gives the name Bharatvarsha for the first time. The Persians called it "Hind," derived from the Sanskrit word "Sindhu" which referred to the Indus River. The Greeks adapted this to "Indos," which became "India" in English. Chinese pilgrims, such as Xuanzang and Faxian, referred to India as "Tianzhu," a name derived from the Persian "Hind." Each name reflects a different aspect of India's geography, culture and its interactions with the outside world.

1. *The Rig Veda uses which name for India ?*
   (*a*) Hind (*b*) India (*c*) Bharata (*d*) Bharatvarsha
2. *The Sanskrit word "Sindhu" refers to which river ?*
   (*a*) Ganga (*b*) Yamuna (*c*) Indus (*d*) Narmada
3. *India was called "Hind" by the*
   (*a*) Persians (*b*) Greeks (*c*) Chinese (*d*) Tibetans

ACTIVITIES & PROJECTS

Multidisciplinary Approach | Creativity and Innovation

1. Create a timeline that shows the evolution of India's names from ancient to modern times.
2. Suppose you had to give a new name to India. Think and write a paragraph on what name you would like to give your country and why ?
3. Create a digital presentation about the different names of India including the time period, cultural significance and related images or videos.

CHAPTER 6

The Beginnings of Indian Civilisation

CG-1 : C-1.1, C-1.2; CG-2 : C-2.1, C-2.2; CG-3 : C-3.1

You read about the Neolithic Age in Chapter 4. The Neolithic Age was followed by the Chalcolithic Age that lasted from 4,000 BC to 2,000 BC. This was an age when copper and bronze came to be extensively used in making utensils and weapons along with the use of stone.

You have already learned that with the advent of agriculture, humans began living a settled life. This gradually led to the development of tribes, communities and villages. These villages grew along the river banks. As people tried to make their lives more comfortable, their needs gradually increased. This led to the rise of many occupations and division of labour. The farmers and the craftsmen produced much more than what they required. This made it essential for people to exchange goods with each other. They assembled at a specific place to exchange their goods for other items that they required. Such a place was called a market that further developed into a market town. Some of these towns grew into big cities. Trade, thus, led to the growth of cities that specialised in crafts and commerce. The villages on the other hand, continued to prosper in agriculture. The growth of trade and cities led to the rise of civilisations.

What's new to learn

- **What is a Civilisation ?**
- **The Indus-Saraswati Civilisation**
- **Extent of the Indus-Saraswati Civilisation**
- **Major centres of the Civilisation**
- **Sources of Information**
- **Main Features of the Indus-Saraswati Civilisation**
- **The End or a New Beginning**

Dholavira site

WHAT IS A CIVILISATION ?

In simple terms, **civilisation means a developed state of human society.** It refers to that stage in human evolution when people started thinking not only of satisfying their basic needs of food, shelter and clothing but they also wanted to accomplish something more. Civilisation is a progressive phenomenon which leads to specialisation in every walk of life. A civilised society has its own social, political and economic structure. Civilisation has an upward trend and leads from simple to complex. Specialisation of labour is the hallmark of a civilisation.

Some of the main features of a civilisation are :

- **An organised government** that provides leadership, maintains law and order and looks after the welfare of its people.
- **A network of cities** that are centres of administration, culture, trade and tradition. The cities are well-planned with efficient irrigation systems, drainage systems, roads and protective walls around them.
- **Surplus food production** with the help of special tools and implements.
- **Distinct social classes** like rulers, priests, soldiers, artisans and farmers, mostly based on occupation, wealth and birth.
- **Specialisation of crafts and occupation** along with an efficient management of raw materials, production and distribution of finished products.
- **Growth and expansion of markets** as well as **internal and external trade.**
- **Emergence of writing** for communication, documentation and to keep records for future generations.
- **Advancement in art, literature, science and technology** that reflects their culture, traditions and values.
- **A specialised religion** with a broader outlook, beliefs and practices.

In short, **a civilisation comes into existence when there is a systematic economic, social and political organisation.** Civilisation is like a ladder comprising steps such as the invention of the wheel, beginning of agriculture, the development of script, mathematics, astronomy, means of communication and transportation, craft work, technology, etc.

The chronology of the four great river valley civilisations of the world that developed about 6,000 years ago are as follows :

DO YOU KNOW?

Why did Civilisations flourish near river valleys ?

A River valley can be termed as the mother of civilisations. All the early civilisations grew up in the river valleys. The main reasons for this were :

- Rivers provided continuous flow of water for agriculture.
- The fertile land near rivers supported settlement.
- Rivers also provided means of transport and communication.
- Rivers flooded every year and thus kept the fertility of soil intact.

TIMELINE

4000-3500 B.C. : **The Mesopotamian Civilisation** on the banks of the Euphrates and Tigris rivers

3100 B.C. : **The Egyptian Civilisation** along the Nile river in Africa.

2600 B.C. : **The Indus-Saraswati Civilisation** or The Indus-Saraswati Civilisation or the Harappan civilisation along the Indus river in the Indian subcontinent.

2000 B.C. : **The Chinese Civilisation** along the Huang Ho river.

Timeline of four great river valley civilisations

Check Your Progress **Understanding**

State whether True or False

1. Villages grew near river banks.
2. Trade led to the growth of cities.
3. A civilisation has a downward trend.
4. The Egyptian civilisation flourished along the river Indus.
5. Well developed markets are an essential feature of a civilisation.

THE INDUS-SARASWATI OR SINDHU-SARASWATI CIVILISATION

Discovery

> **MORE TO KNOW**
>
> Harappa is an ancient city of the Indus-Saraswati Civilisation (c. 2600–1700 BC) in northern Pakistan. The site of the ruins was discovered in 1920.

The Indus-Saraswati Civilisation was first discovered during the excavations conducted by Daya Ram Sahni at Harappa and Rakhal Das Banerji at MohenjoDaro. In 1921, an Indian archaeologist, Rai Bahadur Daya Ram Sahni first found the ruins of the city of Harappa. Later in 1922, Rakhal Das Banerji, an officer of the Archaeological Survey of India discovered the ruins of Mohenjo-daro.

Nomenclature of the Civilisation

The Indus-Saraswati Civilisation belonged to the Chalcolithic Age. In the beginning, the remains of the civilisation were confined to the river Indus and its tributaries— The Ravi, Chenab, Beas, Sutlej and Jhelum rivers. Therefore, the archaeologists named it as the Indus civilisation.

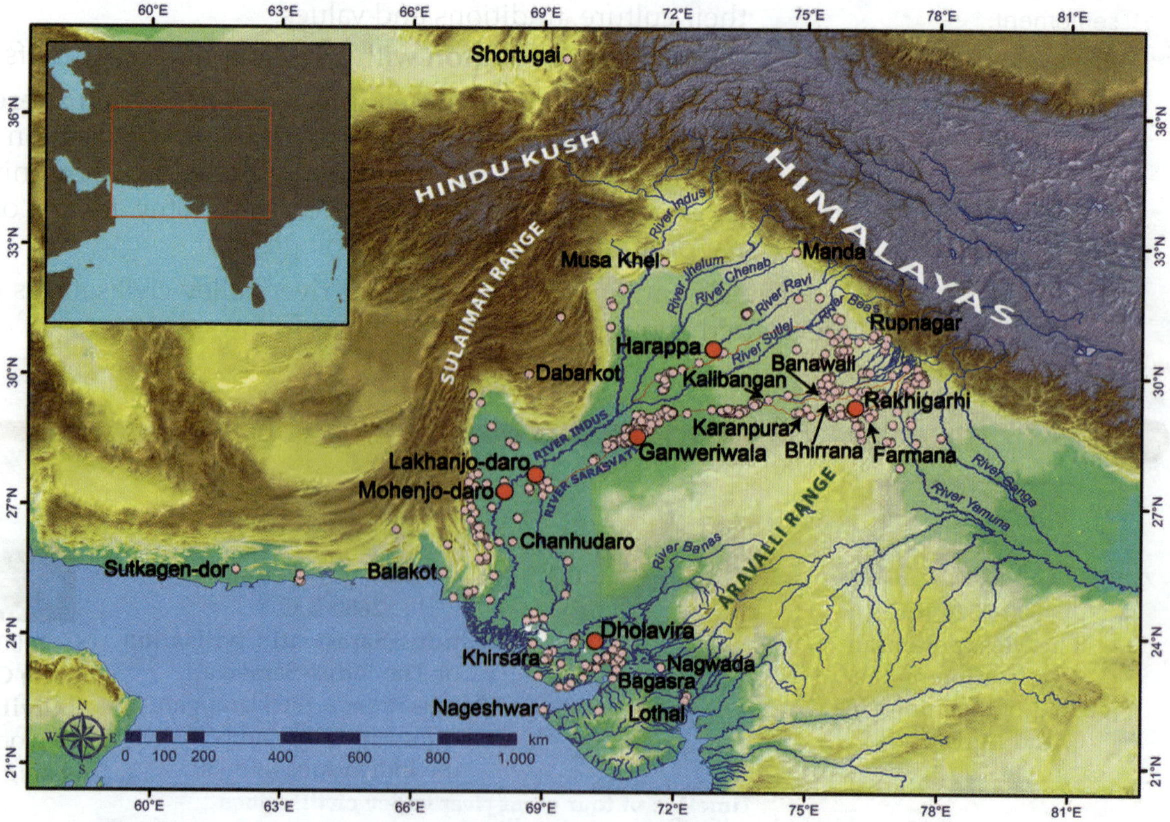

Map of some of the main settlements of the Indus-Saraswati civilisation. Notice the natural boundaries formed by the mountain ranges (in brown colour).

As Harappa was the first city to be discovered from beneath and the chief features of other sites were almost similar to that of Harappa, this civilisation came to be known as the Harappan civilisation. Some archaeologists have also called it the 'Indus-Sarasvati' or 'Sindhu-Sarasvati' civilisation as many sites were also discovered along the river Saraswati. The inhabitants of this civilisation were called Harappans. The excavations of highly planned cities of Harappa and Mohenjo-daro pushed back the history of India by almost 2,000 years.

MORE TO KNOW

The River Saraswati and Indus-Saraswati Civilisation

The River Saraswati is considered a sacred river and is called the "River of Wisdom" in Hindu mythology. Goddess Saraswati is called the "Goddess of Wisdom" and it is believed that Goddess Saraswati herself resided in this holy river.

The river is first mentioned in the Rigveda where it is called the "Naditarna" or the best of rivers. It is identified with the Ghaggar-Hakra channel in Haryana and Rajasthan. The later vedic texts mention that the river gradually dried up and eventually disappeared. As the river no longer exists, it is considered mythical by some historians.

The river plays a significant role in the context of the Indus-Saraswati Civilisation. It originated in the Himalayas and flowed through northwestern India, between the river Indus in the west and Ganges in the east. It passed through Punjab, Haryana, western Rajasthan and Gujarat before emptying into the Arabian Sea.

Many sites of the Indus-Saraswati Civilisation, particularly those in the mature Harappan phase (around 2600-1900 BCE), like Kalibangan, Banawali and Rakhigarhi are found along the banks of the Saraswati River and its tributaries. The river was a boon for the Harappans as it provided water for agriculture, transportation and everyday use. As the river began to dry up slowly due to climatic or tectonic changes, it led to the decline of many Indus-Saraswati cities as there was no water left for agriculture or trade. This led to large scale migration of people from the Saraswati valley to the Ganga Valley and other regions.

Several satellite images have helped to map the course of the river Saraswati which clearly suggests that this river was not mythical but a lifeline for the Harappan civilisation.

EXTENT OF THE INDUS-SARASWATI CIVILISATION

The Indus-Saraswati Civilisation was established around 3300 BC. It flourished roughly between 2600 BC and 1900 BC. With the discovery of nearly 1400 settlements belonging to different parts of the Indian subcontinent, it is the largest civilisation of the ancient world. It is also called the 'First Urbanisation of India'. Out of these 1400 sites, nearly 925 are in India and 475 in Pakistan.

The boundaries of the Indus-Saraswati civilisation are :

West : Sutkagen Dor in Baluchistan

East : Alamgirpur in Uttar Pradesh

North : Manda in Jammu & Kashmir

South : Diamabad in Maharashtra

The civilisation covers a total area of about 12,50,000 sq. km.

MAJOR CENTRES OF THE CIVILISATION

Apart from Harappa and Mohenjo-Daro, where the remains of the Indus-Saraswati Civilisation were first discovered, the other major sites are :

Important sites of the Indus-Saraswati Civilisation

- **Kalibangan** in Ganganagar district of Rajasthan.
- **Ropar** near river Sutlej in Punjab.
- **Banawali** in Hisar district of Haryana.
- **Alamgirpur** in Meerut district of Uttar Pradesh.
- **Lothal, Rangpur, Rojdi** and **Dholavira** in Gujarat.
- **Kotdiji, Amri, Chanhu-Daro** in present-day Pakistan.
- **Sutkagen Dor** on the east coast of South Balochistan (*Pakistan*).

The two new recently excavated sites are Rakhigarhi (Haryana) and Dholavira (in Kutch of Gujarat).

DO YOU KNOW?

Mohenjo-Daro is an ancient city of the Indus-Saraswati Civilisation (c. 2600–1700 BC), which is now a major archaeological site in Pakistan, south-west of Sukur.

SOURCES OF INFORMATION

Our main sources of information for the Indus-Saraswati Civilisation are the archaeological remains unearthed from the various sites. These remains come in the form of seals, sealings, statues, ornaments, pots and buildings like the Great Granary at Harappa and the Great Bath at Mohenjo-Daro. The Indus script, though discovered, has yet not been deciphered and still remains a puzzle for the historians.

MAIN FEATURES OF THE INDUS-SARASWATI CIVILISATION

The ruins of the Indus-Saraswati sites indicate that it was an advanced, well-organised urban civilisation. Some of its striking features are :

- **Town Planning and Buildings :** The Harappan cities were very well-planned. Most of these cities were divided into two parts : the **upper town** or **the citadel** and **the lower town.**

The Citadel

A Citadel refers to a fortified area on high ground in or near a city, where people could go when the city was being attacked. Usually, the citadel was on the western side of the city and smaller in area. It was built on a high platform. High walls of baked bricks were built around the citadel that protected it during floods. The bricks were laid in an interlocking pattern that made the walls strong.

Public buildings or special buildings such as the Great Bath of Mohenjo-daro, store houses, assembly or town hall and fire altars were built on the citadel. Possibly, the ruling classes lived here.

The Great Bath

The Great Bath

It was found in MohenjoDaro. It looks like a special rectangular tank that resembles a large swimming pool. It measures 11.88 metres in length, 7.01 metres in width and is 2.43 metres deep. It was lined with bricks and coated with gypsum plaster. It was made water-tight with a layer of natural tar or bitumen. There were steps leading downwards from two sides. There were rooms which were possibly used as changing rooms. Each room had two openings on all sides. The opening at the top was to let water in from a nearby well. The other opening was to drain out the used water. It is believed that the Great Bath was used either as a bath for the royal family or as a tank for religious rituals and ceremonies.

Store Houses or the Granaries

MohenjoDaro, Harappa and Lothal had elaborate store houses. The largest building found in Mohenjo-Daro is the Granary which is 45.71 metres long and 15.23 metres wide. In Harappa, there were six granaries which were used for storing surplus grains. Near the granaries, circular brick platforms have been found that were probably used for threshing grains.

The Granary

Assembly or Town Hall

A huge structure, measuring 69 metres long and 24 metres wide with walls about 1.5 metres thick, has been found in Mohenjo-Daro. It was used either as an administrative block or as an assembly hall for meetings.

Fire Altars

Fire altars have been discovered from Kalibangan and Lothal. Their discovery suggests that the people of the Indus-Saraswati civilisation performed sacrifices.

The Lower Town

The Lower town was generally in the eastern part of the city. It was larger but lower than the citadel. It was the residential area of the common people. The lower town part was also surrounded by high walls of baked bricks to protect it from floods.

Houses

A Well in the House

The houses of common people were generally one or two storeys high. Rooms were built around a courtyard. The houses were separated by narrow but straight lanes. They were made of baked bricks of uniform size and good quality. Most of the houses had a separate bathroom, a kitchen and a well. Harappan civilisation had the first toilets with flush in the ancient world.

Water Management

A large reservoir cut in the rock at Dholavira, measuring 33 metre in length

The Indus-Saraswati people dug wells to access groundwater. The wells were located inside houses as well as within the city walls. Some wells were also used for disposing wastewater. The plan of cities like Harappa, Mohenjo-daro and Dholavira reveal that the Harappans gave great importance to water management. These cities have evidence of large public baths and water reservoirs. You have already read about the Great Bath at Mohenjo-daro. Excavations have revealed that there were at least six large water reservoirs at Dholavira, the largest measuring 73 metres in length. These reservoirs were either built with stones or cut into the rocks. Most of these were connected to the underground drains for distributing and storing rainwater. The reservoirs thus, helped to manage shortage in water supplies.

Drainage System

The Harappans had an excellent and well planned drainage system. This proves that they paid great attention to sanitation and cleanliness. The drains in houses were connected to the street drains. The smaller drains led into bigger ones. The street drains ran along the streets in straight lines and were usually covered. Each drain had a gentle slope so that water could flow through it. They also had inspection holes at regular intervals to clean them.

Drainage system at Lothal (Gujarat)

A Street in Mohenjo-Daro

Streets

In Mohenjo-daro, the main street was over 800 metres long and 10 metres wide. The streets cut each other at right angles. They had round corners to enable the heavy carts to take an easy turn. Houses were made on both sides of the street. It is likely that houses, drains and streets were planned and built at the same time.

Farming

The farmers grew wheat, barley, pulses, peas, rice, sesame, linseed, mustard and vegetables. The Harappans were the first people to grow cotton in Europe and Asia. They weaved the cotton into clothes.

A new tool, the plough, became very important for the Harappans. It was probably made of wood. It was used to dig the Earth for planting seeds. Although the wooden ploughs have not survived, toy models of plough have been found in excavations. It is supposed that the farmers might have stored water and

The Harappan Plough

supplied it to the fields whenever required. Lothal was an important centre for cultivation of rice.

Herding

The Harappans reared cattle, sheep, goat and buffalo. Though water and pastures were easily available, yet in dry seasons, the herders moved in search of grass and water with their animals. The herders also acted as hunter-gatherers. They collected fruits like ber, caught fish in rivers and the sea and hunted wild animals like the antelope.

Food

The farmers and herders lived in small villages in the countryside. They supplied food to craft persons, scribes and rulers in the cities. The food included grains, milk, meat, fish, eggs and fruits. The Harappan cooking pots with remains of ginger, turmeric and banana have been discovered in the excavations.

Clothing

Cotton was cultivated at Mehrgarh about 7,000 years ago. At Mohenjo-daro, archaeologists have found actual pieces of cloth attached to the lid of a silver vase and some copper objects. They have also found spindle whorls made of terracotta and faience that were used to spin thread. So, archaeologists have sufficient evidence that cotton was woven into cloth in the Harappan civilisation.

Terracotta Figurines

Tool-making and other crafts

The Harappans made tools and weapons out of copper and bronze. These tools included axes, knives, spears, fish hooks, etc. They also continued to make stone tools. Probably, a new class of metal smiths had emerged.

The Harappan Tools

The Harappan Weapons and Implements

DO YOU KNOW?

The metal bronze is obtained by adding copper to tin.

Craft persons generally made things of stone, shell and metals including copper, bronze, gold and silver. These things were made under the supervision of specialists who could have been both men and women.

TIMELINE

c. 2600—1900 BC Period of the Indus-Saraswati Civilisation.

AD 1920-21 Excavations conducted at Harappa and Mohenjo-Daro.

A Brisk Trade

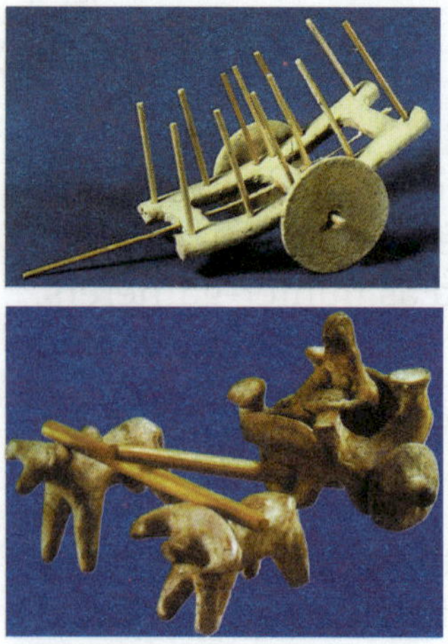

The Harappan Toy Carts

Trade in the Indus-Saraswati civilisation was carried on both by land and sea. Both external and internal trade flourished during this period. While external trade was carried on by ships, the internal trade was carried on by bullock carts. Lothal was an important trading centre for trade with Mesopotamia, Persia, Oman and Afghanistan. The small-sized seals found in the Indus-Saraswati sites were probably used for trade.

The Harappans generally used local raw material but had to bring some items from distant places also. They imported different materials from the following places :

Raw Materials	The Places from where they brought
Copper	Present-day Rajasthan, Oman in West Asia
Tin	Afghanistan and Iran
Gold	Present-day Karnataka
Precious Stones	Present-day Gujarat, Iran and Afghanistan

The items of export were ivory, pearls, gold, ornaments, some food items, timber, designed pottery and cotton cloth. Necklaces made of etched carnelian beads were in high demand. The carnelian beads were drilled and decorated by the Harappan craftsmen using some special technique. Vast quantities of these beads have been found in the Indus-Saraswati sites, Mesopotamia and Ancient Egypt which points to a brisk trade between these places.

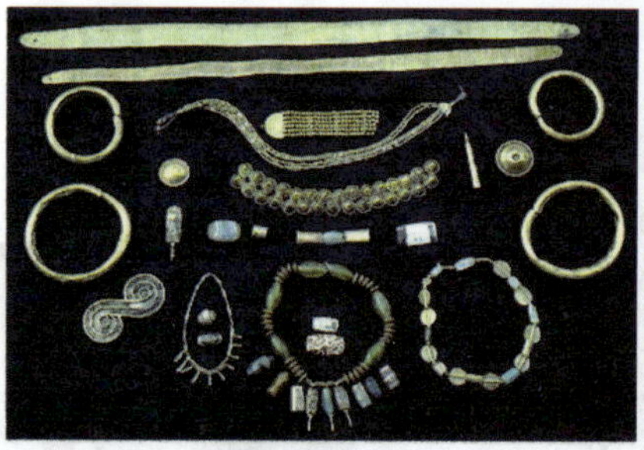

The Harappan Jewellery

Necklace

The Harappan Pottery

DO YOU KNOW?

The Indus-Saraswati seals and beads have been found in Mesopotamia. The Mesopotamian texts mention trade with a region called "Meluhha," which is believed to be the Indus-Saraswati.

Harappan beads of carnelian beads excavated at Susa (present-day Iran)

A dockyard made of bricks has been excavated at Lothal. It measures 217 metres in length and 36 metres in width. It was probably used for the stationing of ships. This discovery reveals that the Harappans were familiar with ships and also had a flourishing overseas trade. The Harappans also developed the earliest system of standardised weights and measures in the history of India. It is believed that the Harappans established trading posts and colonies in other regions to facilitate trade. Evidence of Indus-Saraswati settlements has been discovered in Oman and other parts of the Persian Gulf.

Harappan ivory comb (about 7 cm long) found on the coast of Oman

MORE TO KNOW

Around 4,000 years ago, seals may have been used by the traders to stamp their bags or packets containing goods that were sent from one place to another. A layer of wet clay was applied on the knot after the bag was closed and tied. Later, a seal was pressed on the wet clay. The impression of the seal is known as a sealing.

When the goods arrived with the sealing intact, it was considered that the goods had arrived safely.

Seals

A large number of seals have been found from the Harappan cities. The Harappans usually made seals from stone, terracotta, copper and steatite. The seals are generally rectangular in shape and have an animal carved on them. It is assumed that seals were used to stamp bags and packets that contained goods that were sent from one place to another. After tying the bag, a layer of clay was applied to the knot and the seal was pressed on it. The intact sealing gave the impression that goods had arrived safely.

A Seal depicting Rhino

A Unicorn Seal

THE END OR A NEW BEGINNING

The Harappan or the Sindhu-Saraswati civilisation started declining around 1900 BC and disappeared around 1400 BC. Sites in Sindh and West Punjab were abandoned. Many people moved into newer and smaller settlements to the east and the south.

The reasons for this migration were :

(*i*) Some scholars suggest that with the change in climate, gradually the rivers dried up because of less rainfall. Less rainfall led to less production of crops and less supply of food to the cities.

(*ii*) There may have been floods in some areas.

(*iii*) Possibly, deforestation occurred on a large scale as fuel was required for baking bricks and for smelting copper ores.

(*iv*) It is also likely that grazing by large herds of cattle, sheep and goats may have destroyed the green cover.

Although the cities disappeared, much of the Harappan culture and technology survived and passed on to the next phase of Indian Civilisation about which you will know later.

DO YOU KNOW?

In Sindhi language, 'Mohenjo-Daro' means the 'Mound of the Dead'. The name is derived from the fact that a large number of skeletons of men, women and children were unearthed from the top most levels of the city. The bodies had marks of cuts all over the body, created possibly by a sword or an axe. This suggests that they all met a violent death leading to the downfall of the city.

Skeletons found at Mohenjo-Daro

Check Your Progress — Understanding

Give one word answer for the following

1. The north boundary of Indus-Saraswati civilisation
2. The other name for the upper town
3. Place where cotton was cultivated about 7000 years ago
4. Place from where gold was exported
5. The site where the Great Bath was found

MORE TO KNOW

Lothal

Beside a tributary of the Sabarmati in Gujarat, there was the city of Lothal. It was near the Gulf of Khambat. Raw materials such as semi-precious stones were easily available in the nearby areas. The city became an important centre of production where objects were made of stone, shell and metal. Many seals and sealings (the impression of seals on clay) were found in this storehouse.

Lower Town

A building found at Lothal was probably a bead-making workshop. Pieces of stone, bead-making tools, semi-finished and finished beads have been recovered from the site.

A Dockyard at Lothal

The dockyard at Lothal was a huge tank where boats and ships came in from the sea and through the river channel. Goods were perhaps loaded and unloaded from this dockyard.

NEW WORDS

- **Nomenclature :** Choosing of names.
- **Civilisation :** The process by which a society or place reaches the stage of human social development and organisation.
- **Chalcolithic Age :** An age when tools and implements of metals as well as stone were used.
- **Granary :** A building where grains are stored.
- **Citadel :** A fort-like structure built on a raised ground.
- **Bitumen :** A black sticky substance used for making roofs and roads.
- **Spindle :** A rod used for spinning wool into thread by hand.
- **Specialist :** A person who is highly skilled in a specific and restricted field.
- **Deforestation :** Excess cutting of trees.
- **Seal :** A piece of wax, lead or other materials with an individual design stamped into it.
- **Sealing :** The impression of the seal.
- **Plough :** A tool to dig Earth and turn the soil for planting seeds.

NUTSHELL

- A civilisation means a developed state of human society.
- The Indus-Saraswati Civilisation belonged to the Chalcolithic Age.
- The Indus-Saraswati Civilisation was established around 3300 BC. It flourished roughly between 2600 BC and 1900 BC.
- In 1921, D.R. Sahni discovered Harappa and in 1922 R.D. Banerji discovered Mohenjo-daro.
- Our main sources of information for the Indus-Saraswati Civilisation are the archaeological remains unearthed from the various sites.
- Harappa, Mohenjo-daro, Kalibangan, Ropar, Rakhigarhi, Banawali, Lothal, Dholavira and Alamgirpur are the major sites of the Indus-Saraswati Civilisation.
- Cities were divided into an upper part called citadel on the western side and a lower town on the eastern side of the city.
- The Great Bath, Great Granary, and Town Hall are the main features of Mohenjo-daro.
- Most of the houses had a kitchen, a bathroom and a well. Houses were separated by narrow straight lanes.
- Each house had a well planned drainage system that connected to the street drains. Streets were cut at right angles.
- Crops grown were wheat, barley, pulses, peas, rice, sesame, linseed and mustard.
- The Harappans reared animals like cattle, goats, sheep and buffalo.
- They used clothes made of cotton and wool. Clothes, spindles and whorls have been discovered in excavations.
- The merchants and craftsmen brought raw materials from far off places to make jewellery, sculptures, weapons, tools, toys, utensils, etc.
- The Harappan seals were made of stone, terracotta and copper. They were rectangular in shape and had an animal carved on them.
- This civilisation started declining around 1900 BC and disappeared around 1400 BC.

IMPORTANT NCERT TEXTBOOK QUESTIONS (Solved)

Questions, activities and projects

1. Why does the civilisation studied in this chapter have several names ? Discuss their significance.

Ans. The different names of the civilisation and their significance is as follows :

- **Indus civilisation :** In the beginning, the remains of the civilisation were confined to the river Indus and its tributaries—the Ravi, Chenab, Beas, Sutlej and Jhelum rivers. Therefore, the archaeologists named it as the Indus civilisation.

- **Harappan Civilisation :** As Harappa was the first city to be discovered from beneath and the chief features of other sites were almost similar to that of Harappa, this civilisation came to be known as the Harappan civilisation.
- **Indus-Sarasvati or Sindhu-Sarasvati :** Some archaeologists have also called it the 'Indus-Sarasvati' or 'Sindhu-Sarasvati' civilisation as many sites were also discovered along the river Saraswati like Rakhigarh and Ganweriwala.

2. Write a brief report (150 to 200 words) summing up some of the achievements of the Indus-Sarasvati civilisation.

Ans. The main achievements of the Indus-Sarasvati civilisation can be summed up as under :

- Harappan cities were very well planned. Most of these cities were divided into two parts : the upper town or the citadel on the western side of the city and the lower town, generally in the eastern part of the city.
- The Great Bath, Great Granary, and Town Hall are the main features of Mohenjo-daro.
- Most of the houses had a kitchen, a bathroom and a well. Houses were separated by narrow straight lanes.
- Each house had a well planned drainage system that connected to the street drains. Streets were cut at right angles.
- Crops grown were wheat, barley, pulses, peas, rice, sesame, linseed and mustard.
- The Harappans reared animals like cattle, goats, sheep and buffalo.
- They used clothes made of cotton and wool. Clothes, spindles and whorls have been discovered in excavations.
- The merchants and craftsmen brought raw materials from far off places to make jewellery, sculptures, weapons, tools, toys, utensils, etc.
- The Harappan seals were made of stone, terracotta and copper. They were rectangular in shape and had an animal carved on them.

3. Imagine you have to travel from the city of Harappa to Kalibangan. What are your different options ? Can you make a rough estimation of the amount of time each option might take ?

Ans. The different options for travelling from Harappa to Kalibangan can be as under :

- On foot or using animal driven carts—This would take about 25-30 days as the distance is long enough.
- By boat, I could sail through the river Indus and its tributaries. It would take less time, like 15-20 days.
- A combination of both land and river transport which would take about 20-25 days.

4. Let us imagine a Harappan man or woman being transported to an average kitchen in today's India. What are the four or five biggest surprises awaiting them ?

Ans. The biggest surprises awaiting a Harappan man or woman being transported to an average kitchen in today's India would be :

- Modern electrical appliances like induction cookers, microwave, sandwich makers, refrigerators, etc.
- Water filters or RO.
- Latest modular kitchens with glass-top stoves, electric lights, fans and chimneys.
- Latest utensils like non-stick, microwave safe bowls, etc.
- Variety of packaged and processed foods.
- Variety of spices and different types of ingredients used to make food.

5. Looking at all the pictures in this chapter, make a list of the ornaments / gestures / objects that still feel familiar in our 21st century.

Ans. **Ornaments :** Beads, necklaces and bangles

Gestures : Namaste

Objects : Earthen pots, seals having three-faced deity, swastika symbol, gameboard.

6. What mindset does the system of reservoirs at Dholavira reflect ?

Ans. The system of reservoirs at Dholavira reflects the following mindset :

- It points to efficient water harvesting and distribution in a dry region.
- Understanding the importance of water for everyday needs and agriculture.
- Save water for use in future.
- Sustainable water management.
- Large size of the reservoir reflects the feeling of welfare of the entire community.

7. In Mohenjo-daro, about 700 wells built with bricks have been counted. They seem to have been regularly maintained and used for several centuries. Discuss the implications.

Ans. The implications of maintenance of wells can be as follows :

- High level of urban planning and organisation.
- Knowledge of the importance of water for everyday use and agriculture.
- Distribution of water to a large population through a large number of wells.
- Knowledge of technology and engineering in building brick wells and their regular maintenance.
- Regular maintenance also points to an effective and responsible government.
- Excellent water management with importance to hygiene and sanitation.
- Construction of a large number of wells also points to the awareness of saving water for those times of the year when there was scarcity of water.

8. It is often said that the Harappans had a high civic sense. Discuss the significance of this statement. Do you agree with it ? Compare with citizens in a large city of India today.

Ans. Yes, it is true that Harappans had a high civic sense which is evident from their urban planning, well planned streets, sanitation systems, drainage systems, infrastructure and organisation. The cities were well planned, had separate residential areas and public places like the Great Bath of Mohenjo-daro, store houses, assembly or town hall, etc. People put great stress on sanitation and hygiene. Most of the houses had a kitchen, a bathroom and a well. Houses were separated by narrow straight lanes. Each house had a well planned drainage system that connected to the street drains. Streets were cut at right angles. All the wells were regularly maintained and they saved water for those times of the year when there was scarcity of water.

Even today, the large cities of India have a well-developed infrastructure. Sanitation and drainage facilities are available in big towns and the public is also aware of their rights and facilities they should get from the government. Still, modern cities face problems such as blocked drains, inadequate sanitation facilities, poor waste management, congestion and a lack of public concern towards their civic responsibilities.

EXERCISES
As per NEP-2020 & NCF-2023

I. OBJECTIVE TYPE QUESTIONS

A. Choose the correct answer.

Conceptual Learning | Critical Thinking

1. *One of the oldest cities of the Indian subcontinent is*
   (*a*) Chandigarh (*b*) Noida (*c*) Harappa (*d*) None of these
2. *The earliest cities developed around*
   (*a*) 2,700 years ago (*b*) 4,700 years ago (*c*) 8,000 years ago (*d*) 10,000 years ago

3. *Who planned the construction of the special buildings in the city ?*
(*a*) The farmers (*b*) The herders (*c*) The rulers (*d*) The ministers

4. *Harappan seals are generally of* HOTS
(*a*) square shape (*b*) rectangular shape (*c*) round shape (*d*) none of these

5. *The Harappan city—Dholavira was divided into*
(*a*) three parts (*b*) two parts (*c*) four parts (*d*) five parts

B. Mark the option that matches Column A with Column B.

Conceptual Learning | Problem Solving

Column A	Column B
1. Mohenjo-daro	(*i*) Discovered by Daya Ram Sahni
2. Lothal	(*ii*) Large letters of Harappan script
3. Dholavira	(*iii*) Great Bath
4. Harappa	(*iv*) Dockyard

(*a*) **1.**-(*iv*), **2.**-(*iii*), **3.**-(*ii*), **4.**-(*i*) (*b*) **1.**-(*iii*), **2.**-(*ii*), **3.**-(*iv*), **4.**-(*i*)
(*c*) **1.**-(*iii*), **2.**-(*iv*), **3.**-(*ii*), **4.**-(*i*) (*d*) **1.**-(*i*), **2.**-(*ii*), **3.**-(*iii*), **4.**-(*iv*)

C. Fill in the blanks

Problem Solving

1. The Egyptian civilisation flourished along the ________________ river.
2. ________________ discovered the ruins of Mohenjo-daro in 1922.
3. Mohenjo-daro means ________________.
4. Banawali is situated in the state of ________________.
5. The Citadel was situated in the ________________ side of the city.

D. State True or False

Problem Solving

1. A very special tank, 'the Great Public Bath' was found in Mohenjo-daro during excavation.
2. Fire altars have been found in Kalibangan and Lothal.
3. A specialist is a person who is trained to do several kinds of work.
4. The raw materials like copper, tin, gold, silver and precious stone used by Harappans, were available locally.
5. The cities of Dholavira and Lothal give glimpses of Harappan culture.

E. Assertion-Reason

Critical Thinking

For question numbers 1 to 4, two statements are given—one labelled Assertion (A) and the other labelled Reason (R). Select the correct answer to these questions from the codes (*a*), (*b*), (*c*) and (*d*) as given below :

(*a*) Both Assertion (A) and Reason (R) are true and Reason is the correct explanation of the Assertion.
(*b*) Both Assertion (A) and Reason (R) are true but Reason is not the correct explanation of the Assertion.

(*c*) Assertion (A) is true but Reason (R) is false.

(*d*) Assertion (A) is false but Reason (R) is true.

1. **Assertion (A)** : Actual ploughs have not been found in the excavations.
   Reason (R) : They were made of wood and may have been destroyed.

2. **Assertion (A)** : Ropar is situated in Punjab.
   Reason (R) : Lothal is situated in Haryana.

3. **Assertion (A)** : Crops grew easily in the Indus-Saraswati region.
   Reason (R) : Evidence of fire altars have also been found in many sites.

4. **Assertion (A)** : Granary has been found at Kalibangan.
   Reason (R) : The Great Bath is in Mohenjo-daro

II. SHORT ANSWER TYPE QUESTIONS

Knowledge Application | Critical Thinking

1. Discuss the main features of the Great Public Bath in Mohenjo-daro.
2. List the uses of copper and bronze for the Indus-Saraswati people. HOTS
3. How do we know that cloth was used in the Harappan civilisation ? HOTS
4. When and where was cotton first grown ?
5. Who was a specialist in the Harappan civilisation ?

III. LONG ANSWER TYPE QUESTIONS

Knowledge Application | Critical Thinking

1. Discuss the extent of the Indus-Saraswati civilisation.
2. How were the cities planned in the Harappan cities ? Describe its divisions and important buildings.
3. Write a note on the dress and ornaments of the Indus-Saraswati people.
4. Describe the main features of the Harappan religion.
5. Discuss the main reasons for the decline of the Indus-Saraswati civilisation.

IV. PICTURE STUDY

Conceptual Understanding | Critical Thinking

This is a picture of a ruined city of an ancient civilisation of the world located on the banks of a river.

1. Identify the civilisation from the ruins in the picture.
2. When and by whom were the ruins of this civilisation discovered ?
3. These ruins show the excellent
   (*a*) town planning; and
   (*b*) drainage system of this period.
   Write a few lines on both of them.
4. What were the main reasons for the decline of this civilisation ?

V. SOURCE BASED QUESTIONS

Analysing | Conceptual Understanding

- This civilisation began to end around 3,900 years ago. Sites in Sindh and West Punjab were abandoned. Many people moved into newer and smaller settlements to the east and the south.

  The reasons for this migration were :

  (*i*) Some scholars suggest that the rivers dried up.

  (*ii*) There may have been floods in some areas.

  (*iii*) Possibly, deforestation occurred on a large scale as fuel was required for baking bricks and for smelting copper ores.

  (*iv*) It is also likely that grazing by large herds of cattle, sheep and goats may have destroyed the green cover.

  The waste from drainage was disposed of into the river. Waste disposal was not separate from the main river which led to pollution of river water. Since the river was the only source of water, it being polluted might have led to disease and also the elimination of the only water-source. This might have also been one of the major factors that led to the decline of the Harappan civilisation.

1. *Which civilisation is being talked about in the above paragraph ?*

   (*a*) Indus-Saraswati (*b*) Egyptian (*c*) Chinese (*d*) Mesopotamian

2. *The other name for Indus-Saraswati Civilisation is*

   (*a*) Egyptian (*b*) Harappan (*c*) Chinese (*d*) Mesopotamian

3. *What are the possible reasons for the decline of this civilisation ?*

   (*a*) Drying up of rivers (*b*) Floods (*c*) Deforestation (*d*) All of these

4. *This civilisation was discovered by*

   (*a*) D.R. Sahni (*b*) R.D. Banerji (*c*) Both (*a*) and (*b*) (*d*) None of these

VI. MAP SKILL

Knowledge Application | Experiential Learning

1. Mark the river Indus and its tributaries on an outline map of India.
2. Mark the following important sites of the Indus-Saraswati on an outline map of India—

   (*a*) Harappa

   (*b*) Mohenjo-Daro

   (*c*) Lothal

   (*d*) Kalibangan

   (*e*) Dholavira

   (*f*) Banawali

ACTIVITY & PROJECTS

Multidisciplinary Approach | Creativity and Innovation

1. Indus-Saraswati civilisation is the first planned civilisation in the Indian subcontinent. It was famous for its town planning.

   Activity:

   - Make a picture album showing the different features of Indus-Saraswati civilisation along with some details. Use your creative ideas to prepare the picture album.
   - The album should include the following features:

     (*a*) The Great Bath

     (*b*) The Citadel

     (*c*) Houses

     (*d*) Granaries

     (*e*) Drainage system

     (*f*) Upper and lower town

2. Visit any old monument or historical building of your city. Observe its architecture carefully and find out information about the art, architecture and religion prevalent during that period.
3. Explore the ancient seals used by the Indus-Saraswati people. Discuss their purpose and significance. Design and create your own seals using soft carving material like foam sheets and ink. Now, use these seals to create impressions on clay or paper.

ROLE PLAY

Collaboration | Communication

Work in pairs as archaeologists. Suppose you have found many objects while digging a site. Prepare a report on the objects found at the site, their uses and significance.

WEB LINKS

Digital Literacy

For further information log on to the following links :

- *http://en.wikipedia.org/wiki/Lothal*
- *http://www.harappa.com/har/haro.html*

CHAPTER 7

Theme C—Our Cultural Heritage and Knowledge Traditions

India's Cultural Roots

CG-1 : C-1.1; CG-2 : C-2.1, C-2.2; CG-3 : C-3.1; CG-4 : C-4.1; CG-7 : C-7.3

India is known for its rich cultural traditions and diversity. You must have celebrated various festivals, listened to many stories of Gods, goddesses and ancient heroes, tasted a variety of foods with distinct flavours, witnessed different styles of dances, music, clothing, arts and crafts. All these are a part of India's unique culture, traditions and practices that have been passed down through generations. Our traditions are deeply rooted in spirituality, philosophy, values and mutual respect for diversity.

Major religions like Hinduism, Buddhism and Jainism originated here. Along with different religions, some schools of thought also exist in India that have significantly influenced Indian philosophy, religion and culture. These schools of thought offer different ways to understand the world and live a good life. They give us great learnings on the self, our actions and the ultimate goals of life.

What's new to learn

- **The Vedas and Vedic Culture**
- **The Vedic Society**
- **The Upanishads**
- **Buddhism**
- **Jainism**
- **Folk and Tribal Roots**

Lord Buddha

Lord Mahavira

Bodhi tree

In the present chapter, we shall study about some such schools of thought and two major religions of India, Jainism and Buddhism.

THE VEDAS AND VEDIC CULTURE

The word 'Veda' is derived from the root word, 'vid' which means 'to know'. Thus, the word 'Veda' means 'knowledge'. It is supposed that the ancient rishis (male sages) and rishikas (female ones) wrote the vedic hymns under inspiration from the gods. They were then handed down from generation to generation. When the Aryans settled in India, these Vedic hymns were compiled into books and given their present form.

Most of the hymns of the Vedas are dedicated to various deities such as Agni (god of fire), Indra (king of gods), Varuna (god of water and law), Surya (Sun god), Saraswati (goddess of wisdom), Usha (goddess of dawn), Ratri (goddess of night), etc. The hymns praise the gods in poetic and metaphorical language and invoke their blessings. The hymns also give details of rituals to be performed and the purpose and significance of the rituals. It is supposed that the deities maintain the cosmic order (Rta), sustain the truth (Ritam) and bring prosperity and well being.

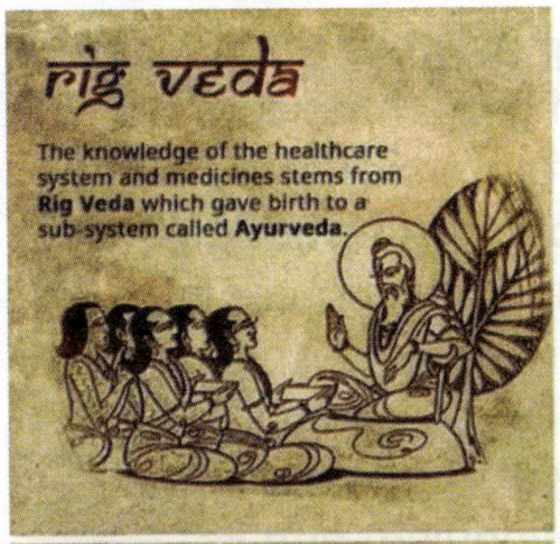

The Rig Veda is the oldest of the four Vedas. It was composed about 3,500 years ago in old or Vedic Sanskrit which is different from the Sanskrit you study in school. The Rigveda is divided into 10 'Mandalas' or volumes. It contains 1028 hymns sung in the praise of various gods and goddesses of the Aryans. Among the gods, three were prominent : Indra, the god of war and rain; Agni, the god of fire and Soma, a plant from which a special drink was prepared.

Some of the hymns in the Rigveda are in the form of dialogues. One such famous dialogue is between a sage named Vishvamitra and the two rivers, the Beas and the Sutlej. The rivers like the Indus and its tributaries, the Saraswati, the Ganga and the Yamuna are mentioned in the hymns.

The Rig Veda gives us information about the political, social, economic and religious life of the Early Vedic Period.

The Sama Veda or the 'Book of Chants' contains hymns that are sung at the time of sacrifices.

The Yajur Veda or the 'Book of Sacrificial Prayers' lays down the procedures for the performance of various sacrifices.

The Atharva Veda is a collection of songs, spells and magical charms to control and ward off the demons and evil spirits.

The Vedas were passed on orally from one generation to another. The priests taught the students to recite and memorise each verse of the Veda word by word with great care. This process continued for several centuries before the Vedas were finally written down. Further, they were printed less than 200 years ago. The Vedas became the basis of Hinduism which is one of the oldest surviving religions in the world.

The Vedas, together with the Brahmanas, the Upanishads, the Puranas and the Epics collectively form the 'Vedic Literature'.

THE VEDIC SOCIETY

Some of the main features of Vedic society were was follows :

- The Vedic people had a joint family that was headed by the senior-most male member of the family called the Grihapati.
- The word Jana was used to describe the people or the community as a whole. A group of villages inhabited by the people of a particular tribe was called the Jana. The Rig Veda mentions the names of over 30 Janas, some of them being the Pancha Jana, Yadava Jana , Puru Jana and Bharat Jana.
- Each Jana was under a Rajan or king who was the protector (Gopa) of the Jana or people.
- The whole country was called Rashtra.
- The rajan or king was assisted by many officials like the Purohita (chief priest), the Senani (leader of the army) and the Gramani (leader of the village).
- Assemblies such as the Sabha and the Samiti existed to aid and guide the king. The Sabha was a council of elder members of the tribe who gave advice to the king on important issues. The Samiti was a general assembly of all the people of a tribe. The most important function of the Samiti was to elect a king.
- Girls were educated and were not married at a tender age. The Rig Veda mentions the names of learned women like Ghosha, Apala and Vishwavara, who attained the ranks of rishis and even composed hymns.
- Agriculture was the main occupation. Barley, wheat, cotton and oil seeds were grown.

DO YOU KNOW?

Sanskrit is considered to be a part of the Indo-European family of languages. This family includes Indian languages like Sanskrit, Hindi, Assamese, Gujarati, Kashmiri, Sindhi and European languages like English, French, German, Greek, Italian and Spanish. The languages like Tamil, Telugu, Kannada and Malayalam belong to the Dravidian family of languages. Languages spoken in north-east India belong to the Tibeto-Burman family. The languages spoken in Jharkhand and some parts of Central India belong to the AustroAsiatic family of languages.

MORE TO KNOW

The Vedic hymns were transmitted orally through generations. The Vedas are often referred to as the "books of knowledge" because of their vast content of poetry, philosophy, collection of songs, spells and magical charms. They also offer valuable insights into Hinduism and its various doctrines. The language of the Vedas has been derived from classical Sanskrit and the verses are traditionally chanted and recited during religious ceremonies as well as daily offerings to deities. The tradition of Vedic chanting is considered as the oldest unbroken oral tradition still in existence.

This tradition of Vedic chanting has been inscribed by UNESCO in the Representative List of the Intangible Cultural Heritage of Humanity on November 7, 2008. UNESCO recognised vedic chanting as "a masterpiece of the oral and intangible heritage of humanity".

- The Aryans ate wheat, barley, vegetables, fruits and meat. Milk and its products were also consumed.
- They domesticated animals like the cow, horse, dog, goat, ass and sheep.
- A number of professions existed in the Rig Vedic Age. The Rig Veda refers to priests, weavers, dyers, metalworkers, builders, healers, dancers, carpenters, tanners, potters, etc.
- Both internal and external trade was carried out in the Vedic Age. Commerce was controlled by a group of people called Pani.
- The chief means of transport by land were chariots drawn by horses and wagons drawn by oxen. Boats were used for trade by rivers.
- In the Later Vedic Period around 3,000 years ago, some men began to be recognised as rajas by performing very big sacrifices like the Ashvamedha Yajna and Rajasuya Yajna. Religious ceremonies and rituals became very complicated, expensive and necessary to be performed by every householder. Numerous offerings were made to Agni, the God of Fire. It was believed that Agni was the intermediary between the Gods and men. Religion also became philosophical. The doctrines of Punarjanma, Karma and Moksha began to rule the minds of people.

Think & Answer

Compare the Vedic society with our modern society. List any three similarities and three differences.

THE UPANISHADS

The word, 'Upanishad' is a combination of three syllables—upa, ni and shad. Here, 'upa' means near, 'ni' means down and 'shad' means to sit. In this way, Upanishad means to sit at the feet of the Guru or teacher to receive his teachings.

The Upanishads are considered to be a part of the Later Vedic texts. They contain conversations between the teachers and students. They have teachings of many religious teachers and saints. Most of the ideas in the Upanishads are presented through simple dialogues.

Upanishadic Teacher and Students

Most historians hold that there are 108 Upanishads. Out of them, 11 are considered to be the main Upanishads. They were written by the learned Hindu sages, most of them being men, especially Brahmins and Rajas. However, there were also a few renowned women thinkers such as Gargi, Apala, Ghosha and Maitreyi who took part in the debates of royal courts. In the 8th and 9th centuries, a great sage, Adi Guru Shankaracharya developed many of the ideas of the Upanishads.

MORE TO KNOW

The doctrine of Punarjanma states that only the body is mortal, while the soul is immortal. After death, the soul passes in another body and again into another, till it becomes free from imperfections and mingles with the universal soul.

The doctrine of Karma states that all actions, whether good or bad, bear their fruits and souls have to be born again and again to reap the fruits of their deeds (Karma) of previous lives. So one should always strive to do good deeds.

The doctrine of Moksha states that a time comes when the soul is liberated from the cycles of births and deaths and migrates into the universal soul. A man should, therefore, always keep the ideal of Moksha in his mind and strive for it throughout his life.

Teachings

The Upanishadic thinkers tried to answer many difficult questions. They wanted to know about life after death. Some thinkers wanted to know why sacrifices should be performed. According to them, there is something permanent in the universe that lasts even after death. They called it the Atman (the Individual soul) and the Brahman (the Universal soul). They believed that ultimately, the Atman and the Brahman are one and the same. If anybody neglects the individual soul, actually he/ she neglects the universal soul.

The Upanishads deal with the Indian philosophy and evolved the theories of Karma—Maya and Mukti. They state that the individual soul can unite with the universal soul or the Brahma by doing right Karma. The Upanishads discuss creation of the world, creation of man, ideal human conduct, the practice of Yoga, meditation, Karma and truths about life and death.

During the Later Vedic Age, many other great literary works were also produced. They were related to grammar, poetry, astrology, astronomy, medicine (Ayurveda), art of warfare (Dhanurveda), music (Gandharvaveda), etc. A famous scholar, Panini prepared a grammar for Sanskrit. He arranged the vowels and the consonants in a special order and then used these to create formulae. He used these formulas to write down the rules of the language.

DO YOU KNOW?

The names of main Upanishads :

1. Katha
2. Taittiriya
3. Chandogya
4. Isha
5. Kena
6. Prasna
7. Mandukya
8. Aitareya
9. Mundaka
10. Svetasvatara
11. Brihadaranyaka

DO YOU KNOW?

The Six Schools of Indian Philosophy

The six schools of Indian philosophy and their founders are :

1. Vaisheshika by Konada
2. Nyaya by Gotama
3. Samkhya by Kapila
4. Yoga by Patanjali
5. Purva Mimansa by Jaimini
6. Vedanta or Uttara Mimansa by Vyasa.

These six schools although seem different from one another, yet they have an underlying harmony in their intellectual exploration of truth. These philosophies still guide the scholarly discourses in our country. According to German born British indologist, Max Muller, these six systems of philosophy have developed over many generations in which many thinkers have made their individual contributions

Check Your Progress

Understanding

A. Fill in the blanks

1. The word "Veda" means ____________________.
2. Saraswati was the Goddess of ____________________.
3. ____________________ is the Book of Chants.
4. ____________________ means to sit at the feet of the Guru or teacher to receive his teachings.
5. ____________________ prepared a grammar for Sanskrit.

B. Do you know any Vedic hymn ? To which Veda does it belong ? Tell its meaning to your friends.

BUDDHISM

Buddhism was founded by Gautama Buddha (c. 563-483 BCE) in India, about 2500 years ago. He did not stick to the strict rules of religion but advocated the middle path that made Buddhism popular among the common masses.

A statue of Buddha from Sarnath, 4th century BC.

Early Life

The real name of the Buddha was Siddhartha Gautama. He was a Kshatriya prince. He was born in 563 BC in the forest of Lumbini, near Kapilvastu, in the foothills of present-day Nepal. His father Suddhodana was the head of the Shakya Gana of Kapilvastu. His mother was Mahamaya who passed away when Siddhartha was just 7 days old. Being a prince, Siddhartha lived a very comfortable and luxurious life. At the age of 19, he married princess Yasodhara and had a son named Rahul.

Lumbini Pillar

The Four Great Signs

One day, while riding through the city in his chariot, Siddhartha first saw an old man, then a very sick man and further, he saw a dead body. These sights affected him deeply and he got disturbed. Finally, he saw an ascetic, who seemed unaffected by the worldly affairs around him. Siddhartha now wanted to know the mystery of life and death. At the age of 29, he left his home in search of truth. The sight of the old man, the sick man, the dead man and the ascetic are referred to as the **'Four Great Signs'** by Buddhist scholars.

Search for Truth

Siddhartha wandered for six years. He then sat under a Pipal tree at Gaya and began to meditate. On the forty-ninth day, at the age of 35, he attained Supreme Knowledge or the Enlightenment . He now came to be known as the **'Buddha' or 'The Enlightened One'.**

Gautam Buddha undertaking extreme ascetic practices before his enlightenment on the bank of river Falgu in Bodhgaya, Bihar.

For the next forty-five years, Gautama Buddha dedicated his life to the service of people.

The pipal tree under which he attained supreme knowledge came to be known as the **Tree of Wisdom or the Bodhi Vriksha.** He delivered his first **Sermon at Sarnath** near Varanasi. This was called the **Dharmachakra Pravartana** or 'setting in motion the wheel of dharma'. Gautama Buddha then travelled to many parts of the country on foot. He died at the age of 80 in 483 BC at Kushinagar in Uttar Pradesh.

Sarnath Stupa

Teachings of Buddhism

The main teachings of Buddhism are contained in the Four Noble Truths and the Eightfold Path.

DO YOU KNOW?

The Stupa at Sarnath was built to mark the place where Buddha taught his first sermon.

The Four Noble Truths

1. The truth of suffering (Dukkha)
2. The truth of the cause of suffering (Samudaya)
3. The truth of the end of suffering (Nirodha)
4. The truth of the path that leads to the End of suffering (Magga)

The Eightfold Path (Ashtangika Marga)

This includes :

1. Right belief or understanding
2. Right thought
3. Right speech
4. Right action
5. Right means of livelihood
6. Right effort
7. Right memory
8. Right meditation, concentration or absorption

The Dharma Wheel, often used to represent the Noble Eightfold Path

Gautama Buddha believed that this Eightfold Path led a person to the Middle Path or the path of balance. By following this path, a man ultimately freed himself from the cycle of birth, death and rebirth and finally attained Nirvana or Moksha. Buddha condemned animal sacrifices and rituals. He strongly preached Ahimsa or non-violence for all living beings. He laid great stress on conduct or Karma.Good deeds are rewarded and bad deeds are punished. Buddha preached equality of all men and women and strongly opposed the caste system. He laid stress on the moral values of honesty, kindness, respect for elders, etc. He encouraged people to think for themselves rather than simply accept what he or anybody else said.

Think & Answer

Which teachings of the Buddha did you like the most and why ?

There were many ways in which Buddha tried to spread his message to the people. He preached in Prakrit, the language of the ordinary people, so that people could easily understand his message. All men and women could join the Buddhist Sangha. The Buddhist Sangha was a community of bhikshus (monks) and bhikshunis (nuns) who practised and spread the teachings of the Buddha.

The simplicity of Buddha's teachings and the principle of equality greatly appealed to the people. Gradually, Buddhism spread not only in India but also to other countries like Tibet, China, Nepal, Sri Lanka, Burma (Myanmar), Mesopotamia, Syria, Egypt, Macedonia, Central Asia, Japan, etc.

Buddhist Councils

After the death of Gautama Buddha, four councils were held at different places to pen down his teachings and sermons and compile them into books.

- **First Council :** at Saptaparni cave near Rajgir.
- **Second Council :** at Vaishali
- **Third Council :** at Pataliputra
- **Fourth Council :** at Kundalvana, Kashmir

DO YOU KNOW?

According to a Buddhist text, just as the waters of different rivers lose their names and separate identity when they flow into the mighty ocean, so are Varna, ranks and family forgotten when the followers of Buddha join the order of the monks.

Buddhist Texts

The Buddhist religious texts called Tripitaka (The Three Baskets) contain the teachings of the Buddha.

They are written in Pali language and are divided into three sections :

(*i*) Sutta Pitaka

(*ii*) Vinaya Pitaka

(*iii*) Abhidhamma Pitaka

The **Jatakas** are stories about the previous lives of Gautama Buddha.

Statue of the Buddha at Bodh Gaya

Buddhist Sects

In the first century AD, during the reign of king Kanishka, Buddhism split into two sects : the **Hinayana,** which viewed the Buddha as a preacher; and the **Mahayana,** which worshipped the Buddha as a god.

Spread of Buddhism

Several factors were responsible for the popularity of Buddhism both in India and abroad.

- **Simplicity of Teachings :** The Buddha was against rituals, sacrifices and superstitions. He laid stress on truth and Karma. His simple teachings appealed to all people.

- **Spirit of Equality :** He condemned the caste system and the superiority of the Brahmin class. He was democratic in his ideas and treated all men equally.
- **Easy Adaptability :** The simple teachings of Buddhism could be easily adapted according to the needs of different countries. Thus, Buddhism spread to many countries outside India.
- **Language :** Gautama Buddha preached in Prakrit which was the language of the common people. Thus, his teachings could be understood by a wider section of people.

DO YOU KNOW?

Ashoka especially appointed a class of officers called the Dhamma-Mahamattas, who went on tours and spread the message of the Buddha among people.

Pali language

- **Personality of the Buddha :** Gautama Buddha left a luxurious life to strive for the common man. His virtues, his love for truth, his intelligence and simple life attracted people towards him.
- **Royal Patronage :** Kings like Ashoka and Kanishka were followers of Buddhism and sent missionaries to other countries for the spread of Buddhism.
- **Buddhist Sangha :** The Sangha established by Gautama Buddha preserved and spread his teachings among the common man. The Buddhist Missionaries became important centres of learning.

Decline of Buddhism

Although Buddhism became quite popular in India, it did not succeed in completely overshadowing Hinduism. Over time, it began to decline under the Hindu kingdoms of the Guptas and the Rajputs.

Sri Adi Shankaracharya (AD 788-820)

The main causes of its decline were :

- Decline of the Buddhist Sangha.
- Revival of Hinduism under Sri Adi Shankaracharya.
- The support of Gupta rulers to Hinduism.
- Split in Buddhism.
- Loss of Royal Patronage under Hindu kings.
- Support given to Hinduism by the Rajput kings who were great fighters and did not believe in the principles of Ahimsa.

MORE TO KNOW

Viharas

Initially, both the Jainas and Buddhists adopted an identical pattern of teaching people by moving from place to place throughout the year. The rainy season was the only time when they stayed in one place, as travelling during this period was very difficult. Their supporters built temporary shelters for them in gardens. Sometimes, they lived in natural caves in hilly areas during the rainy season. With the passage of time, many supporters of the bhikkhus and bhikkhunis realised that there should be more permanent shelters, and thus, monasteries were built. These were known as viharas. The material used in building the earliest viharas was wood and later, bricks were used. Some of the viharas were even made in the caves that were dug out in the hills, especially in Western India. Mostly, the donor of the land on which the vihara was built, was either a king, or a land owner, or a rich merchant. The requirements of food, clothing and medicines for the bhikkhus and bhikkhunis were met by the gifts brought in by the local people. In return, the monks taught the people. Over the centuries, Buddhism spread to many parts of the subcontinent and beyond.

Mulagandhakuti Vihara, a Buddhist Temple at Sarnath.

Check Your Progress

Understanding

Give one word answer for the following

1. The tree under which Buddha attained enlightenment
2. The place where Buddha delivered his first sermon.
3. The place where the third Buddhist council was held.
4. A king who was a follower of Buddhism.
5. Language in which Buddha preached.

JAINISM

Vardhamana Mahavira is considered to be the founder of Jainism. He was the twenty-fourth and the last Tirthankara or the teacher, who gave shape to the ideals of Jainism. His teachings constitute the core of Jainism. The first Tirthankara was Rishabhadeva and the twenty–third Tirthankara was Parshvanath. The main teachings of Parsvanath were : Non-injury, non-stealing, non-lying and non-possession.

परस्परोपग्रहो जीवानाम्

He left a well formed organisation behind him. The followers of this religion are known as Jains.

Vardhamana Mahavira (540-468 BC)

It is Vardhamana Mahavira, who gave a proper direction to Jainism and shaped its philosophy and teachings.

Early Life

Mahavira was born in 540 BC at Kundagrama, near Vaishali in present day Bihar. He belonged to a royal family of the Kshatriyas. His father, Siddartha, was the head of a Kshatriya clan called the Jnatrikas. His mother Trishala was a Lichchhavi princess. Vardhamana got his early education in all the branches of knowledge and art. He was married to Yasodhara and had a daughter. At the age of thirty, Mahavira left his home in search of truth.

Miniature Painting of Mahavira

DO YOU KNOW?

The term 'Jina' was used for a person who had subdued his desires and passions and attained supreme knowledge.

Search for Truth

Vardhamana wandered from place to place for twelve years practising meditation. In the 13th year, he attained Nirvana under a Sal tree on the outskirts of a town called Jrimbhikagrama. He was now called Mahavira, the great hero or Jina, the conqueror. His followers came to be known as Nirgranthis or free from bonds. For the next thirty years, he went from place to place and preached his doctrines. He died in 468 BC at the age of seventy two at Pavapuri near Rajgir, Bihar.

Teachings of Mahavira

The teachings of Mahavira can be summarised as follows :

- Mahavira laid great stress on Ahimsa or non-violence. He said, 'All beings long to live. To all things, life is dear.' He was of the view that along with men and animals, fire, wind and plants too, had souls. Therefore, no injury should be inflicted on any living creature, including insects and plants.
- Mahavira advocated a simple living. He was against the accumulation of property. He said that those who wish to know the truth must first

Idol of Lord Mahavira at Shri Mahavirji (Rajasthan)

give up all their belongings. He called this "Aparigraha" which means 'non-possession'.

- He asked people to be true and honest. He said that truth has many aspects and cannot be described by a single statement. He called this "Anekantavada" which means "not just one".
- He did not believe in the existence of God. He was against the recitation of mantras or performance of rituals and sacrifices.
- He believed that all men are equal and rejected all forms of caste based discrimination.
- He believed in the doctrine of Karma and Moksha. He advocated good actions (Karma) for the attainment of Moksha *i.e.*, freedom from the cycle of birth, death and rebirth. He said that Moksha was possible by following the **Tri-ratnas or Three Jewels of Jainism** namely—(*i*) Right Belief (*ii*) Right Conduct (*iii*) Right Knowledge.

Mahavira preached in Prakrit, the language of the masses. Soon, his ideas and teachings gained support among the masses.

DO YOU KNOW?

Several forms of Prakrit language were used in different parts of the country. They were named after the regions in which they were used. *For example*, the forms of Prakrit used in Magadha and Mithila were known as Magadhi and Maithili respectively.

A Jain Scripture in Prakrit

Jain Councils

Two Jain councils were held after the death of Mahavira to compile all his doctrines and teachings. These councils organised them into texts. The first council was held at Pataliputra in the 3rd century BC. The second council was held at Valabhi in Gujarat in the 5th century AD.

TIMELINE

- **540–468 BC :** Vardhamana Mahavira
- **c. 563–483 BC :** Gautama Buddha
- **3rd century BC :** The First Jain Council at Pataliputra
- **5th century AD :** The Second Jain Council at Valabhi.

Jain Texts

The sacred literature of the Jains is called the Agama-Siddhanta. The 12 Angas are the first and very important part of their sacred texts. The Siddhanta comprises 45 to 50 books. Later on, 12 Upangas or minor sections were also added. The teachings of Mahavira are written in Ardha-Magadhi Prakrit. The Jain monks also wrote Niryuktis or commentaries. They were initially written in Prakrit, but later, Sanskrit was also used.

Jain Sects

In about 300 BC, Jainism split into two sects—the Digambaras and the Svetambaras. Digambara means 'sky-clad' or 'naked'. The followers of the Digambara sect do not wear clothes and strictly follow the original teachings of Lord Mahavira.

A Digambara Jain

A Svetambara Jain

Svetambara means 'white-clad'. The followers of this sect wear white clothes and do not believe in a life of hard penance. In course of time, the Digambaras made South India their centre while the Svetambars settled down in Rajasthan and Gujarat.

Spread of Jainism

The main reasons for the spread of Jainism among the common masses were :

- **Simplicity of language :** Mahavira preached in Prakrit, the language of the common people, which made it easy for them to understand his teachings.
- **Spirit of Equality :** Mahavira condemned the caste distinctions and regarded all men as equal. He opened the doors of the new religion to people of all sections of society. This attracted a large number of followers.

Lord Mahavira's attainment of Kevalajnana

- **Personality of Mahavira :** Mahavira himself set up an ideal before the people for the attainment of truth. He left his home, became a wanderer for many years, and practised several austerities before teaching these things to people.
- **Royal Patronage :** The great Maurya Emperor Chandragupta was a devout Jain. King Kharvela of Kalinga advocated the teachings of Jainism and set up Jain images himself. Jainism was an important religion in Mathura during the Kushana period and in Eastern India during the reign of Harsha. Later on, many royal dynasties of South India embraced Jainism. They supported the development of Jain art and literature, gave donations to Jain monks and encouraged the building of Jain temples.

Decline of Jainism

The factors that led to the decline of Jainism were :

- Lack of royal patronage under the Gupta rulers.
- Split in Jainism.
- No popular preacher after Lord Mahavira.
- The lower sections of society had their own internal differences and they could not unite for a religious cause.
- Jainism had to compete both with Buddhism and the counter-reformation movement of the Hindus.

Jainism was supported mainly by the traders. It spread to several parts of North India, Gujarat, Tamil Nadu and Karnataka. The teachings of Mahavira and his followers were passed down orally for centuries. It is only about 1,500 years ago that they were written down in the present form at Valabhi in Gujarat.

Think & Answer

Do you find any similarities in the teachings of Buddhism and Jainism ?

Write them in your notebook.

Jains, today, are predominantly found in Maharashtra, Rajasthan, Gujarat, some districts of Madhya Pradesh and Karnataka. They are mostly rich and prosperous traders and have founded many charitable institutions like dispensaries, rest houses (dharamshalas) and houses for animal protection. They are constantly involved in the reformation of the society, spread of education and revival of their faith.

Check Your Progress — Understanding

State True or False :

1. The twenty-third Tirthankara was Parsvanath.
2. Mahavira attained Nirvana under a Pipal tree.
3. The first Jain council was held at Vaishali.
4. The teachings of Mahavira are written in Ardha-Magadhi Prakrit.
5. The Gupta rulers were followers of Hinduism.

FOLK AND TRIBAL ROOTS

The rich diversity of India is also reflected by the various tribal and folk cultures, each having their distinct traditions, language, customs, beliefs, art and dance.

A group of families related to one another and living together in small villages or settlements form a tribe. Generally, two or three generations of a family live together in a tribe.

The first references to tribes in India are found in the ancient Vedic texts, particularly the Rigveda. You have studied earlier in this chapter that the Rig Veda mentions the names of over 30 tribes or communities known as "janas", some of them being the Pancha Jana, Yadava Jana , Puru Jana and Bharat Jana. These early tribes were often semi-nomadic and engaged in pastoralism, agriculture and warfare. According to the 2011 Census, there are 705 tribes in India. They represent 8.6% of India's population which amounts to 104 million people. Let us first study the main features of tribes.

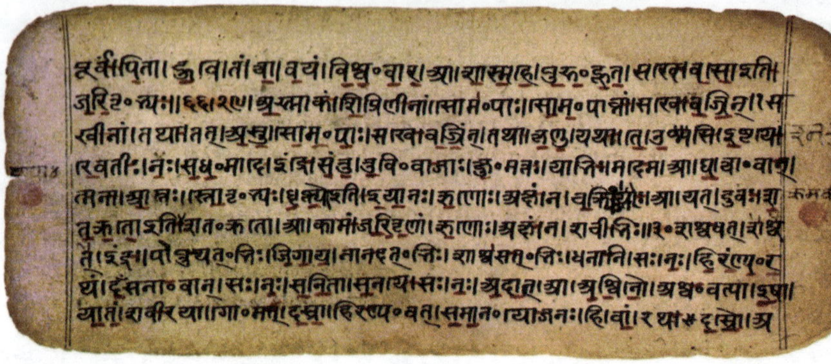

Rig Veda

Chief Features of Tribes

The main features of tribes are as follows :

- Tribes adopt occupations such as gathering, hunting, herding, fishing and farming for their livelihoods. Agricultural work, such as preparing the ground, sowing the seeds, taking care of growing plants and harvesting of grain is performed by the women folk, whereas the men folk lead the herds of animals in search of pastures. Children usually look after plants and drive away stray animals and birds that might destroy or eat them. Taking care of animals and milking is done by both men and women. Together they also make baskets, pots, tools and huts.
- Both men and women participate in dancing, singing and decorating their huts.
- Tribes have their own language, music, stories and paintings, which are part of their rich and unique cultural traditions. In addition, they have their own gods and goddesses.
- There are some men who are regarded as leaders by the tribal people because of their inherent qualities. They could be old and experienced men or priests or young brave warriors. Old women are respected for their wisdom and experience.
- Land, forests, grasslands, water and their usage are regarded as the wealth of the entire tribe. They are shared and used by all men together. Rich and poor live in harmony without any sharp differences between them. This harmony makes the tribes different from many other societies.

The folk culture constitutes the traditional art, music, dance and customs followed by the country's rural and tribal communities. Folk culture is a living tradition in India that has been passed down through generations in the form of folk tales, myths, legends, songs ,stories and proverbs. These tales, myths, legends, songs and stories have not been written anywhere but have been transmitted orally by the common people and tribes. Understanding the tribal and folk culture provides a rich insight into our country's ancient history and traditions.

MORE TO KNOW

The Gond tribe of Chhattisgarh has a traditional system of self-governance called the Ghotul, where young people learn about community values and responsibilities. The Ghotul is considered an autonomous children's republic. It is a gathering place for unmarried boys and girls, where they participate in various activities such as singing, dancing, storytelling and discussing cultural heritage. They also learn the values like discipline, hard work, respect for elders and community service.

Gond tribe of Chhattisgarh

Most of the folk culture and traditions of the tribes are similar to Hinduism. All have a deep connection with nature, traditions and local beliefs. They all worship deities primarily connected to nature like the Sun, Moon, mother Earth, water, etc. and seek their guidance and blessings. The worship of Lord Jagannath, particularly in the state of Odisha also has deep connections to tribal traditions. Lord Jagannath is often associated with the tribal deity **Neela Madhava**, a form of Lord Vishnu worshipped by the Sabara tribe, an indigenous community in Odisha. The tribals also worship deities associated with fertility, agriculture, ancestral spirits and cycle of life.

Some common deities worshipped by the folks and tribes of India are :

- **Gramadevata (Village deities) :** These were local guardian deities often represented by stone idols in village temples. They protected the village and its inhabitants. *e.g.*, Ayyanar (Tamil Nadu) and Khandoba (Maharashtra).

Ayyanar (guardian deity), Tamil Nadu

- **Mother Goddess :** A Goddess associated with fertility, femininity, abundance, prosperity and protection. A number of Mother Goddess figurines were also excavated from the Indus Valley sites. She was worshipped through various rituals associated with fertility, festivals and offerings.

Toda tribes, Tamil Nadu

Lord Donyipolo

- **Nature Spirits :** These are spirits that reside in the natural elements like the mountains, rivers, trees and forests. They are invoked for their blessings through various rituals, prayers and offerings. *e.g.*, the rivers like Ganga and Yamuna, the forest spirit Bonbibi of Bengal and the Nilgiris of Tamil Nadu. The Toda tribes reside in the Nilgiri hills of Tamil Nadu. They consider over thirty peaks of the Nilgiri mountain range as the residence of some god or goddess. These thirty peaks are regarded so sacred by the Toda tribes, that they avoid pointing towards them with a finger.
- **Creator deities :** These are gods and goddesses who have created the world and its people. They are worshipped through rituals and festivals. *e.g.*, God Dharmesh and Singbonga worshipped by the Munda and Santhal tribes of Chotanagpur, Lord Donyipolo, a combined form of the Sun and the Moon worshipped by the tribes of Arunachal Pradesh and God Khandoba worshipped in parts of Central India.

Due to urbanisation, deforestation, displacement and loss of traditional lands, the tribal communities face numerous challenges, but still they have shown extraordinary resilience over the years. They continue to thrive and protect their identity and cultural heritage.

Think & Answer

Think of some measures that can be taken to improve the life of the tribals.

Check Your Progress

Understanding

State whether True or False

1. Many tribal communities in India have their own unique festivals.
2. The Rig Veda mentions the names of over 30 tribes or communities.
3. Folk music and dance in India are performed only during religious festivals.
4. Folk literature includes oral traditions, myths, legends, stories, proverbs and epic tales.
5. God Khandoba is worshipped in parts of Central India.

NEW WORDS

- **Upanishads :** Later Vedic texts, that contain conversation between the teachers and students.
- **Karma Marg :** The path of good deeds.
- **Gyan Marg :** The path of true knowledge.
- **Bhakti Marg :** The path of divine devotion
- **Tirthankara :** A saint or religious teacher.
- **Jina :** A person who has subdued his desires and attained supreme knowledge.
- **Gana :** Clan or tribe.
- **Ascetic :** A self-disciplined man.
- **Enlightenment :** Attain knowledge of the ultimate Truth.
- **Sermon :** Religious teaching.
- **Moksha :** Freedom from the cycle of birth, death and rebirth.
- **Nirvana :** Freedom from worldly desires and suffering.
- **Viharas :** A residence of Buddhist and Jaina monks.
- **Tanha :** A desire to get more things.

- **Ahimsa :** Non-violence.
- **Atman :** The spiritual life principle of the universe
- **Monk :** A man who, giving up the usual life in the world, dedicates himself to religious or spiritual pursuits. A monk usually takes vows, that is, commits himself to follow strict rules for a disciplined life.
- **Nun :** The female equivalent of a monk.
- **Consciousness :** The quality or state of being aware, for instance of something within oneself.
- **Healer :** Someone who uses traditional practices to relieve or heal diseases.
- **Spiritual :** Concerned with the spirit or soul (atman in Sanskrit and many Indian languages). Spirituality is the search for a deeper or higher dimension beyond our current personality.
- **Cosmic :** Connected with space or the universe.
- **Ascetic :** Someone who engages in a rigorous discipline to attain a higher consciousness.
- **Attachment :** The condition of having a bond with someone or something, usually through sentiment or habit.

NUTSHELL

- The word 'Veda' is derived from the root word, 'vid' which means 'to know'. Thus, the word 'Veda' means 'knowledge'.
- The Four Vedas are :
  1. **Rigveda :** A collection of hymns sung in praise of Hindu Gods and Goddesses.
  2. **Samaveda :** A collection of songs taken mainly from the Rigveda.
  3. **Yajurveda :** A collection of sacrificial formulas.
  4. **Atharvaveda :** A collection of songs, spells and magical charms to control or ward off evil spirits.
- The word 'Upanishad' means to 'sit at the feet of Guru to receive his teachings'.
- The Upanishadic thinkers wanted to know about life and death, the reason behind sacrifices, the creation of man and the world, the practice of yoga, meditation, karma, etc.
- **Buddhism :**
  1. Founder : Gautam Buddha
  - Born : Lumbini near Kapilvastu.
  - Mother : Mahamaya
  - Son : Rahul
  - Father : Shuddhodhan
  - Wife : Yashodhara
  - Left home at the age of 29 years
  - Attained enlightenment at Bodh Gaya in Bihar
  - First Sermon at Sarnath, near Varanasi.

  2. Teachings :
  - The Four Noble Truths
  - Preached Non-violence
  - Condemned the caste system.
  - The Eightfold Path
  - Believed in Karma

  3. Buddhism spread to many parts of India, Tibet, China, Nepal, Sri Lanka, Burma, Japan, etc.
- **Jainism :**
  1. Founder : Vardhamana Mahavira
  - 24th Tirthankara
  - Father : Siddharth
  - Wife : Yashoda
  - Born at Kundagrama near Vaishali in Bihar.
  - Mother : Trishala
  - Left home at the age of 30
  - After attaining enlightenment, he was called the Jina (the Conqueror)
  - Died at Pawapuri in Bihar
  - Preached in Prakrit

2. **Teachings :**
   - Follow the rules of Ahimsa.
   - Leave home to know the truth.
   - Be honest, do not steal, do not lie.
   - Observe celibacy.
   - Preached Triratnas (Right Knowledge, Right Belief, Right Conduct)
3. **Jainism became popular among traders. Spread to several parts of North India, Gujarat, Tamil Nadu and Karnataka.**

- A group of families related to one another and living together in small villages or settlements form a tribe.
- The first references to tribes in India are found in the ancient Vedic texts, particularly the Rigveda.
- The folk culture constitutes the traditional art, music, dance and customs followed by the country's rural and tribal communities.
- Folk culture is a living oral tradition in India that has been passed down through generations in the form of folk tales, myths, legends, songs, stories and proverbs.

IMPORTANT NCERT TEXTBOOK QUESTIONS (Solved)

Questions, activities and projects

1. If you were Nachiketa, what questions would you like to ask Yama ? Write them down in 100-150 words.

Ans. If I were Nachiketa, I would ask Yama questions on the origin and philosophy of life, Doctrine of Karma, Cycle of Birth and Death, Moksha, etc. Some of the questions would be as follows :

- How did life originate in the world and how did we come into existence ?
- What happens to the body after death ?
- What is Atman ? Does it really exist ?
- Are Atman and God the same ?
- How does our Karma affect our lives ?
- How can we get rid of the cycle of birth and rebirth ?
- What can we do in this life to attain Moksha ?

2. Explain a few central ideas of Buddhism. Briefly comment upon them.

Ans. The central ideas of Buddhism are contained in the Four Noble Truths and the Eightfold Path.
The Four Noble Truths

1. The truth of suffering (Dukkha)
2. The truth of the cause of suffering (Samudaya)
3. The truth of the end of suffering (Nirodha)
4. The truth of the path that leads to the End of suffering (Magga)

The Eightfold Path (Ashtangika Marga)

This includes :

1. Right belief or understanding
2. Right thought
3. Right speech
4. Right action
5. Right means of livelihood
6. Right effort
7. Right memory
8. Right meditation, concentration or absorption

The Four Noble Truths and the Eightfold Path guide us to lead a simple life, away from greed and desires as this would prevent us from further suffering. They lead us towards an ethical life, discipline, wisdom, good deeds etc that pave our way towards enlightenment.

3. Discuss in class the quotation of the Buddha which begins with "Not by water is one made pure, though many people may bathe here [in sacred rivers]" to make sure that its meaning has been understood by all.

Ans. This quotation means that any person cannot be made pure by bathing in the waters of sacred rivers, but instead a person becomes pure by following the path of truthfulness, righteousness, compassion, honesty, purity of inner self and non-violence towards others.

4. Explain a few central ideas of Jainism. Briefly comment upon them.

Ans. The central ideas of Jainism and their explanation is as follows :

- Mahavira laid great stress on Ahimsa or non-violence. He said, 'All beings long to live. To all things, life is dear.' He was of the view that along with men and animals, fire, wind and plants too, had souls. Therefore, no injury must be inflicted on any living creature including insects and plants.
- Mahavira advocated a simple living. He was against the accumulation of property. He said that those who wish to know the truth must first give up all their belongings. He called this "Aparigraha" which means 'non-possession'.
- He asked people to be true and honest. He said that truth has many aspects and cannot be described by a single statement. He called this **"Anekantavada"** which means "not just one".
- He did not believe in the existence of God. He was against the recitation of mantras or performance of rituals and sacrifices.
- He believed that all men are equal and rejected all forms of caste based discrimination.
- He said that Moksha was possible by following the **Tri-ratnas or Three Jewels of Jainism** namely *(i)* Right Belief *(ii)* Right Conduct *(iii)* Right Knowledge.

5. Consider and discuss in class Andre Beteille's thoughts.

"The thousands of castes and tribes on the Indian subcontinent have influenced each other in their religious beliefs and practices since the beginning of history and before. That the tribal religions have been influenced by Hinduism is widely accepted, but it is equally true that Hinduism, not only in its formative phase but throughout its evolution, has been influenced by tribal religions."

Ans. Andre Beteille says that the interaction between tribal religions and Hinduism is not a one-way process but a mutual exchange that has been ongoing since ancient times. The ever evolving, dynamic and diverse nature of Hinduism can be attributed to the wide influence of tribal culture and traditions. Similarly the vibrant culture of tribals has been influenced by the Hindu culture and practices.

6. Make a list of popular gods and goddesses in your region and the festivals they are associated with.

Ans. Popular gods and goddesses in my region and the festivals they are associated with are as follows :

- **Goddess Durga :** Navratri and Durga Puja
- **Goddess Saraswati :** Basant Panchami
- **Lord Ram :** Ram Navmi and Deepawali

- **Lord Krishna :** Janmashtami and Holi
- **Lord Shiva :** Shivratri

7. As a class activity, list two or three tribal groups from your region or State. Document some of their art and belief systems.

Ans.

Tribal group	Art	Belief System
1. Kondh	Dhokra Art (metal casting using lost-wax technique)	Worship Earth Goddess and practice rituals to appease Mother Earth.
2. Gadaba	Create terracotta figurines and intricate textiles.	Practice Animism (spirits inhabit natural objects and phenomena)
3. Santhal	Wall paintings using natural pigments.	Worship nature and ancestors. Believe in a supreme deity called Marang Buru (Great Mountain).

True or False

1. **The Vedic hymns were written on palm-leaf manuscripts.**
2. **The Vedas are India's oldest texts.**
3. **The Vedic statement ekam sat vipra bahudha vadanti reflects a belief in the unity of cosmic powers.**
4. **Buddhism is older than the Vedas.**
5. **Jainism emerged as a branch of Buddhism.**
6. **Both Buddhism and Jainism advocated for peaceful coexistence and the avoidance of harm to all living beings.**
7. **Tribal belief systems are limited to belief in spirits and minor deities.**

Ans. **1.** False, **2.** True, **3.** True, **4.** False, **5.** False, **6.** True, **7.** False

Class activity

1. **Stage a small play with Yama, god of death, surrounded by several Nachiketas asking him questions about life.**

Ans. Students will do themselves.

EXERCISES As per NEP-2020 & NCF-2023

I. OBJECTIVE TYPE QUESTIONS

A. Choose the correct answer.

Conceptual Learning | Critical Thinking

1. *Mahavira was the ____________ Tirthankara.*
   (*a*) 21st (*b*) 22nd (*c*) 23rd (*d*) 24th
2. *Mahavira died at*
   (*a*) Gaya (*b*) Kashi (*c*) Pavapuri (*d*) Haridwar

3. *Mahavira preached doctrines in* ________ *, the language of masses.*

(*a*) Pali (*b*) Prakrit (*c*) Sanskrit (*d*) English

4. *The Second Jain Council was held at*

(*a*) Pataliputra (*b*) Ujjain (*c*) Valabhi (*d*) Vaishali

5. *Gautama Buddha was born at*

(*a*) Pataliputra (*b*) Gaya (*c*) Varanasi (*d*) Lumbini

6. *Gautama Buddha was married to*

(*a*) Radha (*b*) Rukmini (*c*) Yasodhara (*d*) Sita

7. *Gautama Buddha attained Enlightenment under the* ________ *tree.*

(*a*) Pipal (*b*) Teak (*c*) Sal (*d*) Sandalwood

8. *Gautama Buddha delivered his first sermon at*

(*a*) Prayag (*b*) Kashi (*c*) Mathura (*d*) Sarnath

B. Mark the option that matches Column A with Column B.

Conceptual Learning | Problem Solving

Column A	Column B
1. Second Council of Buddhism	(*i*) Rishabhadeva
2. Fourth Council of Buddhism	(*ii*) Pataliputra
3. First Council of Jainism	(*iii*) Vaishali
4. The Founder of Jainism	(*iv*) Kashmir

(*a*) **1.–(*iv*), 2.–(*iii*), 3.–(*i*), 4.–(*ii*)** (*b*) **1.–(*i*), 2.–(*ii*), 3.–(*iv*), 4.–(*iii*)**

(*c*) **1.–(*ii*), 2.–(*i*), 3.–(*iv*), 4.–(*iii*)** (*d*) **1.–(*iii*), 2.–(*iv*), 3.–(*ii*), 4.–(*i*)**

C. Fill in the blanks

Knowledge Application

1.

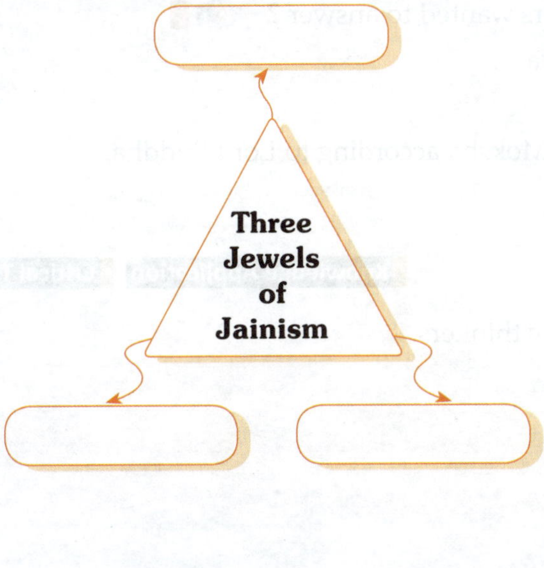

2

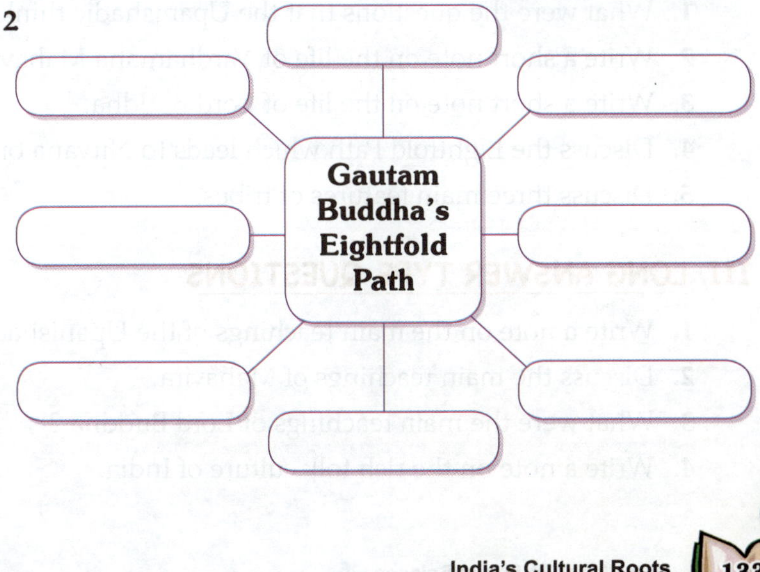

D. State True or False

Problem Solving

1. Buddha attained enlightenment at Kusinara.
2. According to Buddha, the only reason for our sufferings is the thirst of getting more and more.
3. The followers of Jainism were supposed to be truthful and honest.
4. The followers of Buddhism and Jainism were allowed to stay apart from their homes, at separate dwellings known as Sanghas.
5. The Later Vedic texts which contain the conversation between the teacher and students are called Upanishads.

E. Assertion-Reason

Critical Thinking

For question numbers 1 to 4, two statements are given—one labelled Assertion (A) and the other labelled Reason (R). Select the correct answer to these questions from the codes (*a*), (*b*), (*c*) and (*d*) as given below :

(*a*) Both Assertion (A) and Reason (R) are true and Reason is the correct explanation of the Assertion.

(*b*) Both Assertion (A) and Reason (R) are true but Reason is not the correct explanation of the Assertion.

(*c*) Assertion (A) is true but Reason (R) is false.

(*d*) Assertion (A) is false but Reason (R) is true.

1. **Assertion (A)** : Buddha preached the Eightfold Path.
   Reason (R) : Mahavira was against killing living beings.
2. **Assertion (A)** : Gautam Buddha was born at Lumbini.
   Reason (R) : He passed away at Pavapuri.
3. **Assertion (A)** : The Upanishads did not believe in Karma.
   Reason (R) : They believed in ideal human conduct and Yoga.
4. **Assertion (A)** : At the age of 35, Siddhartha attained Supreme Knowledge or the Enlightenment.
   Reason (R) : He now came to known as the 'Buddha' or 'The Enlightened One'.

II. SHORT ANSWER TYPE QUESTIONS

Conceptual Learning | Knowledge Application

1. What were the questions that the Upanishadic thinkers wanted to answer ? HOTS
2. Write a short note on the life of Vardhamana Mahavira.
3. Write a short note on the life of Lord Buddha.
4. Discuss the Eightfold Path which leads to Nirvana or Moksha according to Lord Buddha.
5. Discuss three main features of tribes.

III. LONG ANSWER TYPE QUESTIONS

Knowledge Application | Critical Thinking

1. Write a note on the main teachings of the Upanishadic thinkers.
2. Discuss the main teachings of Mahavira.
3. What were the main teachings of Lord Buddha ?
4. Write a note on the rich folk culture of India.

IV. PICTURE STUDY

Analysing | Critical Thinking

A. 1. Identify and name the person.

2. Which religion did he belong to ?

3. Where did he attain Nirvana ?

4. Into how many sects was Jainism divided ? What was the difference between them ?

5. What were the 'Tri-Ratnas' of this religion ?

B. 1. Identify and name the person.

2. Name the religion found by him.

3. Where did he attain Enlightenment ?

4. Into how many sects was Buddhism divided ? What was the difference between them ?

5. What was the Middle Path of this religion ?

V. SOURCE BASED QUESTIONS

Analysing | Conceptual Understanding

- The Upanishadic thinkers tried to answer many difficult questions. They wanted to know about life after death. Some thinkers wanted to know why sacrifices should be performed. According to them, there is something permanent in the universe that would last even after death. They called it the Atman or the Individual soul and the Brahman or the Universal soul. They believed that ultimately, both the Atman and the Brahman are the same. If anybody neglects the individual soul, actually he/she neglects the universal soul.
  - The Upanishads deal with the Indian philosophy and evolved the theories of Karma—Maya and Mukti.
  - The Upanishads state that the individual soul can unite with the universal soul or the Brahma by doing right Karma.
  - The Upanishads discuss creation of the world, creation of man, ideal human conduct, the practice of Yoga, meditation, Karma and truths about life and death.

1. *The Upanishads were written in*

(*a*) Rigvedic Age
(*b*) Later Vedic Age
(*c*) Harappan Age
(*d*) None of these

2. *According to historians, how many Upanishads are there ?*

(*a*) 106
(*b*) 107
(*c*) 108
(*d*) 109

3. *The Upanishadic thinkers wanted to know about*

(*a*) Life After Death
(*b*) Why sacrifices are performed
(*c*) Both (*a*) and (*b*)
(*d*) None of these

4. *The thinkers discussed about*

I. Creation of world
II. Creation of man
III. Meditation and yoga

(*a*) Only I
(*b*) Both I and II
(*c*) Both II and III
(*d*) All I, II and III

ACTIVITIES & PROJECTS

Multidisciplinary Approach | Creativity and Innovation

1. List at least five teachings of Buddha and Mahavira which you think are significant and important even today.
2. Organise a group discussion in the class on the following topics :
   - The Ideas of Ahimsa
   - The Four Noble Truths
   - The Nirvana
   - The Eightfold Path.
3. Describe how you will convince your parents to allow you to become a monk.
4. Make a PowerPoint presentation on the life of Lord Buddha.
5. Visit any museum and see the Buddhist stupas kept there. Write a paragraph on them.
6. Collect pictures of Buddhist and Jain symbols such as the lotus, Dharma wheel, Bodhi tree, Swastika and Ahimsa hand. Paste them separately on a blank sheet and explain their meanings and significance.

WEB LINK

Digital Literacy

For further information log on to the following link :

- *http ://en.wikipedia.org/wiki/Jainism*
- *http ://en.wikipedia.org/wiki/Buddhism*

CHAPTER 8

Unity in Diversity, or 'Many in the One'

CG-7 : C-7.1, C-7.3; CG-10 : C-10.1

Diversity means the state of being diverse or different. We see different types of people in our surroundings. They are in different dresses e.g., some wear dhoti-kurta, while some other wear kurta-pyjamas, etc. They speak different languages e.g., Hindi, Urdu, Bengali, Marathi, Punjabi, etc. They follow different religions, e.g., Hinduism, Islam, Christianity, etc. In fact, diversity is a range of many people or things that are very different from one another.

What's new to learn

- **A Rich Diversity**
- **Food for All**
- **Textiles and Clothing**
- **Festivals Galore**
- **An Epic Spread**

Diversity adds to our lives. The various differences that diversity includes, actually enhance our lives in many ways :

- **Cultural enrichment :** Societies that have a diverse population witness a rich cultural exchange among its citizens through a variety of festivals, traditions, cuisines, languages, attires, etc.
- **Better representation and effective governance :** A diverse society often leads to better representation of all classes of society and effective governance. The government has to keep in mind the interests, needs and concerns of all its citizens in making policies.
- **Economic Growth :** A country with a diverse population often witnesses a large economic growth as people with diverse skills, abilities and experiences lead to increased productivity.
- **Increased tolerance and acceptance :** A diverse population respects each other's views and differences, thus leading to a culture of tolerance and respect.
- **Social harmony and understanding :** The diverse groups in a society develop a sense of empathy and understanding among each other. This leads to the creation of a harmonious society.

A RICH DIVERSITY

India is a land of diversities. This diversity is reflected in the geography of India, its religions, culture, traditions, languages, cuisines, occupations and more. The landscape of India varies from the lofty Himalayas in the north to the deserts in the northwestern parts of the country, and from the fertile plains of the Ganges to the tropical forests of the south and northeast. The people of India follow different religions, celebrate different festivals, speak a number of languages and eat various types of foods.

Cultural Diversity of India

India is home to over 1.4 billion people which constitutes nearly 18% of the world population. India has 22 officially recognized languages, with hundreds of dialects spoken across different states. Hindi, Punjabi, Bengali, Gujarati, Assamese, Telugu, Marathi, Tamil and Urdu are some of the major languages spoken in India. The "People of India" project, conducted by the Anthropological Survey of India, is one of the largest anthropological studies in the world. Launched in 1985, the project studied the diversity in Indian population, covering mainly the ethnic, lingual and cultural aspects. Completed in the early 1990's, the survey studied over 4,635 communities across India. It recorded around 325 languages and dialects that use 25 scripts. It also studied the major religions and belief systems prevalent in the country. It emphasised the unity in diversity which is one of the main features of our nation.

India : Unity in Diversity

Diversity or the different regional, cultural or religious background of people, help to make India very interesting and diverse. The term, 'unity in diversity' is an appropriate term to describe India. This phrase was coined by Pt. Jawaharlal Nehru. He talked about Indian unity in his famous book, 'The Discovery of India'. He says that Indian unity is not something that is from the outside, but it is something deeper. He further says that in India, the widest tolerance of belief and custom is practised and every variety is acknowledged and even encouraged. Let us now study some aspects of Indian life that are true examples of "Unity in Diversity".

FOOD FOR ALL

India is famous for its wide variety of dishes and cuisines, each having its distinct flavour, ingredients and methods of preparation. The dishes vary from state to state and from place to place according to the climate, culture and availability of local ingredients. You must have experienced that while North India is famous for its wheat -based dishes like chapati and paranthas, South India is famous for rice- based dishes like idli and dosa. Yet, people from different parts of the country enjoy all the varieties of food with the same excitement.

DO YOU KNOW?

Khichdi, a simple dish made of rice and lentils, is often considered a comfort food that represents the essence of Indian cuisine.

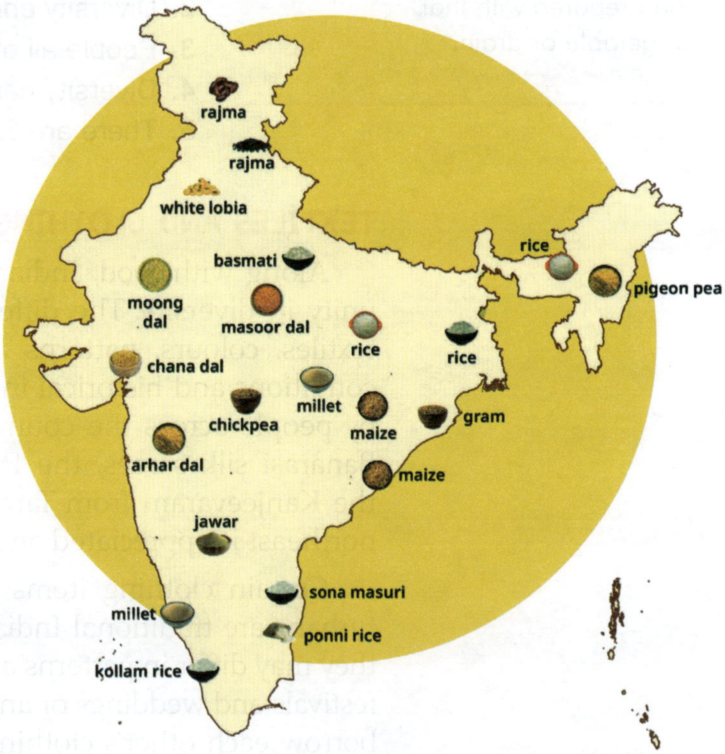

Few examples of cereals and pulses from different regions of India

Despite diversity in dishes, there are many staple foods that unite the country. Cereals like rice, wheat and barley, millets (Jowar, Bajra and Ragi), pulses and lentils, and spices like turmeric, chilli, cumin, ginger etc are used almost in all regions of the country. These common ingredients create a sense of unity amidst the diversity of dishes. You must have witnessed in your homes how a common ingredient (unity) can be used to prepare a variety of dishes (diversity). *For example,* a very common vegetable potato can be used as an ingredient in a number of dishes like pakoda, paratha, dosa, poha, potato curry, tikki, etc.

A *thali* with a variety of dishes

Similarly, the concept of "thali" in Indian culture also represents the idea of unity in diversity. A "thali" is a large platter with a variety of dishes. It contains different flavours of food like sweet, sour, tangy, spicy, etc. just like the diverse population of India living together.

India also has a culture of sharing food and dishes with family, friends and neighbours during festivals and special occasions. This exchange of flavours creates special bonds among people and promotes unity in diversity.

Think & Answer

Like Potato, think of any other vegetable or grain that is used to make a variety of dishes. Name some dishes too, that can be prepared with that vegetable or grain.

Check Your Progress — Understanding

State True or false :

1. India is a land of diversities.
2. Diversity enriches our lives.
3. People all over India speak only one language.
4. Diversity hampers economic growth.
5. There are 22 officially recognized languages in India.

TEXTILES AND CLOTHING

Along with food, Indian textiles and clothing also present an example of unity in diversity. The different regions of India are famous for their unique textiles, colours, patterns and clothing styles depending upon the climatic conditions and historical influences. Yet, the different fabrics are worn proudly by people across the country and reflect unity despite cultural diversity. The Banarasi silk sarees, the Pashmina from Kashmir, the Bandhani of Gujarat, the Kanjeevaram from Tamil Nadu, and the Kantha work of Bengal and the northeast is appreciated and admired by people across India.

Certain clothing items like the saree, salwar-kameez, kurta-pyjama and turbans are traditional Indian attires that are worn throughout India although they may differ in patterns and styles. They are worn by people especially during festivals and weddings or any special occasions. Different regions also adopt and borrow each other's clothing styles and this mutual exchange promotes unity and mutual respect.

Banarasi sari

Kanjeevaram sari

Bandhani sari

Patola sari

Chanderi sari

Tussar silk sari

The sari is a perfect example of unity in diversity in India. It serves as a symbol of cultural heritage that unites women from all parts of the country.

This traditional attire is commonly worn by women in India and is loved and cherished during festivals, weddings and formal occasions. Saris come in different varieties, the most famous being the Banarasi sari from Uttar Pradesh, the Kanjeevaram sari from Tamil Nadu, the Bandhani sari from Gujarat and Rajasthan, the Patola sari from Gujarat, the Tant sari from West Bengal, the Chanderi sari from Madhya Pradesh, the Tussar Silk sari from Bihar, the Muga Silk sari from Assam, the Pochampally sari from Telangana, the Paithani sari from Maharashtra and the Kasavu sari from Kerala. They also come in different fabrics like silk, cotton and synthetic materials and feature numerous colours and patterns. All the varieties of saris have their own unique weaving techniques, fabric, design, draping styles and cultural significance. They represent the regional diversity of India, but the way they have been adopted by women all across India has made the saree a symbol of Indian identity and an example of unity in diversity.

Tant sari

Pochampally sari

The saree is draped in numerous styles. Each style represents our country's rich cultural heritage and creativity. The most common styles are the Nivi Style (Andhra Pradesh and Telangana), the Bengali Style (West Bengal), the Gujarati Style (Gujarat), the Maharashtrian Style (Maharashtra), the Coorgi Style (Karnataka), the Madisar Style (Tamil Nadu) and the Sambalpuri Style (Odisha). Even today, several new styles of draping are being invented owing to the popularity of sari among Indian women.

Nauvari Saree (Maharashtra)

Nivi Style (Andhra Pradesh and Telangana)

Bengali Style (West Bengal)

Gujarati Style (Gujarat)

Different draping styles of sari

In rural areas, the women often drape the saree in a shorter style, making it comfortable for doing agricultural work, household work or carrying heavy loads. Women also use the sari's *pallu* as a veil to protect themselves or their small children from Sun or dust or as a shawl in cool weather.

Different uses of sari

You will be surprised to know that the history of sari can be traced back to the Indus-Saraswati Civilization. The excavations at Mohenjo-Daro and Harappa have revealed small terracotta figurines of women wearing a cloth wrapped around their waist and draped over their shoulder, reminiscent of the modern-day sari. The Rig Veda, one of the oldest texts in the world, mentions the wearing of such garments that correspond to the modern sari. During the Vedic period, women wore a single piece of cloth that evolved into the saree. This garment was known as 'Poshak' and was worn with a band of cloth tied around the waist, known as 'Mekhala.'

Cloth wrapped around the waist of a terracotta figurine

DO YOU KNOW?

The word "sari" comes from the Sanskrit word Satika, which is derived from the three-piece ensemble known as poshak. The poshak includes the antariya (lower garment), uttariya (veil worn over the shoulder), and stanapatta (chest band).

Gradually the saris became more ornate, with elaborate borders and motifs and women wore it with intricate pleats and drapes.

Think & Answer

If you get a chance to wear a sari, which fabric and draping style would you choose for yourself and why ?

Along with a perfect example of unity in diversity, the sari is also a symbol of national pride. Wearing a sari is more than just a fashion choice, it's a sign of respect for elders and family values. Although there are so many varieties of dresses today, the saree remains the undoubtable symbol of Indian heritage.

MORE TO KNOW

Leaders like Indira Gandhi popularised the wearing of handloom sarees to promote self-reliance and support the Indian textile industry.

Check Your Progress — Understanding

Mention the states to which the following saris belong :

1. Banarsi sari
2. Kanjeevaram sari
3. Patola sari
4. Tant sari
5. Chanderi sari

FESTIVALS GALORE

Just like diversity in food, clothing, traditions, culture, languages, etc., the different festivals celebrated in India are also a vibrant reflection of diversity. Festivals like Diwali, Durga Puja, Holi, Eid-ul-Fitr and Christmas are celebrated all across India. These festivals bring people together and strengthen the bonds of harmony and unity irrespective of regional,linguistic or religious backgrounds.

Republic Day

Makar Sankranti

Festivals like Diwali, Makar Sankranti and Navratri are perfect examples of unity in diversity as they are celebrated all across India with regional variations. In North India, Diwali is celebrated to mark the return of Lord Rama to Ayodhya after 14 years, while in the South, it is celebrated as Naraka Chaturdashi. In the east, Diwali is associated with the worship of Goddess Kali.

Dandiya in Gujarat

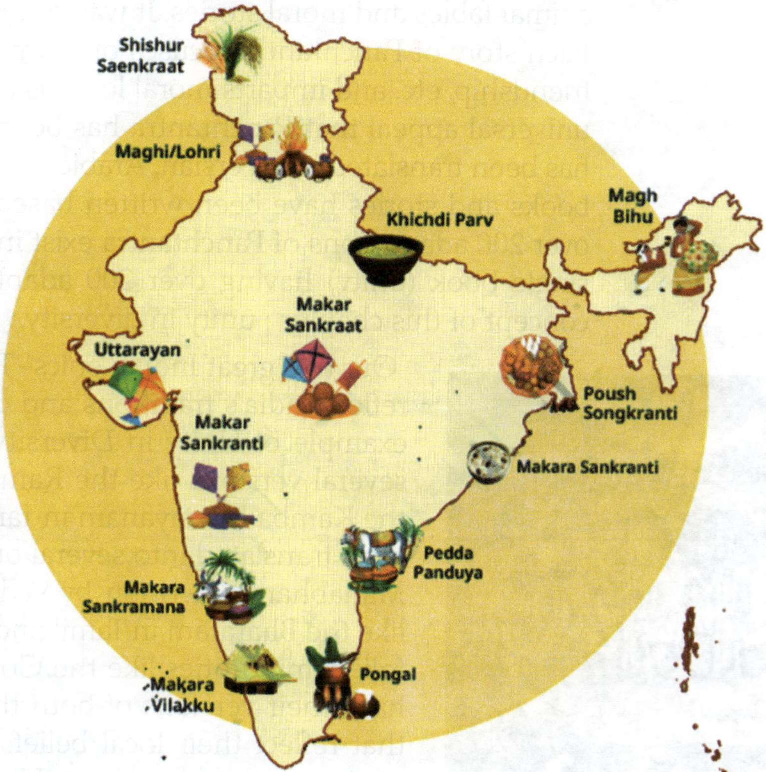

Different names of similar festivals across India about the same date

Makar Sankranti, celebrated in North India as a harvest festival, marks the transition of the Sun into the zodiac sign of Capricorn. It is celebrated on or around 14 January in different parts of India with different names like Pongal in Tamil Nadu, Magh Bihu in Assam, Khichdi Parv in Uttar Pradesh, etc. Similarly, Navratri is celebrated as Durga Puja in Bengal, Dussehra in North India and Garba and Dandiya in Gujarat.

National festivals like Republic Day and Independence Day unite the entire country, as they are celebrated with great pride by all the people of our country.

Think & Answer

Make a list of the festivals celebrated in your surroundings. Write a note on how they are celebrated and how they promote unity in diversity.

AN EPIC SPREAD

Indian literature also sets an example of unity in diversity. The literature of India clearly reflects the vast linguistic and cultural diversity along with unity of thoughts, morals and values.

India has 22 officially recognised languages and hundreds of dialects. Each language has its unique literature that reflects the culture, history and social values of its region. Despite their diversity, these literatures share common themes, narratives and motifs. They all convey universal moral and social values such as equality, love and devotion. Several literary works have been translated into different languages to promote cultural exchange and enhance our understanding of the beliefs and traditions of various regions and communities.

The literary works of Kabir, Guru Nanak, Tulsidas, Amir Khusro, etc. have been translated into many different languages and they all promote love, tolerance, unity and social harmony. The Panchatantra is an ancient Indian collection of animal fables and moral stories. It was composed in Sanskrit by Vishnu Sharma. Each story of Panchtantra focuses on human traits like loyalty, greed, wisdom, friendship, etc. and imparts moral lessons to its readers. The stories have such a universal appeal that Panchtantra has been translated and adopted globally. It has been translated into Persian, Arabic, Latin and European languages. Several books and stories have been written based on Panchtantra. It is believed that over 200 adaptations of Panchtantra exist in more than 50 languages. Thus, one single book (unity) having over 200 adaptations (diversity) also explains the concept of this chapter : unity in diversity.

'Pancha Pandavar', a carved stone in a forest of the Nilgiris, Tamil Nadu, depicting the five Pandava brothers. The shrine containing this stone is maintained by Irula tribals to commemorate the Pandavas' passing through the area.

Our two great Indian epics- The Ramayana and the Mahabharata reflect India's traditions and diverse cultures and set an excellent example of Unity in Diversity. Written by Valmiki, Ramayan has several versions like the Ramcharitmanas by Tulsidas in Awadhi, the Kamba Ramayanam in Tamil and the Ramakien in Thai. It has been translated into several other Indian languages. Likewise, the Mahabharata, written by Ved Vyasa has many regional versions like the Bharatam in Tamil and the Mahabharata in Telugu. Various folk communities like the Gonds, the Mundas and the Bhils also have their versions of both the Ramayana and the Mahabharata that reflect their local beliefs, values and practices. Many tribes of the northeast and the Himalayan regions including Kashmir have transmitted their adaptations of the Ramayana and the Mahabharata orally to their future generations. Their legends also contain details on how the different characters of the two epics visited the regions where the tribes now live. The translations and adaptations of these epics ensures that they are accessible to people across different regions. This has further enhanced cultural exchange and dialogue among different communities. Both these epics have also been recited, enacted and celebrated in various art forms like poetry,drama, music, painting and sculpture.

"Indrajit meets with Ravana, then binds Rama and Laksmana with magic serpents; Sita is told they are dead," folio from the Yuddha Kanda of the Ramayana, by Sahib Din, Udaipur, c. 1650-52,

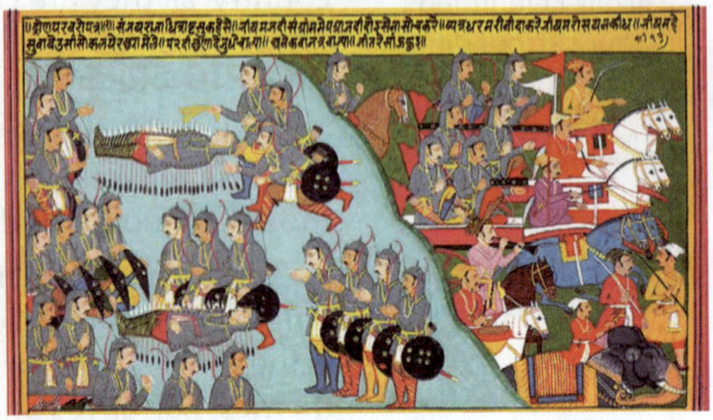

A painting from volume 3 of the set showing Bhishma falling on the battlefield at Kurukshetra

DO YOU KNOW?

The Story of Mahabharata

Pandu was the king of Hastinapur. He had five sons named, Yudhisthir, Bhima, Arjuna, Nakul and Sahadeva. They were called the Pandavas.

Draupadi *Cheer Haran*

When Pandu died, his blind brother Dhritarashtra became the king. He had one hundred sons. Duryodhana was the eldest of them. They were known as Kauravas.

Dhritarashtra divided the kingdom by giving Hastinapur to his sons and the Khandava forest to his nephews. The Pandavas made their capital at Indraprastha. Duryodhana was very jealous of Pandavas. The Kauravas invited the Pandavas to a game of dice and defeated them by tricks. The Pandavas lost everything in the game including their kingdom, wealth and even their wife, Draupadi. They had to go on 13 years' exile. On their return, they demanded their kingdom back, but the Kauravas refused. This resulted in a fierce 18 days battle in the plains of Kurukshetra. Lord Shri Krishna was in favour of the Pandavas and became the Chariot-driver of Arjuna. Ultimately, the Pandavas won the battle and Yudhisthir became the king of Hastinapur.

Gita Updesh by Lord Krishna to Arjuna

Apart from the story of war, the Mahabharata also includes the Bhagavad Gita, which contains the teachings given by Lord Krishna to Arjuna on the battlefield.

DO YOU KNOW?

The Story of Ramayana

Rama was the eldest son of King Dasharatha who was the ruler of Kosala (Awadh). Ayodhya was the capital of Kosala. Dasharatha had three queens. To keep a promise made to his second queen, Kaikeyi, Dashratha sent Rama to exile for 14 years. Rama's wife, Sita and brother, Lakshman also went with him. During the exile Sita was abducted by Ravana, the king of Lanka. Rama had to fight a battle with Ravana to get his wife back. He won that fierce battle and rescued Sita. After completing 14 years in exile, they returned to Ayodhya. The people of Ayodhya celebrated their return by lighting earthen lamps.

Lord Rama seated with his wife Devi Sita

Even today, Hindus celebrate Diwali in the memory of their return. Rama became the King of Kosala and established an ideal state based on equality and justice. This is called Ramarajya.

Rama (right) seated on the shoulders of Hanuman, battles the demon-king Ravana.

Despite variations in themes, characters and adaptations, both the epics are famous for imparting moral values like sense of duty, love, truth, justice, sacrifice, respect towards elders and the triumph of good over evil.

India's unity in diversity is evident in many other forms like art, music, paintings, architecture and sculpture. It is embedded in the very soul of India and we witness it in many forms in our

Think & Answer

Which character of the Ramayana or Mahabharata do you like the most and why ? Give reasons for your answer.

everyday lives. While diversity fosters creativity, inclusiveness and mutual respect for each other's culture and traditions, the underlying unity promotes a sense of cooperation and harmony among citizens.

MORE TO KNOW

Diversity has also been a source of strength for India. During our freedom movement, men and women from different linguistic, cultural, religious and regional backgrounds came together to oppose the British colonial rule. The British thought that they could divide the Indians because of their diversity and rule them.

The people of India showed the British that they could be different and still get united in need. People from every walk of life planned together, worked together and went to jail together during the National Freedom Movement. Poems, songs, plays and symbols served as a constant reminder of our country's rich tradition of respect for diversity. For example, the Indian flag was used as a symbol of protest against British rule by the people of the whole country. The following song was sung after the Jallianwala Bagh Massacre in Amritsar in which a large number of unarmed and innocent people were killed by the British, on the day of Baisakhi.

Jallianwala Bagh Massacre

Don't forget the days of blood, O friend
In the midst of your happiness remember to shed a tear for us
The hunter has torn away every single flower
Do plant a flower in the desert garden dear friend
Having fallen to bullets we slept in Jallianwalla Bagh
Do light a lamp on this lonely grave, O friend
The blood of Hindus and Muslims flows together today
Do soak your robe in this river of blood dear friend
Some rot in jails while others lie in their graves
Do shed a few tears for them O friend.

Source : *Indian People's Theatre Association (IPTA)*

Thousands of men and women, Hindus, Sikhs and Muslims, rich and poor had gathered and sung this song to protest against the diabolic colonial rule. This was one of the strongest example of India's "Unity in Diversity".

Check Your Progress

Understanding

State True or False :

1. In North India, Diwali is celebrated to mark the return of Lord Rama to Ayodhya after 14 years.
2. Pongal is celebrated in Tamil Nadu.
3. Republic day is a National festival.
4. Panchatantra was composed in Awadhi.
5. The Ramayana and the Mahabharata have not been translated into any other languages.

NEW WORDS

- **Diversity :** The state of being different or varied.
- **Enrichment :** The action of improving the quality or value of something.
- **Cultural Exchange :** The sharing and exchange of cultural aspects such as traditions, festivals and practices among people of different cultures.
- **Representation :** The act of speaking or acting on behalf of someone or a group.
- **Productivity :** The rate at which goods are produced or services are performed.
- **Tolerance :** The ability or willingness to accept opinions, behaviors, or people that one may not agree with.
- **Empathy :** The ability to understand and share the feelings of another.
- **Ethnic :** Relating to a population subgroup with a common national or cultural tradition.
- **Dialect :** A particular form of a language which is specific to a region or social group.
- **Anthropological :** Relating to the study of human societies, cultures and their development.
- **Flavour :** The distinctive taste or aroma of food.
- **Staple :** A main or important element of something, especially in terms of food that is a basic or essential part of a diet.
- **Platter :** A large plate or dish used for serving food.
- **Textiles :** Types of cloth or woven fabric.
- **Ornate :** Highly decorated in detail.
- **Figurines :** Small carved or moulded statues, often made of stone, clay, or plastic.
- **Motif :** A decorative design or pattern.
- **Adaptation :** A modified version of a text, idea, or object to fit a different context or environment.
- **Folklore :** The traditional stories, customs and beliefs of a community, passed through generations.
- **Sculpture :** The art of making two- or three-dimensional representative or abstract forms, especially by carving stone or wood or by casting metal or plaster.

NUTSHELL

- India is a land of diversity in terms of religion, culture, language, cuisine, clothing and geography.
- Diversity enriches life by fostering cultural exchange, better governance, economic growth, tolerance and social harmony.
- India's geography ranges from the Himalayas to deserts and from plains to tropical forests.
- India has over 1.4 billion people, 22 officially recognized languages and hundreds of dialects.
- The "People of India" project highlighted the ethnic, lingual and cultural diversity of the country, documenting over 4,635 communities.
- Indian cuisine varies by region but shares common ingredients such as rice, wheat, pulses and spices.
- The concept of "thali" symbolises unity with a variety of dishes on one platter.
- Different regions are famous for unique textiles but share traditional attires like sarees, salwar-kameez and turbans.
- Festivals like Diwali, Holi, Eid, Christmas and Makar Sankranti are celebrated across India with regional variations, fostering unity among different communities.
- National festivals like Republic Day and Independence Day unite the entire country.
- The Panchatantra and epics like the Ramayana and Mahabharata have numerous regional versions and adaptations, symbolising unity in diversity.
- The Ramayana and Mahabharata have been adapted across regions and communities, promoting moral values of duty, love and justice.
- These epics unite the country through shared narratives despite regional variations.

IMPORTANT NCERT TEXTBOOK QUESTIONS (Solved)

Questions, activities and projects

1. Conduct a class discussion on the two quotations at the start of the chapter.

Oh, grant me my prayer, that I may never lose the bliss of the touch of the one in the play of the many.

—Rabindranath Tagore

... The principle of unity in diversity which has always been normal to [India] and its fulfilment the fundamental course of her being and its very nature, the Many in the One, would place her on the sure foundation of her Swabhava and Swadharma.

—Sri Aurobindo

Ans. (*a*) **Quote by Rabindranath Tagore**

"The One" refers to the divinity or the higher spiritual power. It also refers to the spirit of Unity or Oneness. Tagore mentions that he attains a feeling of bliss or happiness when he is connected to the divinity or the spiritual power.

"The Many" refers to the diversity of life we encounter in our daily lives, the different people we meet, the different experiences we have, etc.

Thus, Tagore wishes to retain the connection of oneness with the inner self or divinity while dealing with the diversities of life.

(*b*) **Quote by Sri Aurobindo**

"The principle of unity in diversity which has always been normal to [India] " this suggests that the unity which lies within the diversity of cultures, traditions, languages, religions, faiths, etc. is not something new to India. This underlying unity has always been there amidst all the different forms of diversity. It has been an integral part of Indian culture for centuries.

"Its fulfilment the fundamental course of her being and its very nature, the Many in the One, would place her on the sure foundation of her Swabhava and Swadharma" this means that the achievement of this unity in diversity is essential for the fulfilment of India's identity and true nature. India's identity lies in its strength to embrace different cultures, beliefs and traditions. Within the unity of India, there co-exist various diversities. By adhering to the principle of unity in diversity, India sticks to its basic "Swabhava" or true nature and fulfils its "Swadharma" or its true purpose and responsibility.

2. Read the National Anthem and its translation in the preliminary pages of this textbook. Where do you see the diversity ? And where is the unity ? Write two or three paragraphs on this.

Ans. Diversity in the National Anthem : Diversity is evident in the mention of the names of different geographical regions like Punjab, Sindh, Gujarat, Maratha, Dravida (*South India*), Utkala (*Odisha*) and Bengal where different languages are spoken and different cultures are followed. Diversity is also reflected in the mention of different physical features of India from the mountains to the rivers and seas like the Vindhyas, Himalayas, Yamuna, Ganga and the Indian Ocean. The mention of both the different states and geographical features suggest that India is full of diversities in landscapes, communities, languages, etc.

Unity in the National Anthem : Unity is expressed in the very first line of the National Anthem in the phrase "Jana Gana Mana Adhinayak". The phrase invokes the Supreme entity that binds all the Indians together despite so many diversities. The phrase "Bharata-bhagya-vidhata" has been repeated. It lays emphasis on the common national identity of all Indians that shape our country's future.The collective identity and a sense of sharing and belonging binds all the Indians together. All Indians are united in their respect for the nation and its values. The last lines "Jaya he, jaya he, jaya he, jaya jaya jaya, jaya he" express the spirit of victory, triumph and glory of the nation and an aspiration for its continued unity.

3. Select a few stories from the Pañchatantra and discuss how their message is still valid today. Do you know of any similar stories from your region ?

Ans. Students will do themselves.

4. Collect a few folk tales from your region and discuss their message.

Ans. Students will do themselves.

5. Is there any ancient story that you have seen being depicted through a form of art ? It could be a sculpture, a painting, a dance performance, a movie ... Discuss with your classmates.

Ans. The ancient story of Ramayana is depicted through various art forms like sculptures, paintings, music, dance performances,movies, etc. all over India.

The Ramayana is the story of Rama, the king of Ayodhya, his wife Sita, his brother Lakshmana and their victory against the demon king Ravana.

The Ellora caves of India have many carvings and sculptures of scenes from the Ramayana. The stories of Ramayana are also enacted in various dance forms like the Bharatanatyam and Kathakali. The entire story of Ramayana is also portrayed on stage in most parts of India during Dussehra. Several films and serials have also been made on the story of Ramayana like the television series "Ramayana" and the animated version named "Ramayana : The Legend of Prince Rama".

6. **Discuss in class the following quotation by India's first prime minister, Jawaharlal Nehru, when he travelled to many parts of India before Independence :**

"Everywhere I found a cultural background which had exerted a powerful influence on their lives. ... The old epics of India, the Ramayana and the Mahabharata and other books, in popular translations and paraphrases, were widely known among the masses and every incident and story and moral in them was engraved on the popular mind and gave a richness and content to it. Illiterate villagers would know hundreds of verses by heart and their conversation would be full of references to them or to some story with a moral, enshrined in some old classic."

Ans. Through this paragraph, Jawaharlal Nehru emphasises the impact of our ancient epics the Ramayana and the Mahabharata on the general public of India especially before independence. Both the epics conveyed morals and values like respect, obedience, duty, justice, righteousness and morality. Because of these morals, they were popular among all masses of people throughout India and left a deep impact on their minds. Even the villagers knew many verses of both the epics by heart and they tried to inculcate their meanings and morals in their lives and their conversations.

EXERCISES As per NEP-2020 & NCF-2023

I. OBJECTIVE TYPE QUESTIONS

A. Choose the correct answer.

Conceptual Learning | Critical Thinking

1. *Who coined the phrase "Unity in Diversity" in relation to India ?*
   (*a*) Mahatma Gandhi (*b*) Jawaharlal Nehru
   (*c*) Rabindranath Tagore (*d*) Sardar Vallabhbhai Patel

2. *Which of the following is a symbol of unity in Indian cuisine ?*
   (*a*) Chapati (*b*) Thali
   (*c*) Rice (*d*) Idli

3. *The saree is a symbol of unity because it is worn*
   (*a*) Only in the southern part of India
   (*b*) By women across India in different styles
   (*c*) Exclusively by women in rural areas
   (*d*) As a modern dress in urban regions

4. *Which of the following statements is TRUE about Indian festivals ?*
   (*a*) Diwali is celebrated only in North India.
   (*b*) Makar Sankranti is celebrated with regional variations across India.
   (*c*) Holi is only celebrated in Gujarat.
   (*d*) Eid is a festival specific to South India.

5. *Which of the following is a major theme of both the Ramayana and the Mahabharata ?*
   (*a*) Economic growth (*b*) Cultural diversity
   (*c*) Moral values like duty and justice (*d*) Scientific achievements

B. Mark the option that matches Column A with Column B.

Conceptual Learning | Problem Solving

Column A	Column B
1. Panchatantra	(*i*) Valmiki
2. Mahabharata	(*ii*) Moral Stories
3. Ramayana	(*iii*) Jawaharlal Nehru
4. Unity in Diversity Phrase	(*iv*) Ved Vyasa

(*a*) **1.**-(*iii*), **2.**-(*i*), **3.**-(*ii*), **4.**-(*iv*)
(*b*) **1.**-(*ii*), **2.**-(*iv*), **3.**-(*i*), **4.**-(*iii*)
(*c*) **1.**-(*i*), **2.**-(*ii*), **3.**-(*iii*), **4.**-(*iv*)
(*d*) **1.**-(*iii*), **2.**-(*i*), **3.**-(*iv*), **4.**-(*ii*)

C. Fill in the blanks

Knowledge Application

1. The saree is believed to have originated during the ____________ Valley Civilization.
2. The Ramcharitmanas was written by ____________ in Awadhi.
3. Festivals like ____________ in Tamil Nadu and ____________ in Assam are regional names for Makar Sankranti.
4. The famous Bandhani sarees come from the state of ____________.
5. India has ____________ officially recognized languages.

D. State True or False

Knowledge Application | Problem Solving

1. Ramayana has only one version, which is written by Valmiki.
2. Festivals like Diwali, Makar Sankranti and Navratri are celebrated with regional variations across India.
3. Banarasi silk sarees are famous in Tamil Nadu.
4. Saree is worn only in the northern part of India.
5. Panchatantra is a collection of moral stories that originated in Australia.

E. Assertion-Reason

Critical Thinking

For question numbers 1 to 4, two statements are given—one labelled Assertion (A) and the other labelled Reason (R). Select the correct answer to these questions from the codes (*a*), (*b*), (*c*) and (*d*) as given below :

(*a*) Both Assertion (A) and Reason (R) are true and Reason is the correct explanation of the Assertion.
(*b*) Both Assertion (A) and Reason (R) are true but Reason is not the correct explanation of the Assertion.
(*c*) Assertion (A) is true but Reason (R) is false.
(*d*) Assertion (A) is false but Reason (R) is true.

1. **Assertion (A)** : The phrase "Unity in Diversity" was coined by Jawaharlal Nehru.
   Reason (R) : India has only 10 official languages and one cultural tradition.
2. **Assertion (A)** : Festivals in India like Diwali and Makar Sankranti are celebrated with regional variations.
   Reason (R) : India's climate affects how festivals are celebrated across different regions.

3. **Assertion (A)** : The Panchatantra has been translated into several languages across the world.
Reason (R) : It contains stories that focus on human traits and impart moral lessons that appeal to people globally.

4. **Assertion (A)** : The sari is considered a symbol of national pride in India.
Reason (R) : It is worn only by women in rural areas of India.

II. SHORT ANSWER TYPE QUESTIONS

Conceptual Learning | Knowledge Application

1. Write a note on how the food in India reflects the idea of unity in diversity.
2. How does traditional Indian clothing showcase unity in diversity ?
3. Assess the role of Indian festivals in promoting unity in diversity.
4. What does the phrase 'Unity in Diversity' mean in the context of India ?

III. LONG ANSWER TYPE QUESTIONS

Knowledge Application | Critical Thinking

1. Discuss the role of Indian culture in promoting "Unity in Diversity" through its food, festivals and clothing.
2. Explain how the Ramayana and the Mahabharata exemplify the idea of Unity in Diversity in India.

IV. PICTURE STUDY

Knowledge Application | Critical Thinking

Given here is a picture of a traditional Indian attire. Answer the following questions with respect to the picture.

1. Identify the attire.
2. Name any two states that are famous for the production of this attire.
3. Name three draping styles of this attire.
4. Write a note on the evolution of this attire in India.

V. SOURCE BASED QUESTIONS

Analysing | Conceptual Learning | Understanding

Read the given paragraph and answer the following questions.

The history of the sari can be traced back to the Indus-Saraswati Civilization. Terracotta figurines found in Mohenjo-Daro depict women wearing a cloth draped around their waist and over their shoulder, resembling a modern sari. The word 'sari' is derived from the Sanskrit word 'satika,' which refers to a three-piece ensemble. Over the centuries, the sari evolved in different regions of India, adapting to the local climate, culture and traditions."

1. *Which civilization has shown traces of sari ?*
   (*a*) Indus-Saraswati
   (*b*) Chinese
   (*c*) Egyptian
   (*d*) Mesopotamian
2. *"Satika" is a ________ word*
   (*a*) Awadhi
   (*b*) Hindi
   (*c*) Sanskrit
   (*d*) Prakrit
3. *The variations in the fabric of a sari depends on*
   (*a*) Local climate
   (*b*) Culture
   (*c*) Traditions
   (*d*) All of these
4. *The Patola sari originates from*
   (*a*) Tamil Nadu
   (*b*) Kerala
   (*c*) Gujarat
   (*d*) Maharashtra

ACTIVITIES & PROJECTS

Multidisciplinary Approach **Creativity and Innovation**

1. Create a collage reflecting the diversity of India in terms of food, clothing, languages and festivals.
2. Ask your grandmother /mother/ sister to show you her collection of sarees. Observe them carefully and write a note on their texture and fabric and the state to which they belong. Your note should also mention the changes you observe in the texture, pattern, colours, fabric and design of the sarees of the two/three generations. You can also consult your elder family members on the same.
3. Prepare some food that is the speciality of any state and serve it to your family members. Write a paragraph of about 200-300 words on the food habits, language and traditions of that state.

ROLE PLAY

Collaboration **Communication**

- Make 2-3 groups of students. Each group will enact a story based on the Panchatantra or the Ramayana and highlight the morals of the story. Explain the relevance of the morals in present day times.

CHAPTER 9

Theme D—Governance and Democracy

Family and Community

CG-4 : C-4.1, C-4.2; CG-5 : C-5.2

What's new to learn

- Family
- Roles and Responsibilities
- Community
- Roles and Responsibilities

You all must be familiar with the word "family". What comes to your mind when you think of a "family"? Instantly, you are reminded of your parents, grandparents and your brothers and sisters who live with you in your home. A family is our first school where we learn great lessons and values for life. It plays an important role in shaping our personalities and making us responsible citizens.

FAMILY

A family is an ancient and fundamental social unit consisting of individuals related by blood, marriage, or adoption. A family is our first social group in which we are born. Members of a family stay together and share emotional, financial and social responsibilities.

Chief features of a Family

- **Social Unit :** A family is a small group of individuals that are closely related, share a common living space and responsibilities.
- **Emotional Support :** Members of a family provide emotional support to each other. They take care of each other and share love and companionship.
- **Economic Support :** The elders of the household, such as the grandparents and parents, share economic responsibilities and provide essentials like food, shelter, clothing and education for the family members.
- **Shared Responsibilities :** The members of a family share responsibilities among themselves, such as doing household chores, taking care of the elderly or little ones, decision-making, etc.
- **Transmission of Values and Culture :** A family passes down its culture, values, ethics, traditions and customs from one generation to the next.
- **Socialisation :** A family teaches social behaviour, social ethics and values to its members. It prepares the children for greater responsibilities and societal roles.

Types of Family

- **Joint family :** In this type of a family, multiple generations live together under one roof, like grandparents, parents, children and sometimes even uncles, aunts and cousins. All the members share responsibilities and resources among themselves and provide a strong support system to each other.
- **Nuclear family :** This type of family is more prominent in the urban areas and consists of only the parents and their children or sometimes a single parent and children.

Think & Answer

What type of a family do you live in ? What type of families reside in your neighbourhood ? Make a list of any five families and their members.

A joint family

A nuclear family

A nuclear family

MORE TO KNOW

There would be a number of family members in your family whom you call by names such as Dada, Dadi, Nana, Nani, Mama, Mami, Tau, Tai, Bua, Chachi, etc. These are all Hindi names of different relations. There are many such names in other Indian languages too. But, you will be surprised to know that there is no word in Indian languages for the English word "cousin" because in India, cousins are regarded as brothers and sisters.

ROLES AND RESPONSIBILITIES

Let us first read a short story on how different family members help and support each other.

Aditi lived with her family in Mumbai. There were six members in her family-her grandparents, parents and her little brother. It was Aditi's grandmother's 75th birthday and the family decided to celebrate it by preparing a lavish dinner at home and inviting some of her grandmother's friends.

As a lot of work had to be done for the party, all the members of the family sat together and decided to share the responsibilities so that the party could go on smoothly.

Aditi's father Ravi took over the charge of shopping for the dishes and dessert to be prepared, decorative items and return gifts for the guests. Aditi's mother, Veena took upon herself the task of preparing the main dishes that also included Grandma's favourite dishes. She decided to take the help of Aditi in cutting the vegetables and setting the table.

Sharing and caring in the family

Aditi herself loved to bake and decided to prepare her Grandma's favourite pineapple cake. She prepared a list of ingredients she would require for the cake and its icing and handed over the list to her father. Her younger brother Anant took over the charge of decorating the house and main room with balloons, streamers and other items. He took the help of his grandfather in blowing the balloons and fixing the streamers.

By evening, with the help and support of family members, the house was nicely decorated, the cake was baked and all the dishes were prepared on time. The party went on till night and all the guests praised the family for their collective efforts. Grandma was overjoyed and overwhelmed to see the preparations as well as her old friends on her special day.

Veena especially thanked the children for their help and support and taught them the importance of teamwork and cooperation within a family that makes even difficult tasks easy.

By this story, you must have understood how sharing of roles and responsibilities is essential within a family as this ensures that everything runs smoothly. You must also be helping your family members in one or the other ways.

Members of a family are interdependent on each other for their everyday needs. Help and cooperation from different family members develops bonds of love, understanding, mutual respect and care. Cooperation means to work together. Each family member contributes to household chores in different ways, depending on their abilities, age and strengths.

Generally it is the duty of the parents to arrange for the finances of the family, look after their elderly parents, raise their kids in a healthy environment, provide them with basic needs including good health and education and also prepare them for bigger roles as responsible members of the society. The parents also teach their children moral and ethical values as well as their family traditions and culture. A family is regarded as the first school and the parents as the first teachers of children. It is in a family that children learn values such as kindness, gratitude, empathy, honesty, compassion, integrity, responsibility, hard work and helping others.

Think & Answer

In what different ways do you and your brothers/sisters help your parents in household chores ? Think of some other ways also in which you can help them in running your home smoothly.

Children also share responsibilities as they grow up. They help in household chores like cleaning, dusting, setting the table, watering the plants, taking care of younger siblings, etc. By performing small tasks, they prepare themselves for bigger roles in society in the future. As the children grow up, they gradually take on more responsibilities. Some even help their families financially.

The elders of the family like grandparents also have important roles within a family. They guide the family in important matters and in difficult times through their wisdom and experience. They also teach the children important values and family traditions in day-to-day life or through stories. The elders also take care of the younger ones and help with simple household tasks.

Check Your Progress

Understanding

A. State whether True or false

1. A family is our first social group in which we are born.
2, A nuclear family has grandparents and cousins living together.
3. We learn moral values only in the schools and not in our family.
4. A family also provides emotional support.
5. A family prepares the children for greater responsibilities and societal roles.

B. Prepare your family tree.

C. Fill the following table by mentioning the name of the member of your family who performs the task given in the box

Task	Name of the family member and your relation with him/her
Cooks food	
Cleans utensils	
Looks after the garden	
Brings vegetables from the market	
Helps you with homework	
Goes to office	

COMMUNITY

A community is a group of people with common geographic location, beliefs, interests, values or goals. A community may also be called a number of families that live together, support each other and work together.

Chief features of a Community

- **Shared Interests :** Members of a community have some common interests, goals and experiences. These interests could be based on some common location, profession, culture, hobby or belief.
- **Sense of Belonging :** As members of a community share common interests, they feel connected to each other and have a sense of security in each other's company. They develop a sense of belonging and collective identity.
- **Mutual Support :** Members of a community provide support to each other in times of need. This support could be emotional, financial or social. They share all the resources available to them which strengthens their bonds and relationships.
- **Common Values :** Members of a community often share common beliefs, practices, traditions and customs. These common values guide the behaviour and interactions among the community members.

- **Social Interaction :** The community members interact and communicate regularly either through meetings, written communication or through digital platforms. These meetings are held for a common cause like completing any project or doing something for the well being of the community.
- **Shared Responsibilities :** Members of a community are given different roles and responsibilities that help the community to function effectively. Members take collective decisions while addressing common issues or planning activities for the benefit of the community.
- **Geographical Boundaries :** Traditional communities had defined geographical boundaries like a neighbourhood or town. Modern communities are mostly connected through technology like social media groups and online platforms.

Types of Community

- **Geographical Community :** A community in which people live in the same geographic area, *e.g.*, Rural villages, Towns, Countries, etc.

Village

- **Cultural Community :** A community in which people have the same cultural background, traditions, practices, etc. *e.g.*, Native Americans, German-Americans, etc..
- **Religious Community :** A community with people following the same religion and beliefs, *e.g.*, Hindu Community, Buddhist Community, etc.
- **Virtual Community :** A community in which people connect with each other online from different locations, *e.g.*, Social media groups like Facebook, Online forums, etc.
- **Intentional Community :** A properly planned community where people live together to share some common purpose and responsibilities, *e.g.*, Cooperatives, Co-housing groups, Resident Welfare Associations, etc.
- **Interest-based Community :** A community in which people have some common interest or hobbies, *e.g.*, Sports Clubs, Music and dance groups, etc.

Apart from these, there can be several other types of communities like the trading community, the farming community, the business community, political community, school community, etc. Communities are interdependent. This means that they rely on each other for resources, support and proper management of their functions. *For example,* the rural communities depend on the cities for markets and sale of their manufactured products while the urban communities depend on the rural areas for food and raw materials.

Think & Answer

Are you or any member of your family a part of any community ? Give the name of that community and mention its purpose and functions.

MORE TO KNOW

The Toda Community resides in the Nilgiri Hills of Tamil Nadu, India. One of the most fascinating aspects of Toda culture is their traditional architecture, particularly their barrel-vaulted huts called "douglas." These huts are constructed without any nails or metal supports. They are held together by using only bamboo, thatch and intricate weaving techniques. The huts are semicircular in shape to withstand the strong winds and heavy rainfall of the Nilgiri Hills.

The Todas are also famous for their rich tradition of embroidery, known as "pukhoor". The embroidery has intricate geometric patterns and is made with the use of red and black threads with a white cotton cloth background. It is done mainly on shawls and cloaks worn by women and men. This handicraft product is listed as a geographically tagged product and is protected under the Geographical Indications of Goods (Registration & Protection) Act (GI Act) 1999 of the Government of India.

Pukhoor embroidery by Toda tribals of Nilgiris, Tamil Nadu

ROLES AND RESPONSIBILITIES

Let us first consider a few real-life examples to show how the Communities work for welfare programmes in India.

SEWA (Self-Employed Women's Association)—Gujarat

Founded in 1972 by Ela Bhatt, SEWA is a trade union for poor, self-employed women workers. It aims at improving the employment conditions of women workers employed in informal sectors like street vendors, home based workers and agricultural labourers. It also provides child care , health care and housing to its members. Through SEWA, many women have been provided education, are financially secure and are also undertaking cooperative businesses.

SEWA
SELF EMPLOYED WOMEN'S ASSOCIATION

Women at SEWA meet

Chipko Movement—Uttarakhand

Chipko Movement—Uttarakhand

This movement started in the 1970s in Uttarakhand against the cutting of trees by contractors. The local villagers, especially women, embraced the trees to prevent them from cutting. The movement was led by local communities to protect the forests, which were the source of their livelihood. The movement lays stress on a sustainable utilisation of forest resources and the importance of community participation in conservation programmes.

Chipko Movement

The Van Dhan Vikas Yojana for tribal communities

This programme was launched in 2018 and aims at improving the living conditions and livelihood of tribal communities by encouraging the sale of forest-based products. For this, Van Dhan Kendras have been established where tribal self-help groups are trained in sustainable harvesting, improved quality and marketing of minor forest produce. The programme thus serves many objectives like utilization of local resources, ensure environment sustainability and improve the financial condition of tribal communities.

Van Dhan Yojana

Van Dhan Vikas Yojana

A training programme under the Van Dhan Vikas Yojana

Kerala Floods 2018 - Fishermen's Rescue Operations

The fishermen from the coastal communities played an important part in the rescue operations during the devastating floods of Kerala in 2018. The fishermen navigated the flooded areas with their boats and rescued thousands of stranded people. They were hailed as real heroes by the state government and the people for their selfless service and local knowledge of water currents and navigation that saved so many lives.

Kerala Floods 2018

Flood alert

Gujarat Earthquake 2001 – Kutch Community-Led Rehabilitation

After the devastating earthquake of 2001, the people of Kutch came together and helped each other to rebuild their homes and lives. New earthquake resistant houses were built by the efforts of NGOs, local artisans and traders. Local organisations also provided psychological support by providing trauma counselling to the affected people.

Gujarat Earthquake 2001

Earthquake warning system symbol

Community Efforts

By the examples given above, it must be clear to you how the communities play an important part in economic empowerment, environment sustainability and managing natural calamities from rescue to recovery and relief. Many times, local communities are the first to respond in times of need before any external help arrives.

Some important initiatives undertaken by the communities in various fields are discussed as under :

- In many rural areas, the communities often come together to manage and conserve water resources and undertake initiatives like rainwater harvesting, watershed management and construction of dams.

- The communities also play an important part in the conservation and sustainable use of forest resources. This has led to increased forest cover, regeneration of many degraded forests and incensed livelihood opportunities for the local communities.

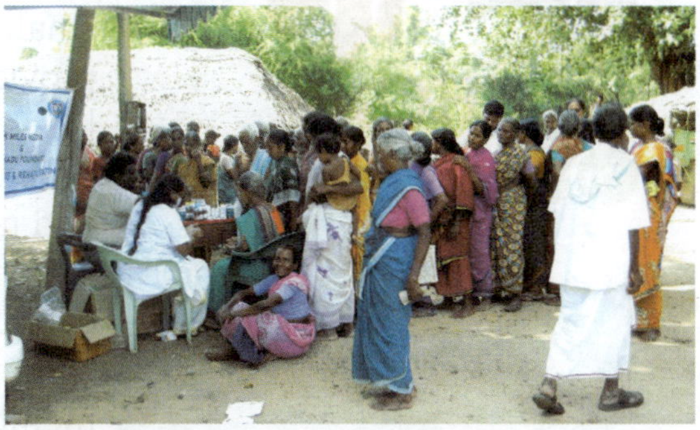

- Communities also organise health camps, awareness and training programmes to address a number of health-related issues and general well being. This has helped in improving maternal and child health, preventing diseases and promoting overall well being of communities.

- Communities also take care of the educational requirements of their members. They establish schools, libraries and carry out educational programs to make the members aware of the importance of education and provide quality education to both children and adults. The efforts of communities has resulted in an increased number of admissions to schools, reduced drop-out rates and improved educational outcomes of students.

- Communities also carry out sanitation drives to promote a clean and healthy environment. They build and maintain sanitation facilities which has resulted in decreased cases of waterborne diseases and enhanced quality of life of community members.

- Communities also undertake agricultural programs in which they encourage sustainable farming practices like organic farming, pest management, proper use of natural resources and improve the living conditions and income of farmers.

- Sometimes communities also undertake disaster management programs that enable them to prepare for and respond to natural disasters like floods, earthquakes, cyclones, etc. Such programs have saved thousands of lives as you have already read in the examples given earlier. They also minimise property damage and facilitate faster recovery from disasters.

- Local communities also provide loans and financial assistance to small businesses and entrepreneurs. Such steps support new and small businesses, provide facility of loans even in the absence of banks and improve the economic conditions of community members. Women usually form Self-Helf Groups (SHGs), where they come together voluntarily to pool savings, provide loans to each other and engage in collective activities.

- Some communities also undertake tourism related activities to promote sustainable tourism, preserve cultural and traditional heritage and also generate new income resources for community members. This has also helped to generate employment and increased income for communities.

Think & Answer

Are you aware of any community based program in your neighbourhood ? If yes, then describe and discuss its objectives and functions in your class.

Thus, we see that communities address various social, economic, traditional, agricultural and environmental issues in India. Their initiatives and solutions have created a positive impact on their members as well as the environment.

Check Your Progress

Understanding

Give one example of each of the following :

1. Cultural Community
2. Geographic Community
3. Interest- based Community
4. Virtual Community
5. Interest-based Community

NEW WORDS

- **Fundamental :** Basic, forming the foundation of something.
- **Socialisation :** The process of learning social behaviours, ethics and values, usually within a family or community.
- **Generation :** All the people born and living at about the same time, regarded collectively.
- **Interdependent :** When two or more people or things rely on each other for resources, support, or success.
- **Responsibilities :** Duties or tasks that one is required or expected to carry out.
- **Compassion :** A deep awareness of and sympathy for another's suffering, often with a desire to help.
- **Sustainable :** Able to be maintained or continued without depleting resources or causing harm to the environment.
- **Conservation :** The protection, preservation, or careful management of natural resources to prevent exploitation or degradation.
- **Geographical :** Related to the physical features, location, or characteristics of a particular area.
- **Intentional :** Done on purpose; deliberate.
- **Empowerment :** The process of becoming stronger and more confident.
- **Cooperation :** The process of working together towards a common goal.
- **Calamity :** A disastrous event causing great damage or distress.
- **Livelihood :** The means by which someone earns a living or supports themselves financially.
- **Artisan :** A worker in a skilled trade, especially one that involves making things by hand.
- **Psychological :** Related to the mind or emotions, often in the context of mental health or well-being.
- **Conserve :** To protect or preserve something from harm, decay, or waste.
- **Sanitation :** Measures taken to maintain cleanliness and prevent disease, especially through the disposal of waste and sewage.
- **Heritage :** The traditions, achievements and beliefs that are part of the history and culture of a group or society.
- **Preserve :** To maintain something in its original state or to protect it from harm or decay.

NUTSHELL

- A family is a fundamental social unit, consisting of individuals related by blood, marriage, or adoption.
- Main functions of a family : Provides emotional and economic support, shares responsibilities such as household chores and decision-making and passes down values, traditions and culture to the next generation.
- Types of Families : Joint Family and Nuclear Family
- A community is a group of people who share common geographic location, beliefs, interests, or goals.
- Main features of a community are : Shared interests and values, a sense of belonging and mutual support, regular social interaction and shared responsibilities.
- Communities rely on each other for resources, support and functioning.
- Communities play a vital role in disaster management, education, health and environmental sustainability.
- They address social, economic and environmental challenges by working collectively.

IMPORTANT NCERT TEXTBOOK QUESTIONS (Solved)

Questions, activities and projects

1. What are some of the rules you follow in your family and neighbourhood ? Why are they important ?

Ans. Some of the rules I follow in my family are :

(*a*) Respect elders.

(*b*) Talk politely and express gratitude.

(*c*) Follow family rules and discipline.

(*d*) Complete the work assigned to me.

(*e*) Follow a timetable for studies and play.

Some of the rules I follow in my neighbourhood are :

(*a*) Greet my neighbours whenever I meet them.

(*b*) Maintain cleanliness.

(*c*) Help my neighbours when they are in need.

(*d*) Do not disturb anyone unnecessarily.

(*e*) No noise after 10 p.m.

(*f*) Participate in neighbourhood activities and programmes.

Rules are necessary both in a family and in our neighbourhood as they help maintain decorum and discipline thus, creating a harmonious atmosphere for a peaceful living.

2. Do you think some rules are unfair to a few people in the family or community ? Why ?

Ans. Rules must always be flexible as strict rules become unfair for people in family as well as community. For example, some family members may not be able to fulfil the tasks assigned to them if they are very busy in their office work or not well. Similarly , in a family, rules based on gender may also be unfair for children, especially girls. Everyone in the family expects girls to do household chores while the same is not expected of boys. This is unfair to girls.

In a community also, aged or busy people cannot take part in all community activities. Similarly, night shift workers cannot be expected to maintain silence after 10 pm.

3. Describe several situations that you have observed where community support makes a difference. You can draw or write about these.

Ans.
1. **Support during illness :** During Covid, many families offered to provide home cooked food to the elderly living alone as house help was not available during those days. Community members also offered to bring vegetables and fruits for the families where all members were suffering from Covid and could not go out of their homes.
2. **Community fundraisers :** Our community also raises funds for the children of some house helps who cannot afford education for their children.
3. **Cleanliness drives :** Our community carries out cleanliness drives on the last Sunday of every month for our colony and a park situated nearby. All elders, parents and children who want to become a part of this programme, participate in this drive and clean our surroundings.

EXERCISES As per NEP-2020 & NCF-2023

I. OBJECTIVE TYPE QUESTIONS

A. Choose the correct answer.

Conceptual Learning | Critical Thinking

1. *What is the primary role of a family ?*
   (*a*) To provide entertainment
   (*b*) To teach values and support its members
   (*c*) To create businesses
   (*d*) To build houses
2. *Which of the following is NOT a characteristic of a joint family ?*
   (*a*) Multiple generations living together
   (*b*) Sharing responsibilities
   (*c*) Living in different locations
   (*d*) Strong support system
3. *Which type of community is based on shared geographic location ?*
   (*a*) Cultural community
   (*b*) Virtual community
   (*c*) Geographical community
   (*d*) Interest-based community
4. *Which of the following best describes community interdependence ?*
   (*a*) Communities rely solely on themselves
   (*b*) Communities rely on each other for resources and support
   (*c*) Communities do not interact
   (*d*) Communities compete against each other
5. *Which of these was a community-led environmental movement in Uttarakhand ?*
   (*a*) SEWA
   (*b*) Chipko Movement
   (*c*) Van Dhan Vikas Yojana
   (*d*) Kerala Rescue Operations

B. Mark the option that matches Column A with Column B.

Conceptual Learning | Problem Solving

Column A	Column B
1. Chipko Movement	(*i*) Women workers' trade union
2. SEWA	(*ii*) Community providing support in natural disasters
3. Van Dhan Vikas Yojana	(*iii*) Protecting forests in Uttarakhand
4. Kerala Fishermen	(*iv*) Supporting tribal communities

(*a*) **1.**-(*iii*), **2.**-(*i*), **3.**-(*ii*), **4.**-(*iv*)
(*b*) **1.**-(*i*), **2.**-(*iii*), **3.**-(*iv*), **4.**-(*ii*)
(*c*) **1.**-(*i*), **2.**-(*ii*), **3.**-(*iii*), **4.**-(*iv*)
(*d*) **1.**-(*iii*), **2.**-(*i*), **3.**-(*iv*), **4.**-(*ii*)

C. Fill in the blanks

Knowledge Application

1. A ______________ family consists of only parents and their children living together under one roof.
2. Members of a community often have shared ______________ , values and experiences, which creates a sense of belonging.
3. The ______________ community played a major role in rescuing people during the Kerala floods of 2018.

4. A family is considered the first ______________ where children learn values like kindness, gratitude and responsibility.

5. In a ______________ family, multiple generations live together and share responsibilities.

D. State True or False

Knowledge Application | Problem Solving

1. SEWA is a trade union for self-employed men in the formal sector.
2. Communities are not interdependent and function independently of each other.
3. A family is considered as the first social group in which we are born.
4. Joint families are more common in urban areas than in rural areas.
5. A nuclear family includes grandparents, parents and children living together.

E. Assertion-Reason

Critical Thinking

For question numbers 1 to 4, two statements are given—one labelled Assertion (A) and the other labelled Reason (R). Select the correct answer to these questions from the codes *(a)*, *(b)*, *(c)* and *(d)* as given below :

(*a*) Both Assertion (A) and Reason (R) are true and Reason is the correct explanation of the Assertion.
(*b*) Both Assertion (A) and Reason (R) are true but Reason is not the correct explanation of the Assertion.
(*c*) Assertion (A) is true but Reason (R) is false.
(*d*) Assertion (A) is false but Reason (R) is true.

1. **Assertion (A)** : A nuclear family consists of parents and their children.
   Reason (R) : In a joint family, multiple generations live together and share responsibilities.
2. **Assertion (A)** : Communities are interdependent on each other for resources and support.
   Reason (R) : Communities function better when they share common interests, values and experiences.
3. **Assertion (A)** : The Chipko Movement focused on protecting forests in Uttarakhand.
   Reason (R) : The movement was primarily led by women of the local communities to prevent cutting of trees.
4. **Assertion (A)** : Communities undertake sanitation programmes.
   Reason (R) : Communities do not undertake disaster management programmes.

II. SHORT ANSWER TYPE QUESTIONS

Conceptual Learning | Knowledge Application

1. Discuss the role of elders in a family.
2. How are communities interdependent ?
3. List the features of a joint family.
4. What was the main purpose of the Chipko Movement ?

III. LONG ANSWER TYPE QUESTIONS

Knowledge Application | Critical Thinking

1. Explain how joint families differ from nuclear families.
2. Describe any three main functions of communities.
3. Discuss the role of a family in the overall development of an individual.

IV. DISTINGUISH BETWEEN THE FOLLOWING

Conceptual Learning | Understanding

1. Joint family and Nuclear family
2. Family and Community

V. PICTURE STUDY

Knowledge Application | Critical Thinking

Given here is a picture of a family. Answer the following questions with respect to the picture.

1. Define a family.
2. Name the type of family you see in the given picture.
3. List some advantages of this type of a family.
4. Discuss the role of elder members like grandparents in a family.

VI. SOURCE BASED QUESTIONS

Analysing | Conceptual Learning | Understanding

Read the given paragraph and answer the following questions.

A community is a group of people who share common interests, values, goals, or geographic locations. Communities foster a sense of belonging, mutual support and shared responsibilities among their members. They come together for a various reasons, such as cultural, religious or professional connections. Whether it's a neighbourhood working on local improvement projects or a group responding to natural calamities, communities play a vital role in providing emotional, social and economic support. For example, during natural disasters, communities often unite to provide aid and relief before external help arrives. Communities not only strengthen bonds among individuals, but also contribute to societal growth by promoting cooperation, understanding and mutual respect.

1. *In a community, people share common*
   (*a*) values (*b*) interests (*c*) goals (*d*) all of these
2. *Which of the following is not true about a community ?*
   (*a*) Community is a group of people who share common interests and values.
   (*b*) Communities foster a sense of belonging and mutual support.
   (*c*) Communities never come together for a variety of reasons.
   (*d*) Communities play a vital role in providing emotional, social and economic support.
3. *The Van Dhan Vikas Yojana is for*
   (*a*) tribal communities (*b*) people living in the villages
   (*c*) people living in metro cities (*d*) none of these
4. *The Chipko Andolan took place in*
   (*a*) Punjab (*b*) Uttarakhand
   (*c*) Uttar Pradesh (*d*) Himachal Pradesh

ACTIVITIES & PROJECTS

Multidisciplinary Approach | Creativity and Innovation

1. Create a family tree of your family. Paste photographs and mention one quality of each of your family members.
2. Talk to your grandmother about her experiences of living in a joint family. Share her experiences in your class.
3. Discuss how roles and responsibilities are divided among different members of your family. How do you contribute as a member of your family ?
4. Create a small community of your friends and carry out a clean-up drive of your locality. Share your experiences in the class.

ROLE PLAY

Collaboration | Communication

- Form pairs as community members. Suppose there is a natural calamity in your locality. Act out what you will do to minimize the effects of the calamity. Discuss all the steps you will take to minimize the harmful effects of the calamity.

CHAPTER 10

Grassroots Democracy – Part 1 : Governance

CG-4 : C-4.1, C-4.2; CG-5 : C-5.2; CG-8 : C-8.3 ; CG-10 : C-10.1

What's new to learn

- Government
- Three Organs of Government
- Three Levels of Government
- Democracy

Once there was a small village where everyone lived in harmony, prosperity and happiness. But, the village had no system to solve the common problems. When the tubewells ran out of water, no one knew how to resume the water supply. If there were floods or drought or no electricity, no one knew how to solve these problems and if there was any dispute among the villagers, no one was there to make fair decisions. To solve these problems, the villagers decided to form a group of elderly and experienced persons to guide the villagers in difficult times and give fair decisions. This group or council was also given the power to make certain rules and regulations for the village like fair distribution of water and resources, maintenance of cleanliness, etc. The appointment of the council proved to be very helpful for all the villagers and life became more organised and simple for everyone. This system of managing, organising and making decisions is called governance.

Different functions of a government

GOVERNMENT

Just like the village in the given story, every city, state, country and organisation needs a system of governance to make decisions and work for the collective good.

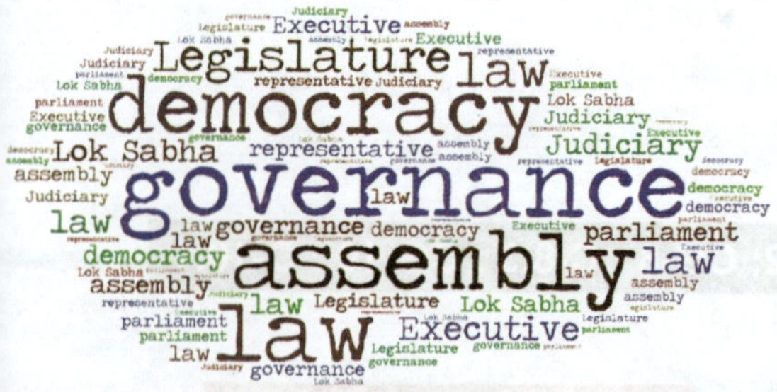

Thus, **governance** refers to the processes, systems and structures that guide, manage and control any organisation or society. A **government** is an institution that makes political decisions to run a country. It refers to the group of people who are responsible for controlling a country or a state. It is an administrative organ of a region or a country. It is a system by which people are governed. The government expresses the will of the state.

Just imagine a situation in your class without a teacher or a school without a principal. There would be a lot of confusion and noise. So, we find it necessary to have somebody or some system to control the situation. Likewise, to maintain law and order, to ensure cooperation among people to make collective decisions and to get things done, a government is needed for the country. The powers and functioning of a government differ from one country to another. Government is the system by which a state is governed. In a democratic country, a government functions according to the Constitution.

Functions of a Government

New Parliament House in Delhi

- **Makes Laws for Everyone :** A government makes rules for the country and the more important rules are called laws. The government makes rules in the form of laws to protect the rights and interests of each of its citizens. The interests of the people of different groups or communities may clash with each other. So, the government takes collective decisions on behalf of its people by exercising leadership. Everyone who lives in a country has to follow these decisions or laws.

Supreme Court of India

- **Maintains Law and Order :** The government ensures law and order within the country. It makes and implements laws for this purpose. In case of any dispute or crime, the government resolves them through courts.
- **Provides Basic Facilities :** The government works for the welfare of the people. It provides basic facilities to the people such as education, healthcare, transportation, electricity, etc. It builds roads, bridges, schools and hospitals, provides supply of electricity and postal and railway services. It also controls the prices of commodities.

Road repair work

Network of Railways

Construction of Bridges

Supply of Electricity

Traffic Police

Construction of Schools

Postal Services

Banking

- **Action on Social Issues :** The government launches several programmes for the poor and needy and implements them. It also makes various laws to prevent female foeticides, ensure equal distribution of resources, etc.

Distribution of Grains

Think & Answer

Has the government provided any basic facility in your neighbourhood like schools, parks, dispensaries, etc. ? Write a paragraph on how you and your neighbours have benefited from it.

Protection of boundaries

- **Protects the Boundaries :** The government protects the boundaries of a country from enemy countries. It also maintains peaceful relations with other countries.

- **Undertakes Relief Measures :** In the case of natural disasters like earthquakes, tsunamis, floods, droughts, etc., the government organises aid and assistance for the affected people.

A relief camp

Check Your Progress — Understanding

State whether true or false

1. A system of governance is required to make decisions and work for the collective good.
2. A government does not make laws.
3. Disputes are resolved through courts.
4. Education, healthcare, transportation etc are basic facilities that the government provides.
5. A government has no role in case of natural disasters.

THREE ORGANS OF GOVERNMENT

Let us get back to the story of the small village that you read in the beginning of the chapter. After the appointment of the council, things went on smoothly in the village for some time. But, after a few months, problems again arose as the council mostly had all elderly members who could not enforce or implement the rules made by the council. So, the council once again called for a meeting with all the villagers. This time, they decided to manage the affairs of the village through three groups or organs : the first group was to be of wise and experienced villagers who would make rules that everyone would follow. This group was called the **Legislature**. The second group consisted of people whose main function was to enforce the rules made by the first group. This group was called the **Executive**. The third group was given the task of setting the disputes and disagreements between the Legislature and the Executive. This group that had to give the right judgements was called the **Judiciary.** As the three groups started functioning for the welfare of the village, life became much smoother for all the villagers. The three groups functioned independently, but also kept a check on one another so that no group could misuse the powers given to it.

Just like the village in the story, our country also has three organs of government namely, the **Legislature**, the **Executive** and the **Judiciary**.

The main functions of these three organs are :

- **Legislature :** It makes or "legislates" new laws for the country. At times, it also updates old laws or removes them if they are no longer required. The making, updating and removal of laws is done by an assembly that is composed of elected representatives. The members of the legislature represent the people and ensure that the laws made by them reflect the needs and aspirations of the people.

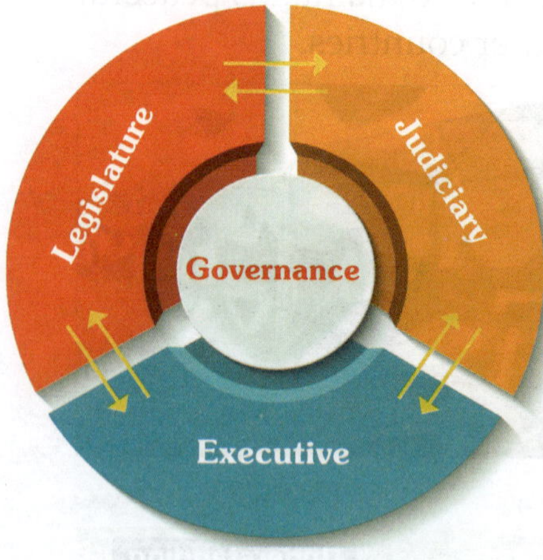

Separation of powers and three organs of the government

- **Executive :** It implements, enforces or "executes" the laws made by the Legislature. It ensures that the laws, programmes and policies made by the government are enforced properly so that their benefits reach the common man. The executive includes the head of the state like the President, Prime Minister or Chief Minister of a state, other government ministers and officials.
- **Judiciary :** It interprets the laws and ensures that justice is given in a fair manner. The judiciary resolves disputes between individuals, organisations, government and people, etc. It protects the rights of citizens and ensures that no one breaks the law. Judiciary also has the power to give punishments to the accused. It also examines the laws made by the legislature and the decisions taken by the executive. It also solves any disputes between the legislature and the executive.

The Separation of Powers

- Power is shared among different organs of the government such as the legislature, executive and judiciary.

- Different organs of government are placed at the same level but they exercise different powers. They are separate and independent from each other although they interact with each other.
- This separation of powers ensures that none of the organs exercise unlimited power and each organ keeps a check on the other organs.
- This system also ensures a balance of power among various institutions. Therefore, it is called **a system of checks and balances.** *e.g.*, while the judges are appointed by the executive, the judges in turn check the functioning of executive or laws made by the legislatures.

THREE LEVELS OF GOVERNMENT

Generally, there are two levels of government in a country : the local level and the national level. In some countries like India, there is also a third level of government known as the Municipal Corporations in towns and Panchayats in villages. The powers of different levels of government are clearly laid down in the Constitution.

The three levels of government in India are :

Local Level

The government in a village, town or locality is known as a local government. This government deals with the problems faced by the local people like water supply, maintenance of roads and street lights, etc. The Panchayati System, Zila Parishad, Municipal Committee, Municipal Corporation, etc. are examples of local government.

A meeting of Panchayat

Local government : Municipal Corporation

State Level/Regional Level

The government at the state level is called the state government. This government deals with the issues related to an entire state like education, health and agriculture. *For example,* the UP Government, Bihar Government, etc. are examples of a State government.

National Level/Central Level

The government at the national level is known as the national government or the central government or the union government. It deals with the issues related to the entire country like defence, economy, national security, etc. *For example,* the Indian Government is the government at the national level.

A Central Level office

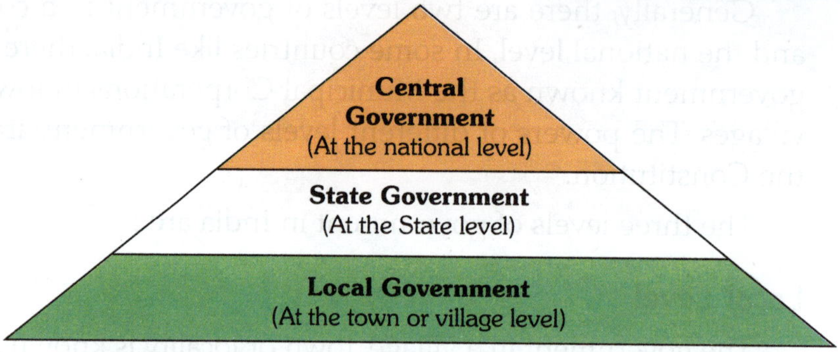

The three levels of government

Given below is a summary of the different organs of government at National and state levels :

1. (a) THE UNION EXECUTIVE

The President

1. The President is the Head of the State and the Supreme Commander of the Indian Armed Forces.
2. The executive power of the Union shall be vested in the President.

The Vice-President

1. The Vice-President is next to the President of India.
2. When the Vice-President acts as President (during casual vacancies in the office or during the absence of the President), he shall not perform the duties of the office of the Chairman of the Rajya Sabha.

Prime Minister and Council of Ministers

1. The Prime Minister is the Head of the Government and the Council of Ministers.
2. He is the leader of his party and usually the leader of the Lok Sabha.

(b) THE STATE EXECUTIVE

Governor of States

1. There shall be a Governor for each State.
2. The Governor is the executive Head of the State.

Chief Ministers and their Council of Ministers

1. The Chief Minister is the real Head of the State Government.
2. The Council of Ministers is collectively responsible to the Legislative Assembly of the State.

2. (a) THE UNION LEGISLATURE (PARLIAMENT)

PRESIDENT

The Council of State (Rajya Sabha)

Maximum Members—250 (238 from the States +12 nominated by the President)

Members at Present—245 (233 + 12)

233 Members are elected by the elected members of the Legislative Assemblies of 28 States and 2 Union Territories (Delhi and Puducherry)

12 Members are nominated by the President from among persons having special knowledge or practical experience in the field of literature, science, art and social service.

The House of the People (Lok Sabha)

Maximum Members—550* (530 from the States + 20 from the UTs)

Members at Present—543 (530 + 13)

530 members are directly elected from territorial constituencies of 28 States and 13 members from 8 Union Territories.

(b) THE STATE LEGISLATURE

GOVERNOR

The Legislative Assembly (Vidhan Sabha)

The Legislative Assembly of a State shall consist of not more than **500** and not less than **60** members exception to **Goa** (40 seats), **Mizoram** (40 seats), **Puducherry** (30 seats) and **Sikkim** (32 seats). Members are chosen by direct election from territorial constituencies.

Nomination of Anglo-Indian

One Anglo-Indian member may be nominated by the Governor to represent the community.

The Legislative Council (Vidhan Parishad)

The Legislative Council shall not exceed **1/3rd** of the total membership of the Legislative Assembly of the State concerned subject to a minimum of 40.

The members are elected as under :

1. **1/3rd** of its members are elected by the members of the Legislative Assembly (MLAs).
2. **1/3rd** by local government bodies.
3. **1/6th** nominated by the Governor.
4. **1/12th** are elected by teachers of the concerned state.
5. **1/12th** are elected by graduates of the concerned state.

The following States have a Legislative Council :

1. Andhra Pradesh
2. Bihar
3. Karnataka
4. Maharashtra
5. Telangana
6. Uttar Pradesh

** Earlier the number of members in Lok Sabha was 552. By the 104th Amendment (Constitution Act 2019), the provision for reservation of the Anglo-Indian Community (2 members nominated by the President in the Lok Sabha) has been abolished in 2020.*

3. THE JUDICIARY

The Union Judiciary

The Supreme Court

- The highest constitutional court with the power of constitutional review.
- It consists of a Chief Justice of India and 30 other Judges.
- It has Original, Appellate and Advisory Jurisdictions.
- The Chief Justice is appointed by the President in consultation with other Judges of the Supreme Court and the High Courts.
- Every Judge of the Supreme Court holds office till he attains the age of 65 years.
- A Judge may be removed by an order of the President after following the procedure on the grounds of proven misbehaviour or incapacity.
- The Supreme Court is a Court of Record.

The High Courts in the States

- The Constitution provides for a High Court for each State. However, there may be a common High Court for more than one State or Union Territory.
- Every High Court consists of a Chief Justice and other Judges as the President may deem necessary from time to time.
- Each High Court is a Court of Record and has Original and Appellate Jurisdiction.
- The Chief Justice of a High Court is appointed by the President after consultation with the Chief Justice of India and the Governor of the State concerned. The other Judges are appointed by the President after consultation with the Chief Justice of India, the Chief Justice of the High Court and the Governor of the State.
- Every High Court Judge holds office till he attains the age of 62 years.
- A Judge may be removed from his office in the manner provided for removal of a Judge of the Supreme Court.

The Subordinate Courts

- The Governor of a state appoints district judges in consultation with the High Court of the State.
- Appointment of persons other than District Judges to the judicial service of a state is made by the Governor of the State concerned according to the rules after consultation with the State Public Service Commission and with the High Court of the State concerned.

Think & Answer

(*a*) Who maintains the roads and street lights in your neighbourhood ?

(*b*) What is the name of the MLA and MP of your area ?

Check Your Progress — Understanding

Fill in the blanks

1. There are ______________ organs of the government.
2. ______________ interprets the laws and ensures that justice is given in a fair manner.
3. ______________ updates old laws or removes them if they are no longer required.
4. India has ______________ levels of government.
5. The Municipal Corporation is an example of ______________ government.

DR. A.P.J. ABDUL KALAM

Famous as the "Missile Man of India", Dr. APJ Abdul Kalam was born on October 15, 1931, in Rameswaram, Tamil Nadu in a modest family. His father was a boat owner while his mother was a homemaker. While growing up, Kalam sold newspapers to support his family while attending school.

Kalam as President of India

Since childhood, Kalam was very hardworking and had great interest in studies, especially mathematics and physics. He pursued aerospace engineering at the Madras Institute of Technology (MIT) and joined the Indian Space Research Organisation (ISRO) in 1969. He played a significant role in India's space program and the development of ballistic missile and launch vehicle technology. He worked on the Agni and Prithvi missiles and earned the title of the "Missile Man of India". He also played an important role in the nuclear tests conducted by India in 1998. He served as the Chief Scientific Adviser to the Prime Minister and Secretary of the Defence Research and Development Organisation from 1992-1999.

Dr. Kalam was elected as the 11th President of India and held this post from 2002-2007. He was famous as the " People's President" due to his humble nature and his dedication to public service. He was an inspiration for millions of youth in India and around the world. He encouraged the youth to dream big and motivated them to do something for the growth of their country. He welcomed students, scientists, educators and even ordinary citizens to meet him at the Rashtrapati Bhavan. He always focused on doing service to the nation, scientific advancement and education. He visited many schools and colleges during his tenure as a President. He wrote books like **Wings of Fire, Ignited Minds, India 2020 : A Vision for the New Millennium, Mission India : A Vision of Indian Youth, etc.** to inspire the youth of India and fill in them a sense of pride for the nation.

Dr. APJ Abdul Kalam receiving Bharat Ratna

Dr. Kalam was honoured with numerous awards, including the **Padma Bhushan (1981)**, **Padma Vibhushan (1990)** and the **Bharat Ratna (1997)**, India's highest civilian award.

Dr. Kalam's journey from a small village to the President of India highlights the importance of hard work, dedication and commitment towards one's goals.

Given below are some of the most famous quotes of Dr. Kalam that reflect his vision, wisdom and optimistic view towards life :

"Teaching is a very noble profession that shapes the character, calibre and future of an individual."

"If you fail, never give up because FAIL means 'First Attempt In Learning."

"To succeed in your mission, you must have single-minded devotion to your goal."

"Excellence is a continuous process and not an accident."

"Climbing to the top demands strength, whether it is to the top of Mount Everest or to the top of your career."

"You should not give up and we should not allow the problem to defeat us."

"If you want to shine like a Sun, first burn like a Sun."

DEMOCRACY

The word "Democracy" has been derived from a Greek word *"Demokratia"*, where *"Demos"* means people and *"kratia"* means rule or power. So, democracy is rule by the people.

Abraham Lincoln, one of the greatest Presidents of the United states said, "Democracy is government of the people, by the people and for the people". This means that in a democracy, the government is created and run by the people it serves. The power lies with the citizens and they ensure that the government acts in the interest of all citizens and not just a few.

The main features of Democracy are :

- All major decisions are made by rulers elected by the people.
- Elections are held periodically, offering people the opportunity to choose and change their current leaders.
- The choice and opportunity in elections is given to all people on an equal basis. Each adult citizen has one vote and each vote has one value.
- A democratic government is limited by the basic rules of the Constitution and citizens' rights.

MORE TO KNOW

The Universal Adult Franchise means that all citizens who are 18 years of age and above, irrespective of their caste , gender, education, religion, colour, race and economic status, have the right to vote.

A Representative Democracy

India is a democratic country as the citizens of India have the power to vote and elect their government through free and fair elections. You will be surprised to know that India is the world's largest democracy with a population of more than 1.4 billion people. In 2024, about 969 million people were eligible to vote, including 18 million first-time voters.

People in queue for voting

DO YOU KNOW?

The Electronic Voting Machines (EVMs) were first used in India in the General Elections of 2004. Before that, elections in India were conducted using paper ballots.

With such a vast population, can all people actually rule ? It will not be possible as it would lead to chaos and disorder. Therefore, the citizens elect their representatives to make decisions and pass laws on their behalf. The leaders elected by the people represent their interests in the government. This is called a **Representative Democracy.** It is similar to how your class monitor represents all the students of your class in front of the teacher or principal of your school.

The main features of a representative democracy in India are as follows :

- All people do not rule in a democracy directly. The citizens rule through their Elected Representatives at various levels like local, state or national level. The elected representatives have different names at different levels. At the local level, they are called **Panchs** in rural areas and **Councillors** in urban areas. At the state level, they are called the **Members of the Legislative Assembly (MLAs)** or **Members of the Legislative Council (MLCs).** At the national level, the elected representatives are called the **Members of Parliament (MPs).**

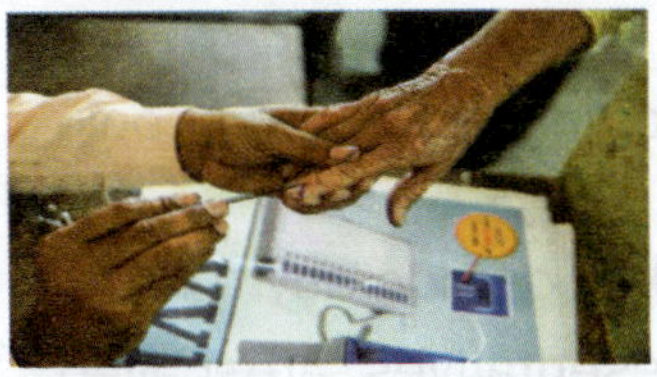

Application of indelible ink on the elector's finger

Electronic Voting Machine (EVM)

- Citizens give their approval to a government by taking part in elections and choosing their representatives. While the winning party forms the government, the other elected representatives form the opposition. Together, they form the Parliament that controls and guides the government.
- In a representative democracy, decisions are taken after many debates, dialogues, consultation and consent of all those who are affected by that decision. The powerful as well as the non powerful have the same say in taking decisions.
- The elected representatives are accountable to the people who elect them and can be voted out in the future elections if they do not fulfil their promises made to the people.

Direct Democracy

Suppose your parents want the entire house to be painted. But, there is a difference of opinion on the colours to be used for painting. Finally, your grandfather decides that everyone should vote on the colour. The options he gives are blue, green, pink and red. Every member of the family is given the right to vote and it is decided that the colour with the most votes would be chosen for painting. This is an example of a **direct democracy** where every member of the family has a direct say in decision making.

Thus, in a direct democracy, citizens directly participate in decision-making and governance, rather than electing representatives to do so on their behalf. They directly vote on laws, policies and important issues themselves and therefore have a more significant role in the functioning of the government. Citizens can even propose new laws or changes to existing laws and vote on them. Switzerland is a notable example of a country that uses direct democracy extensively at the local and national levels.

Think & Answer

In a democracy, people have the right to vote and choose their leaders. Why is it important for everyone to vote for their representatives ? What will happen if only the rich and powerful are allowed to vote ?

Grassroots Democracy

This is a form of democracy where citizens participate directly in decision-making at the local or community level. In this, people at the lowest levels of society (grassroots) are encouraged to take part in governance. It allows the people at the grassroots level to have direct control over decisions affecting their daily lives and ensure that local problems are addressed at the village or community level.

In India, the **Panchayati Raj System** is an example of grassroots democracy where the villagers or community members elect a **Sarpanch** (village head) and other members of the **Panchayat** (village council). The Panchayat makes decisions about local issues of the village like construction and maintenance of roads, management of water resources, schools and healthcare centres. Decisions are taken based on the needs and preferences of the community members.

Check Your Progress

Understanding

State whether True or False

1. In a democracy, the government is created and run by the people it serves.
2. Only the rich and powerful are benefitted by democracy.
3. At the national level, the elected representatives are called MLAs.
4. The Panchayati Raj System is an example of grassroots democracy.
5. In a direct democracy, citizens do not participate in decision-making and governance.

NEW WORDS

- **Governance :** The processes and systems by which a country or organisation is controlled or managed.
- **Institution :** A large organisation or establishment with a specific purpose, often governmental or educational.
- **Dispute :** A disagreement or argument between two or more people or groups.
- **Legislature :** A group of people who have the power to make laws for a country or state.
- **Executive :** The part of the government responsible for enforcing laws and making sure they are carried out.
- **Judiciary :** The system of courts that interprets and applies laws and resolves disputes.
- **Enforce :** To make sure that people obey a law or rule.
- **Implement :** To put a law, decision, or plan into action.
- **Regulation :** A rule or directive made and maintained by an authority.
- **Infrastructure :** The basic physical systems of a country, such as transportation, communication, power supplies and buildings.
- **Natural disaster :** A disastrous event caused by nature, like an earthquake, flood, or drought.
- **Constitution :** A system of basic principles and laws by which a country is governed.
- **Interpret :** To explain or understand the meaning of something, especially laws.
- **Judgement :** A decision made by a court or judge.
- **Checks and balances :** A system where the powers of different organs of government are limited and balanced to prevent any one organ from becoming too powerful.
- **Representative democracy :** A form of democracy where citizens elect representatives to make decisions on their behalf.
- **Direct democracy :** A form of democracy where people directly vote on laws and policies rather than electing representatives.
- **Grassroots democracy :** A type of democracy where people at the local level participate in decision-making about their community or village.
- **House :** An assembly where laws are discussed or passed.
- **Nominal :** In name only. It means, in our case, that the President of India and the Governor of a State are not the actual executive heads. They do have certain powers under special circumstances, but normally do not interfere in the affairs of the Central or State government.

NUTSHELL

- Governance refers to the processes, systems and institutions that guide, manage and control an organisation or country.
- A government is an institution that makes political decisions to run a country.
- Three Organs of Government are :

  (*a*) **Legislature :** Makes laws for the country.

  (*b*) **Executive :** Implements and enforces the laws.

  (*c*) **Judiciary :** Interprets the laws and ensures that justice is served.
- Power is divided among the three organs of government to prevent any one organ from becoming too powerful. This ensures a system of checks and balances.
- Three Levels of Government are :

  (*a*) **Local Level :** Panchayats in villages and Municipal Corporations in towns that handle local issues.

  (*b*) **State Level :** State governments address issues related to the entire state, like education and agriculture.

  (*c*) **National Level :** The central government deals with national matters such as defence and economy.
- The word Democracy has been derived from the Greek word "Demokratia," meaning "rule by the people."
- Citizens elect representatives to make decisions in a Representative Democracy.
- In a representative democracy, decisions are taken after many debates, dialogues, consultation and consent of all those who are affected by that decision.
- In a direct democracy, citizens participate directly in decision-making and governance.
- Grassroots democracy is a form of democracy where citizens participate directly in decision-making at the local or community level, like the Panchayati Raj system in India.

IMPORTANT NCERT TEXTBOOK QUESTIONS (Solved)

Questions, activities and projects

1. Test yourself — What is the meaning of democracy ? What is the difference between direct democracy and representative democracy ?

Ans. The word "Democracy" has been derived from a Greek word "Demokratia", where "Demos" means people and "kratia" means rule or power. So, democracy is rule by the people. In a democracy, the power lies with the citizens. They vote and choose the government of their choice and they ensure that the government acts in the interest of all citizens and not just a few.

In a direct democracy, citizens directly participate in decision-making and governance while in a representative democracy, the citizens elect their representatives to make decisions and pass laws on their behalf.

2. Recall the three organs of government. What are their different roles ?

Ans. The three organs of a government and their different roles are as follows :

(*a*) **Legislature :** It makes or "legislates" new laws for the country. At times, it also updates old laws or removes them if they are no longer required. The making, updating and removal of laws is done by an assembly that is composed of elected representatives.

(*b*) **Executive :** It implements, enforces or "executes" the laws made by the Legislature. It ensures that the laws, programmes and policies made by the government are enforced properly so that their benefits reach the common man.

(*c*) **Judiciary :** It interprets the laws and ensures that justice is given in a fair manner. The judiciary resolves disputes between individuals, organisations, government and people, etc. It protects the rights of citizens and ensures that no one breaks the law. Judiciary also has the power to give punishments to the accused.

3. Why do we need three tiers of government ?

Ans. India is a vast country with a population of more than 1 billion. It is necessary to have different levels of government to effectively manage and govern a vast and diverse country like India. The different regions of India have different climatic conditions and different needs.The three tiers of government can ensure that decisions are made according to the specific needs of people. Different levels also ensure that the responsibility of governing such a vast nation does not fall on a single authority. Three tires also allows participation of the citizens more effectively at the grassroots level and a better utilisation and distribution of the country's resources.

4. Project : Many of you will remember the lockdown that took place during the COVID-19 pandemic. Make a list of all the actions that were taken at that time ? Which tiers of government were involved in managing the situation ? What was the role of each of the organs of government ?

Ans. Actions taken during the lockdown :

- Nationwide lockdown was imposed.
- Schools and Educational institutions were closed.
- Social gatherings were not allowed.
- Online classes for students and work from home for working men/women was followed.
- Social distancing and wearing of masks was made compulsory.
- Quarantine centres and COVID hospitals were established.
- Food and essential supplies were distributed.
- Financial relief was given to affected industries and individuals.
- International and interstate travel was restricted.
- Vaccination programme was carried out for all citizens of India in different phases.

The tiers of government involved in managing the situation :

1. The Central Government

- Imposed the nationwide lockdown
- Restricted international travel
- Provided financial relief to the affected industries and individuals.
- Issued health and safety guidelines.
- Procured vaccines.

2. The State Government :

- Enforced lockdown within their state.
- Established quarantine centres and covid hospitals.
- Issued and implemented health guidelines.
- Took decisions about closing of schools, colleges and universities.
- Restricted interstate travel.

3. Local government :

- Implemented lockdown restrictions at the village, town and city levels.
- Established quarantine centres and covid hospitals at local level.
- Distributed Food and Essential Supplies
- Enforced social distancing norms in markets, streets and public spaces.

Role of different organs of government :

1. **Legislature :** Passed laws related to healthcare, financial aid, relief packages and support to the most affected industries and individuals.
2. **Executive :** Implemented the lockdown, coordinated the healthcare measures, vaccine distribution to different states and managed public communication through media.
3. **Judiciary :** Monitored the actions of the government, heard cases related to healthcare measures, problems faced by migrant workers and any cases related to lockdown measures.

I. OBJECTIVE TYPE QUESTIONS

A. Choose the correct answer.

Conceptual Learning | Critical Thinking

1. *Which of the following is/are functions of the government ?*
   (*a*) Making laws (*b*) Providing healthcare
   (*c*) Solving disputes (*d*) All of these
2. *Which organ of the government makes laws ?*
   (*a*) Judiciary (*b*) Executive
   (*c*) Legislature (*d*) Police
3. *Which of the following is a characteristic of the judiciary ?*
   (*a*) Makes laws (*b*) Ensures that justice is given in a fair manner
   (*c*) Implements government programs (*d*) Controls military operations
4. *Which of the following is an example of local government ?*
   (*a*) Indian Parliament (*b*) Municipal Corporation
   (*c*) State Legislative Assembly (*d*) Supreme Court
5. *Which system in India is an example of grassroots democracy ?*
   (*a*) Parliament (*b*) Supreme Court
   (*c*) Panchayati Raj System (*d*) State Legislative Assembly

B. Mark the option that matches Column A with Column B.

Conceptual Learning **Problem Solving**

Column A	Column B
1. Democracy	*(i)* Citizens elect representatives to make decisions
2. Representative Democracy	*(ii)* Citizens participate directly in decision-making at the local level
3. Direct Democracy	*(iii)* Rule by the people
4. Grassroots Democracy	*(iv)* Citizens participate directly in decision-making and governance

(a) **1.**-*(iii)*, **2.**-*(i)*, **3.**-*(ii)*, **4.**-*(iv)*
(b) **1.**-*(i)*, **2.**-*(iii)*, **3.**-*(iv)*, **4.**-*(ii)*
(c) **1.**-*(i)*, **2.**-*(ii)*, **3.**-*(iii)*, **4.**-*(iv)*
(d) **1.**-*(iii)*, **2.**-*(i)*, **3.**-*(iv)*, **4.**-*(ii)*

C. Fill in the blanks

Knowledge Application

1.

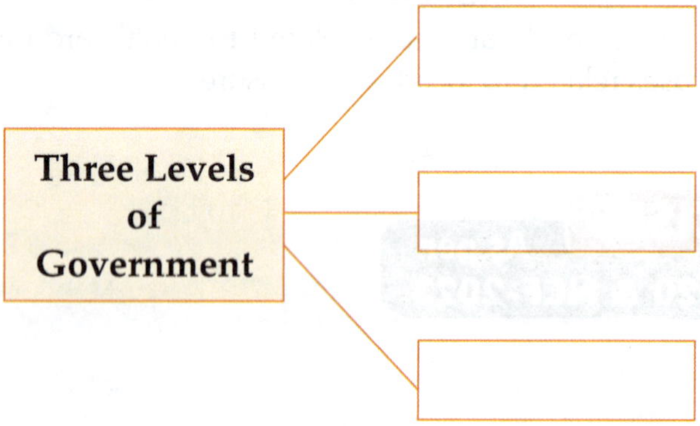

2.

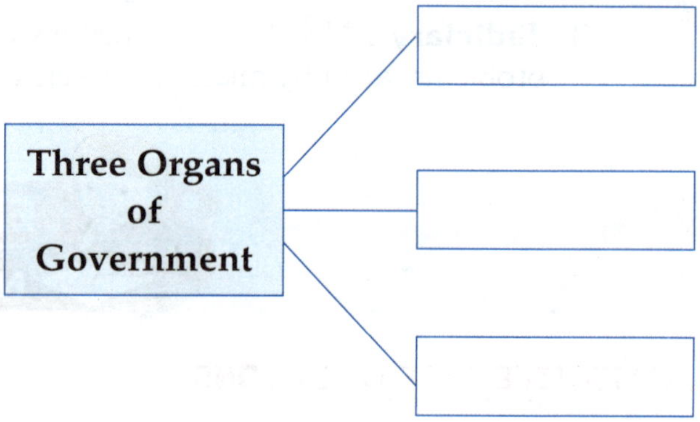

D. State True or False

Knowledge Application **Problem Solving**

1. In a democracy, the government is created and run by the people it serves.
2. The government does not provide basic facilities like education, healthcare and transportation.
3. In a representative democracy, all citizens directly make decisions and pass laws.
4. The Panchayati Raj System is an example of state government.
5. The Legislature updates and removes old laws if they are no longer required.

E. Assertion-Reason

Critical Thinking

For question numbers 1 to 4, two statements are given—one labelled Assertion (A) and the other labelled Reason (R). Select the correct answer to these questions from the codes *(a)*, *(b)*, *(c)* and *(d)* as given below :

(a) Both Assertion (A) and Reason (R) are true and Reason is the correct explanation of the Assertion.
(b) Both Assertion (A) and Reason (R) are true but Reason is not the correct explanation of the Assertion.
(c) Assertion (A) is true but Reason (R) is false.
(d) Assertion (A) is false but Reason (R) is true.

1. **Assertion (A)** : India follows a system of direct democracy.
   Reason (R) : In a direct democracy, citizens vote directly on laws and policies.
2. **Assertion (A)** : The Judiciary ensures that justice is given in a fair manner.
   Reason (R) : The Judiciary enforces the laws made by the Legislature.
3. **Assertion (A)** : The Panchayati Raj System is an example of grassroots democracy.
   Reason (R) : In grassroots democracy, decision-making happens at the local or community level.
4. **Assertion (A)** : There are three levels of government.
   Reason (R) : There are three organs of government also.

II. SHORT ANSWER TYPE QUESTIONS

Conceptual Learning | Knowledge Application

1. Give reasons why governance is important for a country.
2. Write a note on the Judiciary.
3. Explain how the separation of powers acts as a system of Checks and Balances.
4. Discuss the functions of local government.
5. Analyse the importance of representative democracy.

III. LONG ANSWER TYPE QUESTIONS

Knowledge Application | Critical Thinking

1. Describe why separation of powers is important in a government.
2. Explain how grassroots democracy empowers citizens at the local level.

IV. DISTINGUISH BETWEEN THE FOLLOWING

Conceptual Learning | Understanding

1. Legislature and Executive
2. National level and State level of government
3. Representative democracy and grassroot democracy

V. PICTURE STUDY

Knowledge Application | Critical Thinking

Given here is a picture that shows the three organs of the government. Answer the following questions with respect to the picture.

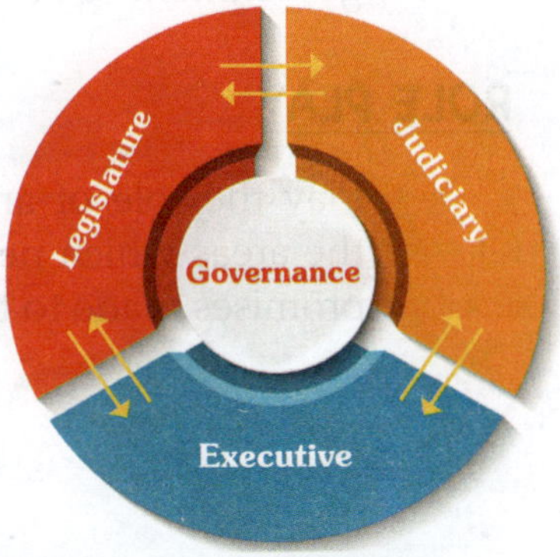

1. Write two functions of each of the organs of the government given in the picture.
2. Explain what is meant by 'Separation of Powers' with respect to the picture.
3. Why were these organs of government required in India ?

VI. SOURCE BASED QUESTIONS

Analysing | Conceptual Learning | Understanding

Read the given paragraph and answer the following questions.

India is a democratic country as the citizens of India have the power to vote and elect their government through free and fair elections. You will be surprised to know that India is the world's largest democracy with a population of more than 1.4 billion people. In 2024, 969 million people are eligible to vote, including 18 million first-time voters.

With such a vast population, can all people actually rule ? It will not be possible as it would lead to chaos and disorder. Therefore, the citizens elect their representatives to make decisions and pass laws on their behalf. The leaders elected by the people represent their interests in the government. This is called a **Representative Democracy.**

1. *What type of government do we have in India ?*
   (*a*) Democratic
   (*b*) Monarchy
   (*c*) Both (*a*) and (*b*)
   (*d*) None of these
2. *Which is the world's largest democracy ?*
   (*a*) USA
   (*b*) India
   (*c*) Sweden
   (*d*) New Zealand
3. *Who are elected representatives at the National level ?*
   (*a*) MLC
   (*b*) MLA
   (*c*) MP
   (*d*) Sarpanch

ACTIVITIES & PROJECTS

Multidisciplinary Approach | Creativity and Innovation

1. Mahatma Gandhi strongly believed that all adults in India should be given the right to vote. Many other people thought that illiterate and poor people should not be given the right to vote. What do you think about this issue ? Arrange a debate on this topic in the class.
2. Organise a mock election in the classroom. Assign roles such as candidates, voters, election officials and observers. Conduct an election using ballot papers or even EVM replicas. After voting, count the votes and announce the winner.
3. Divide the class into three groups : Legislature, Executive and Judiciary. Give any topic to the students like maintaining discipline in the school or cleanliness in the surroundings. Ask each group to act according to their roles i.e. the Legislature will make rules, the Executive will implement them and the Judiciary will resolve any disputes. Finally, hold a discussion in the class on the importance of the three organs of government.
4. Arrange a discussion with your classmates about why it is important for citizens to take part in the government of our country.

ROLE PLAY

Collaboration | Communication

- Play the role of an MLA of your area. Identify your responsibilities as an elected representative and the areas which need your urgent attention. Write a report on all the actions you will take to fulfil your promises made to the public during elections.

CHAPTER 11

Grassroots Democracy –Part 2 : Local Government in Rural Areas

CG-4 : C-4.1, C-4.2; CG-8 : C-8.3; CG-10 : C-10.1

"Independence must begin at the bottom. Thus, every village will be a republic or panchayat having full powers. It follows, therefore, that every village has to be self-sustained and capable of managing its affairs even to the extent of defending itself against the whole world."

—Gandhi ji (Harijan, 28-7-1946; 85:32)

What's new to learn

- **Panchayati Raj System**
- **Gram Panchayat**
- **Child-Friendly Panchayat Initiative**
- **Panchayat Samiti**
- **Zila Parishad**

India is a land of villages. According to the Census of 2011, India has about 649, 481 villages of which 593, 615 are inhabited. The rural population forms 68.84% of the total population of India with the urban population constituting only 31.16%. With so many villages and a vast population residing in them, the villages across India needed a system of governance to solve their day to day problems and manage their affairs. This need led to the creation of a government at the rural level, which is known as the Panchayati Raj System. The ***Panchayat*** *plays an important role in handling local issues like water, roads, education and health. It gives villagers the power to make decisions for their own community.*

In this chapter, we will learn about the Panchayati Raj institutions, their main functions and their importance in governance. But before that, let's dive into the affairs of the village named Anandgram and understand the decision-making process and implementation of decisions in a village.

Anandgram has about 250 houses and a population of about 1000 people. Most of the people are engaged in agriculture while some own small shops in the village or nearby towns. Some people have also migrated to the cities for higher education or in search of jobs. There are several issues in the village such as the problem of water supply, the repair and construction of roads, the finalisation of the list of people below the poverty line, etc.

The Gram Sabha Meeting

The Gram Sabha meeting of village Anandgram was fixed at 11:00 AM. The meeting was attended by the Panchayat President (Mukhia), the members of the Panchayat (the Panchs) and all the people of the village who were 18 years of age and above. First of all, the Panchayat President presented a plan to build a primary school in the eastern outskirts of the village and to repair a road that connects the village to the sub divisional town Sukhgram. Thereafter, the discussion moved to the problem of water and water shortage in the village. A villager, named Praveen raised the issue and said, "The water problem is acute in our village. Women have to walk about 2 km to get water from the river". All the members supported his point. Pushpak suggested constructing an overhead water tank in the village where water from the river would be stored. But, most of the members did not agree to this suggestion because it would be very expensive. Many suggestions were made, but the villagers did not unanimously agree with any of them. Ultimately, Preetam gave the idea of watershed development for which the government also provides assistance. Everybody considered it an innovative and useful idea. So, the Gram Sabha asked the Gram Panchayat to find out about watershed development in detail.

A meeting of the Gram Sabha

The Gram Panchayat Meeting

A Gram Panchayat meeting was held to discuss about watershed development. The meeting was attended by the village President (Mukhia), ward members (the Panchs) and the Secretary. As the Gram Panchayat is accountable to the Gram Sabha, its members discussed the water problem and concluded that there should be both a short-term and a long-term solution for water management.

Gram Panchayat meeting

Short-term Solution

As a short term solution, the village President and the ward members agreed to deepen the existing hand pumps.

The Panchayat President also accepted to approve funds for this. In this way, all the members agreed to the immediate solution to solve water scarcity. The secretary recorded their decision.

Long-term Solution

The members of the Gram Panchayat also discussed a long-term solution. Ultimately, it was decided that the Gram Panchayat would approach the Block Development Officer (BDO) for the arrangement of watershed development in the village.

In the above story, you read terms such as the Gram Sabha, the Gram Panchayat, Panchs, Secretary, etc. All these are a part of the Panchayati Raj System in India. Now, let's study the rural local government in detail.

PANCHAYATI RAJ SYSTEM

The local government at the rural level functions under the Panchayati Raj System. It is a system through which people in the rural areas participate in their own government. The basic idea of the Panchayati Raj System is to provide people with greater opportunities to participate in the government and raise their voices on issues concerning them. The system also ensures that the benefits of government schemes reach people at the grassroots level.

Discussion being held in a village meeting

The Panchayati Raj is a three-tier system which includes the **Gram Panchayat** at the village level, the Janpad Panchayat or the **Panchayat Samiti** at the block level and the District Panchayat or the **Zila Parishad** at the district level.

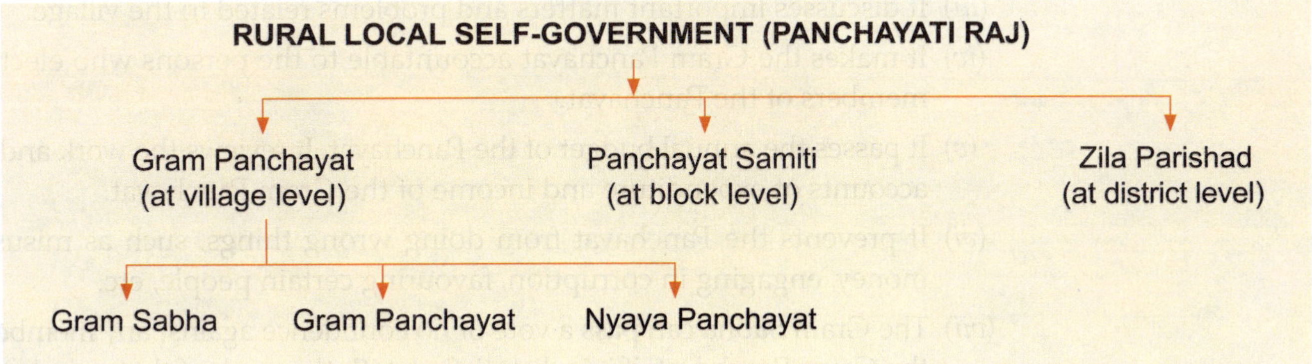

GRAM PANCHAYAT

The Panchayat System is very old in India. The word, 'Panchayat' means a group of five people. It was customary that the villagers elect a group of five elders as 'Panchs' who used to deal with local problems and resolve disputes among villagers. Their decisions were binding upon all the villagers. But, this system became less effective during the British rule because the British sent their own officials to look after rural problems. After Independence, the Panchayat System again gained importance. In 1992, the Central Government formulated rules for the Panchayati Raj System that became effective from April, 1993.

The Panchayati Raj System at the village level consists of three main bodies—the Gram Sabha, the Gram Panchayat and the Nyaya Panchayat.

The Gram Sabha

The Gram Sabha is a meeting of all adults who live in the area covered by a Panchayat. A Panchayat may include one village or a few villages. Every citizen of the village who is 18 years of age and above, *i.e.*, whose name is in the voter list, is a member of the Gram Sabha. It is a meeting where people directly participate and seek answers from their elected representatives. It holds meetings at least twice a year. The Gram Sabha acts as the Lok Sabha in the Centre and Legislative Assembly in the state.

A Gram Sabha

Functions of the Gram Sabha

The Gram Sabha has the following important functions.

(*i*) It elects the representatives who form the Gram Panchayat. These representatives look after the day-to-day working of the Panchayat.

(*ii*) It also elects the Sarpanch or the head of the Gram Panchayat or the village headman or the Mukhia. He/she presides over the meetings of the Gram Sabha.

(*iii*) It discusses important matters and problems related to the village.

(*iv*) It makes the Gram Panchayat accountable to the persons who elect the members of the Panchayat.

(*v*) It passes the annual budget of the Panchayat. It reviews the work and the accounts of expenditure and income of the Gram Panchayat.

(*vi*) It prevents the Panchayat from doing wrong things, such as misusing money, engaging in corruption, favouring certain people, etc.

(*vii*) The Gram Sabha can pass a vote of no confidence against any member of the Gram Panchayat, if it is dissatisfied with the work of that member. As a result, that Panchayat member will have to resign and a new member will be elected in his or her place.

(*viii*) It maintains and promotes social harmony. It involves voluntary workers in different social programmes.

The Gram Panchayat

The Gram Panchayat is an elected body of villagers. It implements the decisions taken by the Gram Sabha. Thus, it acts as an executive body of the Gram Sabha.

Every Panchayat is divided into smaller areas, called **wards.** Each ward elects a representative who is known as the Ward Member or **Panch.** The members of the Gram Sabha directly elect a **Sarpanch** who is the President of the Panchayat. All these elected people form the Gram Panchayat. The Gram Panchayat is elected for a term of five years. One-third of the total seats are also reserved for women.

A Gram Panchayat

DO YOU KNOW?

Some Exemplary Sarpanchs

1. Chhavi Rajawat (Sarpanch of Soda Village, Rajasthan)

Chhavi Rajawat is India's first woman sarpanch with an MBA degree. She implemented many projects in her village successfully like rain water harvesting, sanitation, roads and rural employment. She organised skill development workshops for women like tailoring, handicrafts, digital literacy, etc. and helped women become financially independent. Under her leadership, Soda village became a model for sustainable development.

2. Meena Behen (Sarpanch of Vyara Village, Gujarat)

Meena Behen implemented various developmental initiatives in her village. After 65 years, their village has their own Panchayat board and that too, an all-women Panchayat board. She focussed on improving basic amenities like sanitation, water supply and education. As the accessibility to the village was very poor, she undertook the task of constructing a road in her village. Under a Government scheme that provides housing for the poor, she built over 30 houses in her village and next plans to build a government hospital in the village.

3. Neeru Yadav (Sarpanch of Lambi Ahir Village, Rajasthan)

Famous as the "Hockey Sarpanch," Neeru Yadav promotes education and sports among village children, especially girls. She introduced hockey training sessions and improved educational facilities that brought national recognition to Lambi Ahir for its sports achievements.

4. Chintala Venkat Reddy (Sarpanch of Kowkoor Village, Telangana)

A farmer-turned-sarpanch, Chintala Venkat Reddy is famous for his innovations in organic farming. He introduced sustainable agricultural practices in his village that helped increase crop yields without harming the environment. His work earned him recognition from the government and environmental bodies for promoting eco-friendly farming. He was awarded the Padma Shri in 2020 for his contributions to agriculture.

The state government appoints a **Secretary** for the Gram Panchayat who is also the secretary of the Gram Sabha. The secretary receives a regular salary. He/she is responsible for calling the meetings of the Gram Sabha and the Gram Panchayat. He/she also maintains the record of the proceedings and looks after the functioning of the office of the Gram Panchayat.

Many Gram Panchayats also have an officer called the **Patwari** who maintains land records and collects revenue at the village level. He is also known as the Lekhpal, Kanungo, Karamchari or Village Officer. Each Patwari is responsible for a group of villages.

MORE TO KNOW

The Sarpanch Samvaad App is a digital network that aims to connect ~2.5 lakh Sarpanchs across India, providing a platform for networking, knowledge sharing and collaboration. Through this App, the Sarpanchs can share the developmental activities in their villages and encourage other Sarpanchs to carry out innovative development strategies in their villages.

Think & Answer

Suppose you are the Sarpanch of a village. Make a list of the initiatives you will take to make your village an ideal village of your Block.

Functions of a Patwari

The main functions of a Patwari are as follows :

(*i*) Measure land and keep land records.

(*ii*) Maintain and update the records of a village.

A Patwari showing land records

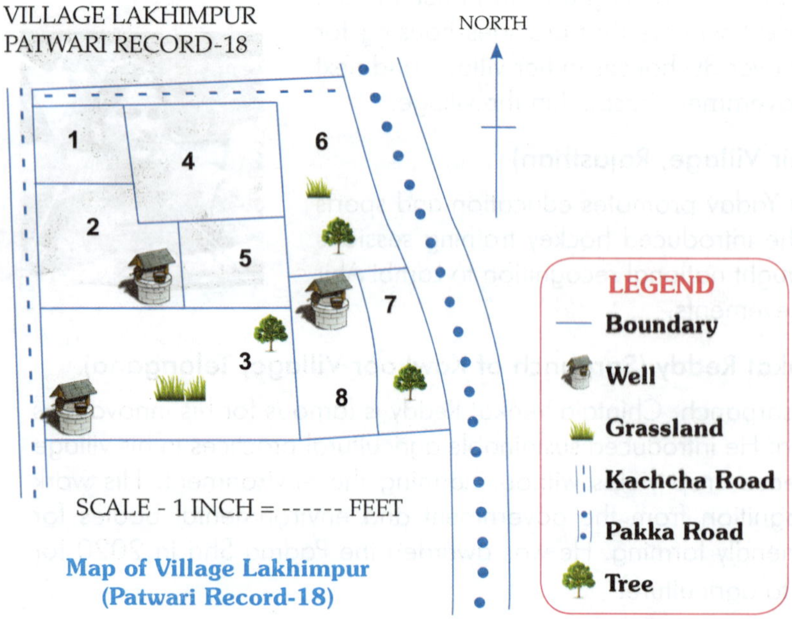

Map of Village Lakhimpur (Patwari Record-18)

The Patwari keeps the maps of land and the corresponding details, such as Khata No., Khasra No., etc. Some of these maps are generations old. The Khasra record of the Patwari provides information regarding the village map. You can easily identify which plot of land is owned by whom. The Patwari generally uses a long chain for measuring agricultural fields.

(*iii*) Collect land revenue from the farmers.

(*iv*) Provide information to the government about the crops grown in the area.

(*v*) Keep a vigil on the village land. The farmers may change the crops grown on their fields or someone may dig a well somewhere— keeping track of all these things is the work of a Patwari.

The Khasra Record of the Patwari of Village Lakhimpur

Khasra No. 3

S. No.	Area in hectare	Name of owner, Father or husband's name, address	If it is rented to some other farmers, their name and rent received	Area cultivated this year			Area not cultivated fallow land	Facilities
				Crop grown	Area	Second crop grown		
	1	2	3	4	5	6	7	8
1.	0.50	Alam, Son of Usman, Village Lakhimpur, owner	No	Lentil	0.50 Hect.			
2.	2.00	Naval Kishore, Son of Awadh Kishore, Village Lakhimpur, owner	No	Lentil, Wheat, irrigated	1.75 Hect.	0.75	0.25	Well-1 working
3.	10.00	Bihar Government Grassland	No	—				Well-1 working Grazing

MORE TO KNOW

A farmer may require a copy of his land's record together with a map in many situations.

These are :

- If a farmer wants to divide his property among his children.
- If a farmer wants to buy/sell a plot of land from/to another.
- If a farmer wants to purchase fertilizers for his field.
- If a farmer wants a loan from the bank to dig a well in his land.

Farmers have the right to obtain information about their records. These records are now computerised and generally kept at the Panchayat Office so that they are more easily accessible and regularly updated. People may obtain related information by paying a nominal fee for this.

Functions of the Gram Panchayat

The Gram Panchayat has the following main functions :

(*i*) It looks after the construction and maintenance of water sources, roads, drainage, school buildings and other common property resources.

(*ii*) It imposes and collects local taxes.

(*iii*) It implements government programmes related to employment generation and poverty alleviation.

(*iv*) It provides health and sanitation facilities.

(*v*) It controls the spread of diseases through vaccination.

(*vi*) It provides primary education facilities in the village.

(*vii*) It maintains records of births and deaths in the village.

(*viii*) It helps the farmers to develop and improve their farms and cattle. It helps in providing good quality seeds and fertilizers.

(*ix*) It looks after the welfare of the weaker sections of the village.

(*x*) It organises cattle fairs and village fairs.

A village school

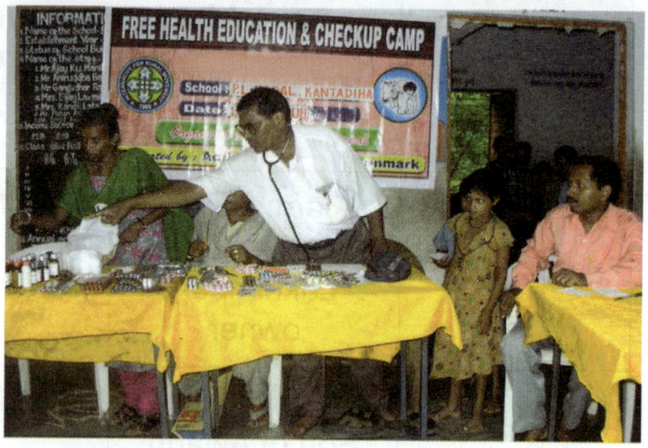

Health Education and Check-up Camp

MORE TO KNOW

The Gram Panchayat also implements plans for water conservation.

Watershed development is a way of conserving water and recharging or refilling it in a high land area.

Benefits : Watershed development benefits an area in the following ways :

(*i*) There is a shift towards the cultivation of commercial crops such as pulses, groundnut, cotton, onion and horticulture crops in the watershed areas.

(*ii*) Increase in the area under cultivation.

(*iii*) Reduction in the migration status.

(*iv*) Improvement in the livestock numbers as fodder production increases in the area.

(*v*) Increase rural non-farm activities in the area.

(*vi*) Increase the income of the land owning families in the area.

(*vii*) More employment generation.

(*viii*) It has a direct positive impact on the economic independence of rural women.

Sources of Income

The Gram Panchayat obtains funds in a number of ways :

(*i*) It obtains funds from the collection of taxes on houses, market places, fairs, etc.

Meeting of a Gram Panchayat

(*ii*) It receives government scheme funds through various departments of the government such as the Janpad and Zila Parishad.

(*iii*) It also receives donations for community works, etc.

(*iv*) It obtains fees for registering the purchase and sale of cattle, land and other property.

(*v*) It receives a share of some taxes and fees collected by the state government.

(*vi*) It obtains funds from the sale of property owned by the community.

(*vii*) It obtains grants from the state government.

The Nyaya Panchayat

A Nyaya Panchayat

The Nyaya Panchayat is a judicial wing of the Panchayati Raj System at the village level. The term of service of the Nyaya Panchayat is also five years. Its members are elected in the same way as the members of the Gram Panchayat.

It hears and decides minor civil and criminal cases. It can fine and punish the guilty within certain limits. But, it can not send a person to jail. The main purpose of the Nyaya Panchayat is to provide speedy justice at minimum expenses.

Check Your Progress — Understanding

State whether True or False

1. The Panchayati Raj is a three-tier system.
2. Rules for the Panchayati Raj System became effective from April, 1994.
3. The Gram Panchayat is elected for a term of five years.
4. The Khasra record of the Patwari gives no information regarding the village map.
5. One-third of the total seats are reserved for women in the Gram Panchayats.

CHILD-FRIENDLY PANCHAYAT INITIATIVE

The Child-Friendly Panchayat Initiative is a concept that caters to the needs of children in rural areas through Bal Sabha and Bal Panchayats. It ensures the well being, safety and protection of children in the rural areas and provides them a platform where they can raise their voices on issues that matter the most to them. It also ensures that the basic needs of children like education, health, sanitation and participation in community matters are taken seriously and considered in all decision-making processes at the local level. Several states have taken steps towards the formation of Bal Panchayats and encouraged children to take active part in its meetings.

A Bal Sabha

A few notable examples of these are as follows :

Thirunelli Panchayat, Kerala

Thirunelli Panchayat, Kerala

The panchayat took steps to prevent child trafficking and improved educational facilities being provided to children. It set up many anganwadis or day -care centres to protect children and ensured that children attend school regularly.

Punnapra Thekku Panchayat, Kerala

It is the first fully child friendly panchayat in the state. It is also the first panchayat in the state to form a Child Protection Committee in all wards. A Child Observatory Committee and a Child Resource Committee have also been formed to monitor the projects related to children. Facilities like one table-one chair, colour tents, playgrounds, enclosure walls, toilet blocks, soak pits, etc. have been provided in schools. Toys, flag posts, wall paintings, pressure cookers and the internet have been provided in Anganwadis.

Dungarpur Panchayat, Rajasthan

The district of **Dungarpur** in Rajasthan has been recognized for its efforts in making Panchayats child-friendly. It has improved the school infrastructure, ensured regular attendance of children and run awareness campaigns for child education and child protection.

Sangkhu Radhu Khandu Gram Panchayat in Dentam, West Sikkim

This panchayat has been declared a child friendly Gram Panchayat for its efforts like building compound walls in schools for child safety and constructing kitchens in the schools to ensure hygienically cooked midday meals. The panchayat aims to deal strictly with issues related with child abuse and other offences against children. It also aims to empower the children in the

Gram Panchayats and make them realise their potential. The Panchayat also aims to sensitize the public at the grass root level about child rights, encourage active participation of the children in community programmes and address their issues actively.

Children's Parliament, Rajasthan

This is an offshoot of the Bunker Roy's **Barefoot College** initiative and has received the World's Children's Honorary Award in 2001. It has played a significant role in empowering children by engaging them in democratic processes and allowing them to understand governance, decision-making and the importance of collective action.

Children's Parliament

An interesting idea of the parliament was to give children roles similar to those in actual government bodies, such as Prime Minister, Ministers and other officials. The children took part in elections and followed all the formal procedures like voter ID cards and campaigning. The elected representatives formed a 'Cabinet' and took part in discussions on matters affecting their community, such as education, health, hygiene, child labour, child marriages, school attendance and malnutrition. This helped them learn about structures, electoral processes and leadership responsibilities.

Think & Answer

- You read about five Child friendly panchayats. Which one influenced you the most and why ?
- If you become a member of any Child friendly panchayat, list the measures you will take to ensure the well-being and active participation of children in your community.

PANCHAYAT SAMITI

The Panchayat Samiti has many Gram Panchayats under it. It is also called the Janpad Panchayat or the Block Samiti. It works at the block level. The **Block Development Officer (BDO)** acts as the secretary of the Panchayat Samiti.

Block Development Officer (BDO)

Functions of the Panchayat Samiti

The functions of the Panchayat Samiti are as follows :

(*i*) The Panchayat Samiti supervises the working of the Gram Panchayats in a block.

(*ii*) It makes plans for the development of the whole block.

(*iii*) It has a team of experts in various fields who guide the villagers over different developmental issues.

(*iv*) It arranges funds from the government for development programmes and government schemes like the Pradhan Mantri Gram Sadak Yojana (for construction of all—weather roads in rural areas), Pradhan Mantri Awaas Yojana—Gramin (to provide affordable housing to the rural poor), Swachh Bharat Mission—Gramin (to eliminate open defecation and improve sanitation facilities in rural areas), etc.

ZILA PARISHAD

The District Panchayat or the Zila Parishad is the highest governing body under the Panchayati Raj System. It works at the district level. An officer of the rank of a District Magistrate is the Chief Executive Officer of the Zila Parishad.

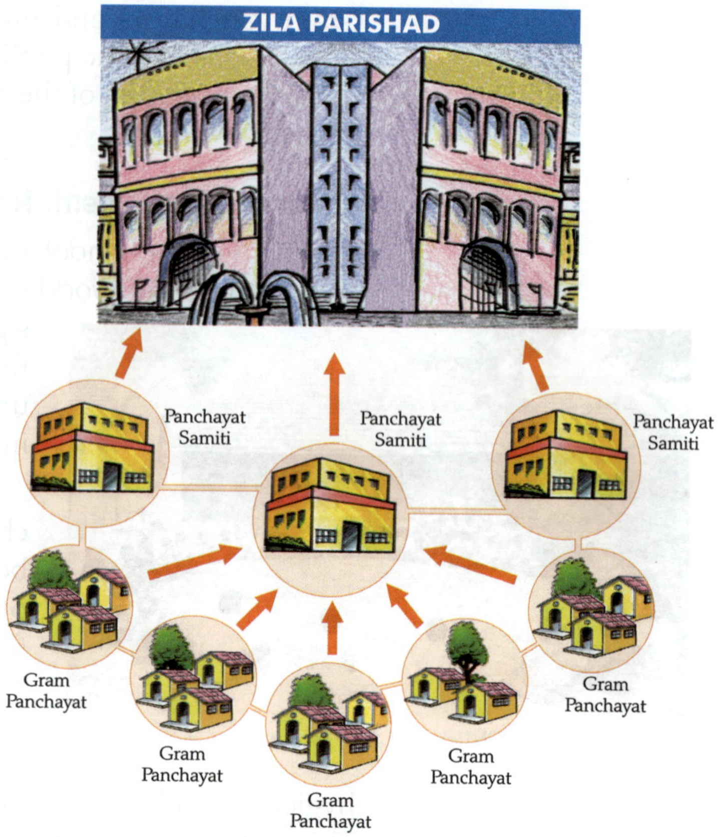

Zila Parishad

Functions of the Zila Parishad

The main functions of the Zila Parishad are :

(*i*) It supervises the working of the Panchayat Samitis, the Gram Panchayats and the projects under the Five-Year Plans.

(*ii*) It makes development plans at the district level.

(*iii*) It regulates money distribution among all the Gram Panchayats with the help of Panchayat Samitis.

(*iv*) It advises the state government on the working of the Panchayati Raj System.

Each state in our country has its own laws with regard to the Panchayats.

Check Your Progress — Understanding

Fill in the blanks

1. The Punnapra Thekku Panchayat is in the state of ______________.
2. The ______________ Parliament received the World's Children's Honorary Award in 2001.
3. The ______________ acts as the secretary of the Panchayat Samiti.
4. The ______________ works at the district level.
5. The ______________ is the highest governing body under the Panchayati Raj System.

NEW WORDS

- **Republic :** A state where power is held by the people and their elected representatives.
- **Inhabited :** A place that is occupied by people living there.
- **Panchayati Raj :** A system of local government in rural areas of India.
- **Mukhia :** The elected head or president of a Gram Panchayat in a village.
- **Watershed development :** A process that involves managing and conserving water resources in a particular area, especially in rural areas.
- **Patwari :** A government official who maintains land records and collects land revenue in rural areas.
- **Lekhpal / Kanungo / Karamchari :** Other names for the Patwari or the officer responsible for maintaining land records in a village.
- **Revenue :** Income that the government receives from taxes or other sources.
- **Khasra Record :** A record that shows details about land and ownership in a village.
- **Khata No./Khasra No. :** Identification numbers used in land records to define specific plots of land.
- **Nyaya Panchayat :** The judicial body in the Panchayati Raj system responsible for resolving minor disputes at the village level.
- **Anganwadi :** Rural child-care centres in India that provide early childhood education and basic health services.
- **Bal Sabha :** A children's assembly in the Child Friendly Panchayat Initiative, where children can voice their concerns.
- **Zila Parishad :** The district-level governing body in the Panchayati Raj system.
- **Pradhan Mantri Gram Sadak Yojana :** A government scheme to provide all-weather road connectivity to unconnected villages.
- **Pradhan Mantri Awaas Yojana-Gramin :** A government scheme to provide housing for the rural poor.
- **Swachh Bharat Mission-Gramin :** A government initiative for improving sanitation and eliminating open defecation in rural areas.
- **Sustainable :** Able to be maintained or continued without causing harm to the environment.
- **Judicial :** Relating to the system of courts or the administration of justice.

NUTSHELL

- The rural population forms 68.84% of the total population of India with the urban population constituting only 31.16%
- The local government at the rural level functions under the Panchayati Raj System. It is a system through which people in the rural areas participate in their own government.
- The Panchayati Raj is a three-tier system which includes the Gram Panchayat at the village level, the Janpad Panchayat or the Panchayat Samiti at the block level and the District Panchayat or the Zila Parishad at the district level.
- The word, 'Panchayat' means a group of five people.
- In 1992, the Central Government formulated rules for the Panchayati Raj System that became effective from April, 1993.
- The Panchayati Raj System at the village level consists of three main bodies—Gram Sabha, Gram Panchayat and Nyaya Panchayat.
- The Gram Sabha is a meeting of all adults who live in the area covered by a Panchayat.

- Every citizen of the village who is 18 years of age and above, *i.e.*, whose name is in the voter list, is a member of the Gram Sabha.
- The Gram Panchayat is an elected body of villagers. It implements the decisions taken by the Gram Sabha. It acts as an executive body of the Sabha.
- The Gram Panchayat is elected for a term of five years.
- The state government appoints a Secretary for the Gram Panchayat who is also the secretary of the Gram Sabha.
- The Patwari maintains land records and collects revenue at the village level.
- The Nyaya Panchayat is a judicial wing of the Panchayati Raj System at the village level.
- The main purpose of the Nyaya Panchayat is to provide speedy justice at minimum expenses.
- The Child Friendly Panchayat Initiative is a concept that caters to the needs of children in rural areas through Bal Sabhsa and Bal Panchayats.
- The Panchayat Samiti has many Gram Panchayats under it. It is also called the Janpad Panchayat or the Block Samiti. It works at the block level.
- The Block Development Officer (BDO) acts as the secretary of the Panchayat Samiti.
- The District Panchayat or the Zila Parishad is the highest governing body under the Panchayati Raj System. It works at the district level.

IMPORTANT NCERT TEXTBOOK QUESTIONS (Solved)

Questions, activities and projects

1. Test yourself—without looking at the text above, can you name the three tiers of the Panchayati Raj system ? What are the key functions of each of the three tiers ?

Ans. The three tiers of the Panchayati Raj System and their functions are :

1. Gram Panchayat (Village Level) :

Functions :

- It looks after the construction and maintenance of water sources, roads, drainage, school buildings and other common property resources.
- It imposes and collects local taxes.
- It implements government programmes related to employment generation and poverty alleviation.
- It provides health and sanitation facilities.

2. Panchayat Samiti (Block Level) :

Functions :

- The Panchayat Samiti supervises the working of the Gram Panchayats in a block.
- It makes plans for the development of the whole block.
- It has a team of experts in various fields who guide the villagers over different developmental issues.
- It arranges funds from the government for development programmes and government schemes.

3. Zila Parishad (District level) :

Functions :

- It supervises the working of the Panchayat Samitis, the Gram Panchayats and the projects under the Five-Year Plans.
- It makes development plans at the district level.
- It regulates money distribution among all the Gram Panchayats with the help of Panchayat Samitis.
- It advises the state government on the working of the Panchayati Raj System.

2. Write a letter to the Sarpanch regarding the issue of plastic bags lying on the roadside in the village.

Ans. Your Name
Your Address
Village Name
Date : [Insert Date]

To

The Sarpanch
[Village Name]
[Block/District Name]

Subject : Request to address the issue of plastic bags littering the roadside

Dear Sir/Madam,

I want to bring your attention to an urgent and important matter regarding the growing problem of plastic bags littering on the roadside throughout our village. These plastic bags pose serious health problems and are a danger to the environment. As these plastic bags are non-biodegradable, they can cause irreparable damage to our soil and water resources.

Due to a huge accumulation of plastic bags in many places, most of the drains are blocked leading to waterlogging. As a result, our village colonies have become a breeding ground for mosquitoes posing health threats. Sometimes even animals like cows, goats and buffaloes consume the plastic bags in search of food and water, which can be fatal to their lives. These bags littered here and there also destroy the beauty of our village.

I humbly request you to take immediate measures to solve this problem as it affects all of us. I also request you to organise a village cleanliness drive in which young and old, all must take an active part. I further urge you to initiate awareness programmes through role-plays and songs and make the villagers aware about the ill-effects of plastic bags. Kindly make arrangements for installing dustbins at different locations throughout the village so that waste poly bags can be disposed of safely.

I hope you will seriously consider my request and take action at the earliest and ensure a clean and safe environment for all of us.

Yours sincerely,
Your Name,
Your Contact Number.

3. In your view, what type of person should be a Gram Panchayat member ?

Ans. A Gram Panchayat member should be responsible and dedicated towards his service for the community. He should have a sound knowledge of all the village members, their problems and concerns and should be prompt in taking decisions for the welfare of the village.

He should have good communication skills to communicate effectively with higher officials and he should also have the patience to listen to the problems and concerns of the community members.

He should also be aware of all the government schemes that have been initiated for the welfare of the villages and know how to implement them in his village. He should be honest and promote inclusivity. He should not be biased towards any member of his community and promote the welfare of all.

He must also have knowledge of the concepts of Bal Panchayats, Sustainable Development, Rainwater Harvesting, etc. and must be eager to implement them in his village to secure the future of upcoming generations.

4. Let us suppose that you study in a village school. The school is located next to a highway and students find it difficult to cross the road when they come to school or leave at the end of the day. What are the options to solve this issue ? Which institutions in the Panchayati Raj can help you ? What can the students do ?

Ans. The different options to solve the issue may be as follows :

- Installation of a zebra crossing near the school so that students can cross the road safely.
- Installation of a foot over bridge to allow safe crossing of road for students.
- Installation of speed breakers and road signs indicating the presence of schools so that the drivers slow down their vehicles.
- Construction of an underpass to enable students cross the road safely.
- Appointment of a traffic police to manage traffic during the heavy traffic hours.

Panchayati Raj institutions that can help me are :

1. **Gram Panchayat :** The Gram Panchayat can raise this issue in its meetings and forward it to the concerned authorities through a letter.
2. **Panchayat Samiti :** It can approve funds for the installation of a foot over bridge, an underpass or a speed breaker.
3. **Zila Parishad :** It will supervise the project, regulate its funds in a proper manner and ensure timely completion of the project.

Actions taken by the students :

1. Students can submit a Petition to the Gram Panchayat, explaining their problem and requesting an immediate solution.
2. They can organise an Awareness Campaign that will emphasise on the importance of road safety measures.
3. They can use social media to highlight their problems and take the matter to the concerned authorities through articles in the newspapers or online tools.
4. They can also take the help of their teachers, parents and press to come to a speedy solution of the problem by putting pressure over the authorities.

EXERCISES As per NEP-2020 & NCF-2023

I. OBJECTIVE TYPE QUESTIONS

A. Choose the correct answer.

Conceptual Learning | Critical Thinking

1. *Who presides over the meetings of the Gram Sabha ?*

(*a*) Ward Member
(*b*) Block Development Officer (BDO)
(*c*) Sarpanch (Mukhia)
(*d*) Patwari

2. *Which of the following is NOT a function of the Gram Sabha ?*
   (*a*) Electing the representatives of the Gram Panchayat
   (*b*) Making the Gram Panchayat accountable
   (*c*) Collecting taxes from the villagers
   (*d*) Passing the annual budget of the Panchayat

3. *What percentage of seats in the Gram Panchayat are reserved for women ?*
   (*a*) 50% (*b*) 25%
   (*c*) 33% (*d*) 20%

4. *Who maintains the land records at the village level ?*
   (*a*) Secretary (*b*) Patwari
   (*c*) Block Development Officer (BDO) (*d*) Sarpanch

5. *What is the primary goal of the Child-Friendly Panchayat initiative ?*
   (*a*) Provide financial aid to children
   (*b*) Ensure children's well-being and participation in local governance
   (*c*) Create jobs for young people
   (*d*) Promote child marriages

B. Mark the option that matches Column A with Column B.

Conceptual Learning | Problem Solving

Column A	Column B
1. Sarpanch	(*i*) Maintains land records
2. Patwari	(*ii*) Secretary of the Panchayat Samiti.
3. Block Development Officer	(*iii*) Village-level elected representative
4. Ward member	(*iv*) President of the Panchayat

(*a*) **1.**-(*iv*), **2.**-(*i*), **3.**-(*ii*), **4.**-(*iii*) (*b*) **1.**-(*ii*), **2.**-(*iii*), **3.**-(*iv*), **4.**-(*i*)
(*c*) **1.**-(*iv*), **2.**-(*ii*), **3.**-(*iii*), **4.**-(*i*) (*d*) **1.**-(*iii*), **2.**-(*i*), **3.**-(*iv*), **4.**-(*ii*)

C. Fill in the blanks

Knowledge Application

1. (*a*) The group of villagers that elects the Gram Panchayat is known as the ______________.
   (*b*) The ______________ is a judicial body in the Panchayati Raj system that handles minor disputes.
   (*c*) The ______________ is an administrative body that works at the block level, coordinating with several Gram Panchayats.
   (*d*) The leader of the Gram Panchayat is called the ______________.
   (*e*) The Child Friendly Panchayat Initiative is a concept that caters to the needs of children in ______________ areas.

2. **The local government at the rural level functions under the Panchayati Raj System. It is a three-tier system which includes various government bodies.**

Complete the following flowchart that describes different levels of Panchayati Raj System :

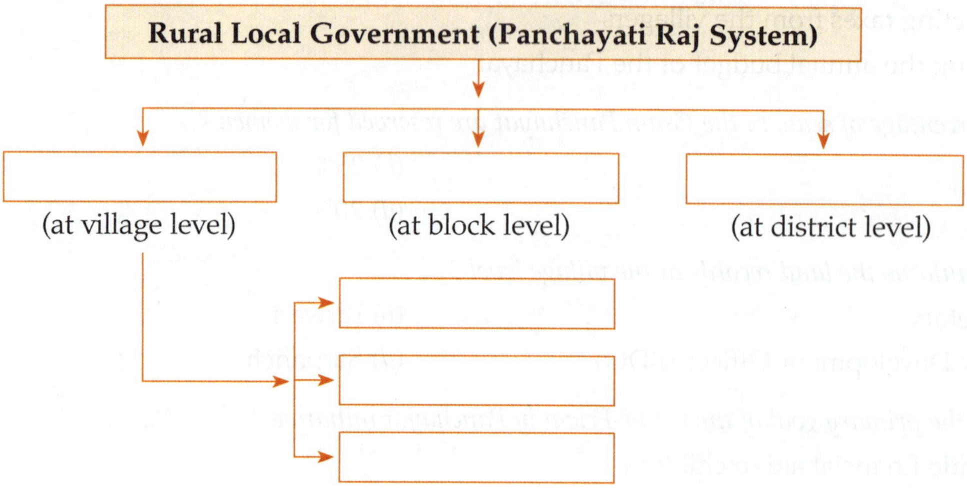

D. State True or False

Knowledge Application | Problem Solving

1. Local Self-Government deals with local problems.
2. The Panchayati Raj System is a two-tier system.
3. The Gram Panchayat cannot impose and collect taxes.
4. Patwari is a senior officer of the revenue department.
5. District Dungarpur lies in Gujarat.

E. Assertion-Reason

Critical Thinking

For question numbers 1 to 4, two statements are given—one labelled Assertion (A) and the other labelled Reason (R). Select the correct answer to these questions from the codes (*a*), (*b*), (*c*) and (*d*) as given below :

(*a*) Both Assertion (A) and Reason (R) are true and Reason is the correct explanation of the Assertion.
(*b*) Both Assertion (A) and Reason (R) are true but Reason is not the correct explanation of the Assertion.
(*c*) Assertion (A) is true but Reason (R) is false.
(*d*) Assertion (A) is false but Reason (R) is true.

1. **Assertion (A)** : The Gram Sabha acts as a legislative body whereas the Gram Panchayat is an executive body at the village level.
   Reason (R) : The minimum requirement of age for the membership of the Gram Sabha is 21 years while a member of the Gram Panchayat should not be less than 18 years.
2. **Assertion (A)** : The State Government appoints a secretary for the Gram Panchayat.
   Reason (R) : He is also the secretary of the Gram Sabha.
3. **Assertion (A)** : The Gram Sabha elects the members of the Gram Panchayat.
   Reason (R) : The Panchayat Samiti has many Gram Panchayats under it.
4. **Assertion (A)** : The Panchayat Samiti operates at the block level.
   Reason (R) : The Panchayat Samiti coordinates development activities in multiple Gram Panchayats within its block.

II. SHORT ANSWER TYPE QUESTIONS

Conceptual Learning | Knowledge Application

1. Write a note on the role of the Gram Panchayat in local governance.
2. Discuss the three-tier system of the Panchayati Raj.
3. What is a Nyaya Panchayat ? What is the basic idea behind its formation ?
4. Name the head of Gram Panchayat. What is he/she responsible for ?
5. Mention the main objectives of Bal Panchayats.

III. LONG ANSWER TYPE QUESTIONS

Knowledge Application | Critical Thinking

1. Discuss the functions and sources of income of the Gram Panchayat.
2. Describe the composition and functions of the Panchayat Samiti.
3. Write a short note on the Zila Parishad.
4. In what ways do you think a Bal Panchayat can influence decision-making in a village ? Write your answer in 100 words.

IV. DISTINGUISH BETWEEN THE FOLLOWING

Conceptual Learning | Understanding

1. Gram Sabha and a Gram Panchayat.
2. Panchayat Samiti and Zila Parishad

V. PICTURE STUDY

Knowledge Application | Critical Thinking

This is a village scene representing an important function of the Gram Panchayat.

(i) (ii) (iii)

1. Name the function.
2. Is it a compulsory function of the Gram Panchayat ?
3. Mention any two other functions of the Gram Panchayat.

VI. SOURCE-BASED QUESTIONS

Analysing | Understanding

Read the given paragraph and answer the following questions.

The Panchayati Raj System is a system of local self-government in India. It aims to decentralise power and promote democratic decision-making at village level. The system consists of Gram Panchayats at the village level, Panchayat Samitis at the block level and Zilla Parishads at the district level.

1. *Which level of the Panchayati Raj System is represented in the picture ?*
(*a*) Gram Panchayat (*b*) Panchayat Samiti (*c*) Zila Parishad (*d*) Vidhan Sabha
2. *What activity is depicted in the picture ?*
(*a*) Villagers participating in a religious ceremony.
(*b*) Villagers attending a political rally.
(*c*) Villagers engaging in discussions for local development.
(*d*) Villagers protesting against the government.
3. *What is the primary objective of the Panchayati Raj System in India ?*
(*a*) To centralise power at the national level.
(*b*) To promote democratic decision-making at village level.
(*c*) To exclude rural areas from governance processes.
(*d*) To establish a monarchy in villages.
4. *What is the role of the Gram Panchayat in the Panchayati Raj System ?*
(*a*) Making decisions at the district level.
(*b*) Planning development projects at the village level.
(*c*) Handling matters related to the state government.
(*d*) Overseeing national policies.
5. *What is the highest level of the Panchayati Raj System in a state ?*
(*a*) Zila Parishad (*b*) Gram Panchayat (*c*) Panchayat Samiti (*d*) State Assembly

ACTIVITIES & PROJECTS

Multidisciplinary Approach | Creativity and Innovation

1. Visit a nearby village and prepare a report on the developmental works being carried out by the Gram Pradhan of the village.
2. Interview a village Sarpanch/Pramukh/member of the Zila Parishad on his/her work and the projects undertaken by him/her.
3. Organise a meeting in your class like the Gram Sabha. Prepare an agenda. Inputs should be provided by the students about issues that concern them. Discuss the measures you will take to solve these issues.
4. Organise a debate in your class on the topic, "How can children's perspectives differ from adults in addressing community issues and whether this difference is beneficial or problematic."

ROLE PLAY

Collaboration | Communication

Topic : Local Self-government

Knowledge to be gained : To know the functioning and administration of Rural Local Government.

- Choose any character and become a member of your own choice from the various tiers of the Panchayati Raj System like the Gram Sabha, Gram Panchayat, Nyaya Panchayat, Panchayat Samiti, etc.
- Dress up accordingly and speak up for 2 or 3 minutes on what you would have done for your village/block if you would have been this person.
- Record your video while you are expressing your points and send it to your subject teacher.

CHAPTER 12

Grassroots Democracy – Part 3 : Local Government in Urban Areas

CG-4 : C-4.1, C-4.2; CG-8 : C-8.3; CG-10 : C-10.1

We have already studied that the Panchayati Raj System has been established to fulfil the civic needs of the people in rural areas. Similarly, in a town or city area, the basic facilities are provided by the Nagar Panchayats, Municipalities and the Municipal Corporations.

The 74th Amendment Act of the Constitution, 1993, has provided these three types of local self-government bodies in the urban areas. The percentage of urban population according to the Census of 2011 is 31.16.

What's new to learn

- Nagar Panchayat
- Municipal Council
- Municipal Corporation
- Functions of the Municipality and the Municipal Corporation
- Sources of Income of the Municipality and the Municipal Corporation

Urban Local Government

- Nagar Panchayats
- Municipalities or Muncipal Councils
- Municipal Corporations

NAGAR PANCHAYAT

A Nagar Panchayat is set up for an area that is in the process of changing from a rural to an urban center. Such a transitional area does not qualify for the setting up of a Municipality, but requires a local governing body for its smooth functioning. The minimum population required for setting up a Nagar Panchayat varies from state to state.

Nagar Panchayat

Composition

The area of the Nagar Panchayat is divided into **wards.** The registered voters of each ward elect a representative, known as the **ward member**. These ward members are the members of the Nagar Panchayat. Apart from these elected members, the Nagar Panchayat also includes some nominated and ex-officio members.

The term of the Nagar Panchayat is five years. However, it can be dissolved earlier if found to be incompetent.

Functions

The Nagar Panchayat looks after water supply, sanitation, healthcare, drainage, street cleaning, street lighting, primary education, parks, public buildings, management of fairs, etc. It also records births and deaths in its area.

Sources of Income

The main sources of income of the Nagar Panchayat are as under :

(*i*) Grants received from the state government.
(*ii*) Property Tax
(*iii*) Sales Tax
(*iv*) Fair Tax

MORE TO KNOW

e-Panchayat Mission Mode Project (MMP)

This project is part of the Digital India Programme and includes the automation of internal processes, capacity building and social audits. Several Nagar Panchayats are now implementing e-governance systems to improve citizen services. From paying property taxes online to applying for building permits, many Nagar Panchayats are adopting digital tools to make local governance more efficient. This has increased transparency, accountability and improved the delivery of services to citizens.

MUNICIPAL COUNCIL

Cities with a population between 20 thousand and 10 lakh have Municipalities. A Municipality is also called a Municipal Council or a Municipal Committee. It is a local self-governing body for small towns or cities.

Composition

The members of a Municipality are directly elected by the registered voters of the city. That is, all citizens of a city who are 18 years of age and above can vote in the municipal election. The candidates who wish to contest the election, must be 21 years of age or above. The number of members in a Municipality varies from city to city depending on the population of the city.

Office of a Municipality

The elected members of the Municipality or Municipal Council are called **Councillors.** The term of a Municipality, unless dissolved earlier, is five years.

For election, the city is divided into a number of wards. Each ward elects one member. The Municipality also has some nominated and ex-officio members. Some seats are filled by members nominated for having special knowledge and experience of municipal administration. The MLAs and MPs elected from the area also form a part of the Municipality. Many municipal bodies in India have reserved seats for women, ensuring their participation in local governance. In 1993, the **74th Constitutional Amendment** reserved 33% seats for women in the municipalities.

The members of the Municipality elect a chairperson who presides over the meetings that are held at regular intervals. They also elect a vice-chairperson who takes charge in the absence of the chairperson.

A Municipality also has some permanent members who assist in its day-to-day functioning. They include Executive Officers, the Secretary, Health Officers, Sanitary Inspectors, Municipal Engineers, Junior Engineers and Education Officers. These officials follow the instructions and implement the policies framed by the Municipality.

Check Your Progress — Understanding

State whether true or False

1. There are three types of local self-government bodies in the urban areas.
2. The minimum population required for setting up a Nagar Panchayat is fixed.
3. The Nagar Panchayat looks after water supply and sanitation.
4. No seats are reserved for women in the municipalities.
5. There is no chairperson in the Municipality.

MUNICIPAL CORPORATION

Municipal Corporation Office

The cities with a population of more than 10 lakh have a Municipal Corporation. The Municipal Corporation is a local self-governing body for big cities. The **Chennai Municipal Corporation**, established in 1688, is the oldest municipal corporation in India. It was formed during the British colonial period to improve urban infrastructure and governance. It is also the second oldest municipal corporation in the world, after the City of London Corporation in the United Kingdom. The **Brihanmumbai Municipal Corporation (BMC)**, founded in 1888, is the richest municipal corporation in India. It handles vast infrastructure projects, public services and urban development.

Chennai Municipal Corporation

Brihanmumbai Municipal Corporation (BMC)

Composition

Like a Municipality, the Municipal Corporation also consists of members elected by the adult citizens of the city. All citizens of the city who are 18 years of age and above, can vote in its election.

The candidates who wish to contest the elections, must be 25 years of age and above. The elected members of the Municipal Corporation are called the **Councillors.** For election, the city is divided into a number of wards, *i.e.*, smaller areas. Each ward elects one member.

Besides the elected members, a corporation also has some nominated and ex-officio members. There are a number of members called Aldermen. They are usually elected by the councillors from among the highly experienced and gifted public workers of the city. The MLAs and MPs of that area also form a part of the corporation.

The members of the Municipal Corporation elect a **Mayor or Mahapaur** and a **Deputy Mayor or Up-Mahapaur** from among themselves. The Mayor is the head of the Municipal Corporation. He/she presides over the meetings of the corporation. In the absence of a Mayor, the Deputy Mayor performs his/her functions.

The Municipal Corporation has a Chief Executive Officer, who is also called the **Municipal Commissioner**. He/she acts as a link between the Municipal Corporation and the state government. He/she implements the laws framed by the corporation. The Officers-in-charge of various departments like health, education, engineering, sanitation, etc. assist him.

The corporation sets up a number of committees to look after its day-to-day functioning. For each subject, there is a committee. *For example,* the Education Committee, Public Health Committee, etc. Each committee consists of 5 to 12 members of the corporation and a chairperson.

DO YOU KNOW?

The Corporation of the City of Panaji is the world's smallest Municipal Corporation, catering to the civic needs of Goa's capital city of Panjim.

FUNCTIONS OF THE MUNICIPALITY AND THE MUNICIPAL CORPORATION

A Municipality and a Municipal Corporation almost have the same functions which are as follows :

Compulsory Functions

1. Public Health

(*i*) Establish and run healthcare centres, dispensaries and hospitals for the common people.

(*ii*) Make arrangements for vaccination and inoculation to prevent the spread of dangerous diseases like tuberculosis, smallpox, malaria, cholera, etc.

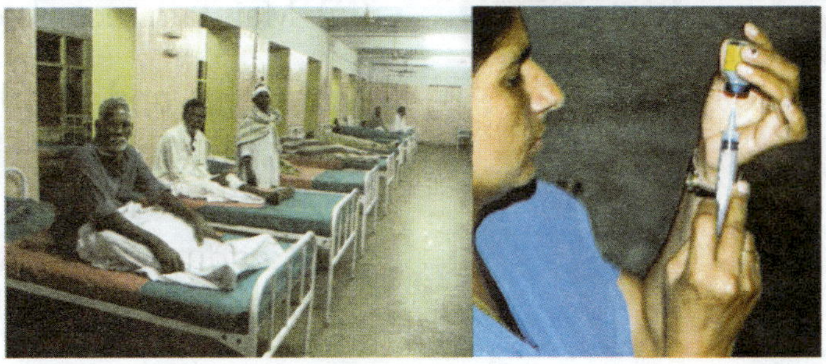

MCD Hospital

2. Sanitation

(*i*) Make arrangements for clearing and disposal of garbage, cleaning roads, markets, drains and public toilets.

(*ii*) Make the public aware of health safeguards through various means.

People Engaged in Sanitation Works

3. Water Supply

(*i*) Maintain the water supply system.

(*ii*) Ensure supply of safe and clean drinking water.

Water supply

4. Education

(*i*) Establish and maintain primary and secondary schools and adult educational centres.

(*ii*) Establish libraries and maintain museums, zoos, etc.

MCD School

5. Lighting

Make arrangements for street lighting, park lighting, etc.

6. Public Security

Fire Brigade

(*i*) Maintain fire brigades to save people from fires.

(*ii*) Pull down old and dangerous buildings which may collapse and cause mishaps.

(*iii*) Take steps for maintaining the quality of goods and check food adulteration.

Repairing Roads

7. Public Works

(*i*) Construct and maintain roads, bridges, public buildings, markets, sports complexes, crematoria and graveyards.

(*ii*) Demolish illegal buildings.

(*iii*) Maintain records of births and deaths.

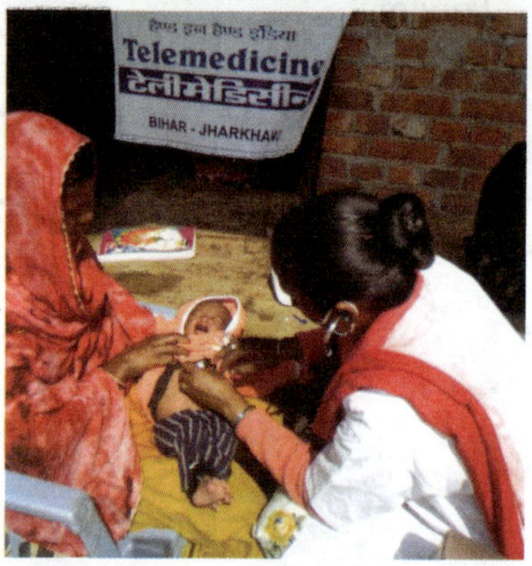

Maternity and Child Welfare

8. Maternity and Child Welfare

(*i*) Establish and maintain maternity and child welfare centres.

(*ii*) Conduct public awareness campaigns for maternity and child welfare.

Optional Functions

The Municipality and the Municipal Corporation have the following optional functions :

(*i*) Establish and maintain public parks, gardens, theatres, picnic resorts, etc.

(*ii*) Construct and maintain old homes, orphanages, night shelters, rest houses, etc.

(*iii*) Ensure supply of cooking gas and milk.

(*iv*) Organise cultural events like exhibitions, sports, fairs, etc.

(*v*) Run a cheap public transport system.

(*vi*) Provide housing facilities.

All these functions of the Municipality and the Municipal Corporation facilitate the life of those living in the cities to a great extent.

India has a **participatory democracy**. It involves the active participation of citizens in decision making and ensuring good governance at all levels of administration. Participatory democracy aims to ensure that democracy is a constant, evolving process that involves everyone, not just during elections but in the day-to-day running of society. The Municipality or the Municipal Corporation play their roles and duties effectively. But it is also our duty as citizens to keep the public spaces clean, dispose of waste properly, pay taxes on

Think & Answer

List the various ways you and your friends can help to make your city clean and a healthy place to live in.

•

Write a paragraph on the civic amenities provided by the Municipality/ Municipal Corporation in your area.

time, abide by the laws and rules made for us, take steps towards conservation of our resources, do not damage public infrastructure like parks, roads and buildings and above all, attend community meetings and voice concerns for better governance. It is then, that the true meaning of Participatory Democracy would be fulfilled.

Decision Making Process of the Corporation

All the decisions that affect the entire city are taken by a group of councillors. The ward councillors present the particular demands of their ward before the entire council. They discuss and debate on the issues in the respective committees. While the councillors' committees and the councillors decide on the issues, the commissioner and the administrative staff implement these decisions

DO YOU KNOW?

A tax is a sum of money that people pay to the government for the services the government provides.

SOURCES OF INCOME OF THE MUNICIPALITY AND THE MUNICIPAL CORPORATION

The Municipal Corporation and the Municipality earn money in the following ways :

(*i*) Property Tax (Property Tax contributes 25-30% of the total money that a Municipal Corporation earns).

(*ii*) Tax on the goods coming into the city, known as octroi.

(*iii*) Income from the water and electricity supplied to the houses and factories.

(*iv*) Money from municipal properties.

(*v*) Vehicle tax levied on cars, motorcycles or carriages.

(*vi*) Education Tax to fund educational activities.

(*vii*) Taxes on businesses and occupations.

(*viii*) Entertainment Tax from cinema halls, theatres, circuses, etc.

(*ix*) Toll tax on the users of roads and bridges.

(*x*) Tax on shopkeepers and traders.

(*xi*) Fees for issuing birth and death certificates.

(*xii*) Grants from the state government for providing specific services to the citizens.

MORE TO KNOW

- Subcontracting refers to a contract in which the work that was earlier being done by government workers is now being done by a private company. *For example*, Municipal Commissioners now hire private contractors to collect and process garbage. This is done to save money. But, these contract workers get paid less. They do not have sufficient safety measures and their jobs are temporary.
- The Indore Municipal Corporation (IMC) has been consistently ranked as the cleanest city in India under the Swachh Bharat Abhiyan (Clean India Campaign) for its sustainable waste management practices and community participation. It is the richest municipal corporation in Madhya Pradesh in terms of revenue.

Think & Answer

List the functions performed by the Municipal Corporation of your city. Also, mention how garbage is cleaned from your neighbourhood by the Municipal Corporation.

Check Your Progress

Understanding

Fill in the blanks.

1. The cities with a population of more than ____________ have a Municipal Corporation.
2. The ____________ Municipal Corporation, established in 1688, is the oldest Municipal Corporation in India.
3. The elected members of the Municipal Corporation are called the ____________.
4. The ____________ is the head of the Municipal Corporation.
5. Sanitation is a ____________ function of the Municipal Corporation.

NEW WORDS

- **Transitional :** The process of changing from one state or condition to another.
- **Ward :** An administrative division of a city.
- **Incompetent :** Inefficient.
- **Nagar Panchayat :** A unit set up for an area that is in the process of changing from a rural to an urban centre.
- **Municipality :** The local body of a city having a small population *i.e.,* between 20,000 and 10 lakhs.
- **Municipal Corporations :** The local body of cities having a large population *i.e.,* more than 10 lakhs.
- **The Municipal Commissioner :** An officer who implements the decisions of the corporation.
- **Councillors :** Elected members of a local government council in cities and municipalities.
- **Ex-officio :** By virtue of one's position or office, usually referring to members who hold a position automatically because of their role in another capacity.
- **Inoculation :** The process of introducing a vaccine into the body to protect against disease.
- **Adulteration :** The act of making something impure or less valuable by adding inferior substances.
- **Dispensaries :** Healthcare facilities that provide medical services and medicines, typically in rural or small urban areas.
- **Crematoria :** Places where bodies are cremated (burnt to ashes) after death.
- **Orphanages :** Institutions that provide shelter and care for children who do not have parents.
- **Mahapaur :** Another term for the Mayor, used in some Indian languages.
- **Tax :** A sum of money that people pay to the government for the services the government provides.
- **Participatory Democracy :** A form of democracy where citizens have direct involvement in decision-making processes, not just during elections but also in everyday governance.
- **Subcontracting :** The practice of hiring another company or individual to perform a specific task that was originally done by an employee or group of employees.
- **Transparency :** The quality of being open, honest and clear in governance, ensuring that actions and decisions are visible and accountable to the public.

NUTSHELL

- In a town or city area, the basic facilities are provided by the Nagar Panchayats, Municipalities and the Municipal Corporations.
- The 74th Amendment Act of the Constitution, 1993, has provided three types of Local Self-government bodies in the Urban areas.
- A Nagar Panchayat is set up for an area that is in the process of changing from a rural to an urban centre.
- The minimum population required for setting up a Nagar Panchayat varies from state to state.
- The term of the Nagar Panchayat is five years.
- The Nagar Panchayat looks after water supply, sanitation, healthcare, drainage, street cleaning, street lighting, primary education, etc.
- A Municipality is also called a Municipal Council or a Municipal Committee. It is a local self-governing body for small towns or cities.
- The cities with a population between 20 thousand and 10 lakh have Municipalities.
- The elected members of the Municipality or Municipal Council are called Councillors.
- In 1993, the 74th Constitutional Amendment, reserved 33% seats for women in the municipalities.
- The cities with a population of more than 10 lakh have a Municipal Corporation.
- The Chennai Municipal Corporation, established in 1688, is the oldest Municipal Corporation in India.
- The members of the Municipal Corporation elect a Mayor or Mahapaur and a Deputy Mayor or Up-Mahapaur from among themselves.
- The Municipal Commissioner acts as a link between the Municipal Corporation and the state government.
- Both the Municipality and the Municipal Corporation have almost the same functions in small towns and big cities respectively. The main functions are to look after Public Health, Sanitation, Water Supply, Education, Lighting, Public Security, Maternity and Child Welfare, etc.
- A participatory democracy involves the active participation of citizens in decision making and ensuring good governance at all levels of administration.

IMPORTANT NCERT TEXTBOOK QUESTIONS (Solved)

Questions, activities and projects

1. On your way to school, you and your friends notice that a water pipe is leaking. A lot of water is being wasted on account of the leak. What would you and your friends do in such a situation ?

Ans. Things me and my friends can do in such a situation :

- If possible, first of all try to stop water leakage by tying the pipe with my handkerchief or any piece of cloth available.
- Report the issue to either my school authorities or the water supply department through helpline numbers.
- Take a photo of the pipe leakage and send the image to the concerned authorities so that they take immediate action.
- Ask the people living nearby to either store or use the water being wasted.

2. Invite a member of an urban local body near you to your class. Discuss with them their role and responsibilities. Prepare a set of questions to ask them so that the meeting is fruitful.

Ans. Set of questions to be asked from the member of an urban local body :

- Please tell your name and share your educational details.
- What is your role in the local body ?
- What are your responsibilities in the local body ?
- Could you explain how decisions are made within the urban local body ?
- What is the criteria of prioritising and addressing the needs of different wards in the city ?
- What are the challenges you face in your duties ?
- What type of work do you like the most ?
- What steps are taken to maintain and improve infrastructure, like roads and street lighting, in the city ?
- How can you encourage community participation in your work ?
- What new initiatives will you take to encourage students and children in community activities ?
- What new technologies do you use in your work ?
- What are your plans for sustainable development and conservation of resources ?
- What advice would you like to give us to make our community, city and nation a better and healthier place to live in ?

3. Discuss with adult members of your family and neighbourhood and make a list of their expectations from the urban local bodies.

Ans. Some expectations from the adult members of my family and neighbourhood from the urban local bodies are as follows :

- Regular supply of safe and clean drinking water.
- Uninterrupted power supply, especially during peak seasons.
- Solve the issue of hanging electrical wires from colonies.
- Regular collection of garbage and waste management services.

- Regular cleaning of drains to prevent waterlogging.
- Maintenance of public parks, walking areas and footpaths.
- Repair and maintenance of roads, especially after monsoons.
- Installation of street lights and ensure safety at night.
- Preventive measures against diseases like dengue, malaria and other infectious diseases.
- Take initiatives to reduce air and noise pollution.
- More cleanliness drives and penalties for littering.
- Initiate programs for rainwater harvesting and conservation of water resources.
- Construction of community halls, libraries and recreational zones where people can meet occasionally.
- Organise awareness programs, role plays and skits to make the public aware of their rights and encourage the people to take part in decision-making through community meetings.

4. Make a list of characteristics of a good urban local body.

Ans. Characteristics of a good urban local body :

- Honest and sincere towards duty.
- Quick response to the needs of citizens.
- Provides essential services like water supply, sanitation, waste management, public transportation and healthcare in an effective manner.
- Provides infrastructure like street lights, clean parks, bus stands, schools and dispensaries.
- Is accountable and answerable to the citizens and their needs.
- Encourages citizen participation in the local decision-making process through community meetings.
- Ensures better use of resources and implements sustainable development.
- Uses new technologies like e-governance for smart solutions and speedy work.

5. What are the similarities and differences between the Panchayati Raj system in rural areas and the urban local bodies ?

Ans. **Similarities :**

- Both represent local self governance.
- In both, members are elected by local people.
- Both bodies have a term of five years.
- Any Indian citizen can take part in the elections of both the bodies.
- Both have $1/3$rd of the seats reserved for women
- Both generate their income through taxes and aids from the government.

Differences :

- The Panchayati Raj governs rural areas while the Urban local bodies govern towns and cities.
- Panchayati Raj caters to smaller rural populations while Urban local bodies manage larger, more densely populated urban areas like cities and towns.
- Panchayati Raj has a three-tier system consisting of Gram Panchayat (village), Panchayat Samiti (block) and Zila Parishad (district), while the Urban local bodies are divided into Nagar Panchayats (for transitional areas), Municipalities (for small towns) and Municipal Corporations (for large cities).
- Panchayati Raj has less sources of income and receives funds primarily through state grants, taxes on land and water usage while the Urban local bodies have many sources of revenue like property tax, vehicle tax, house tax, entertainment tax, business taxes and state grants.

I. OBJECTIVE TYPE QUESTIONS

A. Choose the correct answer.

Conceptual Learning | Critical Thinking

1. *Which option correctly mentions the three types of local governing bodies in urban areas ?*
   (*a*) Gram Sabha, Gram Panchayat and Nyaya Panchayat
   (*b*) Nagar Panchayat, Municipal Council and Municipal Corporation
   (*c*) Gram Panchayat, Panchayat Samiti and Zila Parishad
   (*d*) Legislative Assembly, Legislative Council and the Rajya Sabha

2. *A Nagar Panchayat is set up for*
   (*a*) A transitional area from a rural to an urban centre
   (*b*) A group of villages
   (*c*) An urban area which has a population of more than 1 lakh
   (*d*) An urban area which has a population of more than 5 lakhs

3. *The elected members of the Nagar Panchayat are known as*
   (*a*) Councillors (*b*) Panchs
   (*c*) Ward Members (*d*) MLAs

4. *The cities with population between 20,000 and 10 lakhs have*
   (*a*) Nagar Panchayats (*b*) Municipal Councils
   (*c*) Municipal Corporations (*d*) Zila Parishads

5. *The members of the Municipal Corporation that are usually elected by the Councillors from among the experienced and popular workers of the city, are called*
   (*a*) Aldermen (*b*) Permanent Members
   (*c*) Ex-officio Members (*d*) None of these

B. Mark the option that matches Column A with Column B.

Conceptual Learning | Problem Solving

Column A	Column B
1. Aldermen	(*i*) elected members of the Municipality
2. Councillors	(*ii*) head of the Municipal Corporation
3. Mayor	(*iii*) highly experienced and gifted public workers of the city.
4. Municipal Commissioner	(*iv*) a link between the Municipal Corporation and the state government.

(*a*) **1.**-(*iii*), **2.**-(*i*), **3.**-(*iv*), **4.**-(*ii*) (*b*) **1.**-(*iv*), **2.**-(*iii*), **3.**-(*i*), **4.**-(*ii*)
(*c*) **1.**-(*ii*), **2.**-(*iii*), **3.**-(*i*), **4.**-(*iv*) (*d*) **1.**-(*iii*), **2.**-(*i*), **3.**-(*ii*), **4.**-(*iv*)

C. Fill in the blanks

Knowledge Application

1.

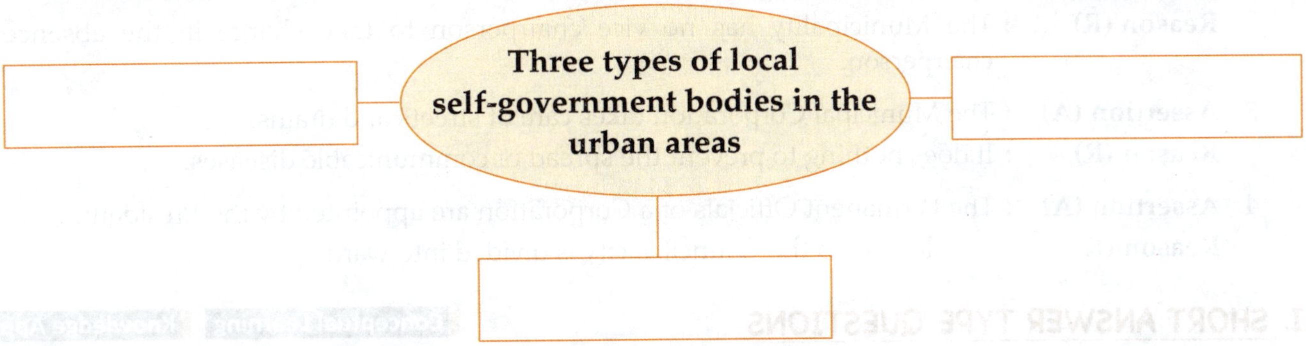

2.

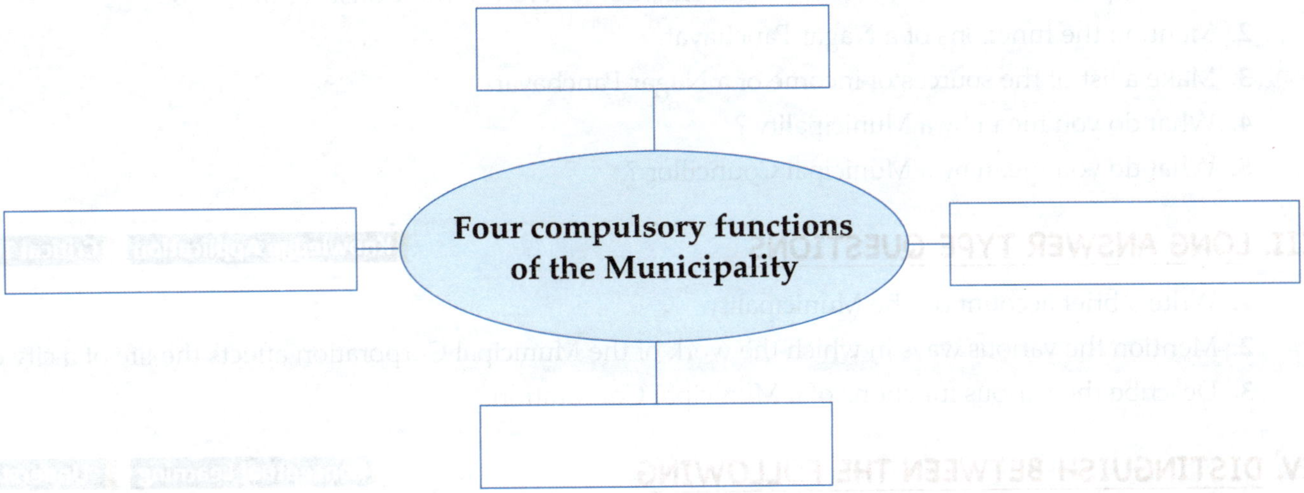

D. State True or False

Knowledge Application | Problem Solving

1. The 74th Amendment of the Constitution was done in 1995.
2. A Nagar Panchayat has a term of six years.
3. The members of Municipality are called Councillors.
4. Cities with a population of more than 10 lakh have Municipal Corporation.
5. The Mayor is the head of Nagar Panchayat.

E. Assertion-Reason

Critical Thinking

For question numbers 1 to 4, two statements are given—one labelled Assertion (A) and the other labelled Reason (R). Select the correct answer to these questions from the codes (*a*), (*b*), (*c*) and (*d*) as given below :

(*a*) Both Assertion (A) and Reason (R) are true and Reason is the correct explanation of the Assertion.

(*b*) Both Assertion (A) and Reason (R) are true but Reason is not the correct explanation of the Assertion.

(*c*) Assertion (A) is true but Reason (R) is false.

(*d*) Assertion (A) is false but Reason (R) is true.

1. **Assertion (A)** : 1/3rd of seats in Municipalities are reserved for women.
   Reason (R) : Women get representation and empowerment through this reservation.

2. **Assertion (A)** : The members of the Municipality elect a chairperson who presides over the meetings that are held at regular intervals.
   Reason (R) : The Municipality has no vice chairperson to take charge in the absence of the chairperson.
3. **Assertion (A)** : The Municipal Corporation takes care of streets and drains.
   Reason (R) : It does nothing to prevent the spread of communicable diseases.
4. **Assertion (A)** : The Permanent Officials of a Corporation are appointed by the President.
   Reason (R) : For election to the Council, a city is divided into wards.

II. SHORT ANSWER TYPE QUESTIONS

Conceptual Learning | Knowledge Application

1. List the provisions of the Seventy-fourth Amendment Act of the Constitution, 1993.
2. Mention the functions of a Nagar Panchayat.
3. Make a list of the sources of income of a Nagar Panchayat.
4. What do you mean by a Municipality ?
5. What do you mean by a Municipal Councillor ?

III. LONG ANSWER TYPE QUESTIONS

Knowledge Application | Critical Thinking

1. Write a brief account on the Municipality.
2. Mention the various ways in which the work of the Municipal Corporation affects the life of a city dweller.
3. Describe the various functions of a Municipal Corporation.

IV. DISTINGUISH BETWEEN THE FOLLOWING

Conceptual Learning | Understanding

1. Nagar Panchayat and Municipality
2. Municipality and Municipal Corporation

V. PICTURE STUDY

Knowledge Application | Critical Thinking

This is a picture of a public park. Answer the following questions with respect to the picture.

1. Who maintains the parks in your locality ?
2. How are seats reserved in the wards for elections ?
3. Write two compulsory and two optional functions of the Municipal Corporation.
4. List three sources of income of the Municipal Corporation.

VI. SOURCE BASED QUESTIONS

Analysing | Conceptual Learning | Understanding

Read the given paragraph and answer the following questions.

Urban sanitation is a form of sanitation which focuses on maintaining sanitary conditions in urban areas. Municipalities have responsibility to ensure the provision of public services, including water supply and sanitation to their residents. Water supply and sanitation services are generally managed within a dedicated municipal department.

1. *What activity is depicted in the picture ?*
   (*a*) A political rally
   (*b*) A school field trip
   (*c*) An environmental clean-up and beautification drive
   (*d*) A protest against the local government
2. *What is the purpose of the activity shown in the picture ?*
   I. To celebrate a festival in the locality.
   II. To protest against environmental issues.
   III. To promote awareness about pollution.
   IV. To improve cleanliness of the urban area.
   (*a*) I and II (*b*) II and III (*c*) III and IV (*d*) II and IV
3. *Which level of Urban Local Self-Government is responsible for overseeing activities like the one shown in the picture ?*
   (*a*) Gram Panchayat (*b*) Municipal Council
   (*c*) Panchayat Samiti (*d*) Zila Parishad
4. *What role do the people in the picture likely have ?*
   (*a*) Local residents discussing community issues.
   (*b*) Students learning about governance of the city.
   (*c*) Municipality officials making efforts to improve sanitation of the city.
   (*d*) Tourists exploring attractions of a new city.

ACTIVITIES & PROJECTS

Multidisciplinary Approach | Creativity and Innovation

1. List the functions done by the Municipal Corporation of your city. Also, mention how garbage is cleaned from your neighbourhood by the Municipal Corporation.
2. List at least five particular demands of the people of your ward and talk to the Councillor in this regard.
3. Visit the office of the Municipality or Municipal Corporation in your area. Collect information and write a report on how it functions.

LIFE SKILLS

Experiential Learning

Topic : Healthcare and Sanitation

Knowledge to be gained : To know about measures that should be taken for proper healthcare and sanitation in your locality.

Activity :

- Frame a constitution for the school on an A4 size sheet, including **Do's** and **Don'ts** that you think should be practised when there is a pandemic.
- Instructions should be very clear as to what should to be done and what should not be done.

For example :

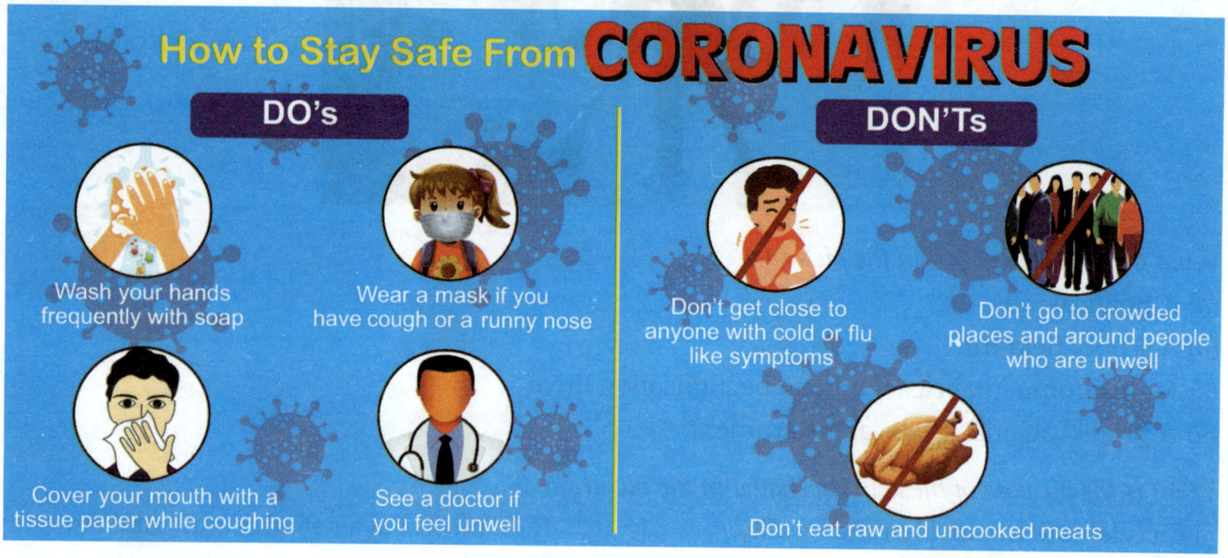

ROLE PLAY

Collaboration Communication

1. Act as if you are a civil engineer who has been given the job to design a road through the landscape for a new community that is moving in. The new road must go from one corner of the model to the other.
2. On your worksheet, draw the landform pictures where you are going to construct the roads using black construction paper. Adjust the route around the terrain and possibly design some bridges using craft sticks and tunnel structures to enable the road to reach the other corner. Use creative ideas to create safe routes.

CHAPTER 13

Theme E—Economic Life Around Us

The Value of Work

CG-4 : C-4.1, C-4.2

You must have heard the famous quote "Work is Worship". You must have also seen people doing many types of work in your surroundings. Let us first take a few examples of different forms of work we generally see in our day to day lives.

What's new to learn

- **Economic Activities**
- **Non-Economic Activities**
- **Types of Economic Activities**
- **The Importance of Non-Economic Activities**

Street Vendor

There are almost one crore street vendors in India. They sometimes sell things or repair them or provide services. They are not employed by anyone but are self employed. So, they have to organise their own work. They plan what to sell and how much stock they should purchase, as well as from where to source it from and how to set up their shops. Their shops are usually temporary structures.

A street vendor—vegetable seller

The vegetable vendors generally use their own carts. Sometimes, they simply use a plastic sheet and spread it on the pavement. Their temporary shops are not secure. They can be dismantled anytime by the police. In certain parts of the city, the hawkers are not even allowed to enter.

Many hawkers sell eatables like snacks, etc. They prepare these at home with the help of family members.

Every morning, Lalu, a street vendor, arranges vegetables like potatoes, tomatoes, pumpkins, cucumbers, etc. in different baskets at his stall. He uses cycle trolleys to carry vegetables and sell them to people at their houses. He usually earns ₹ 100-150 per day. Earlier, street vending was considered as an obstruction to traffic and to the people walking on roads. But now, it is recognised as a general benefit and as a right of the people to earn their livelihood. People feel that mobile vendors should be allowed to move around freely and hawking zones must be created for them in towns and cities.

Domestic Servant

Some people in the urban areas earn their livelihoods by working as domestic servants.

A domestic servant

Rupa works as a domestic help in a posh colony in Delhi. She migrated from UP with her husband seven years ago. She cleans utensils, washes clothes, sweeps and mops the floor. She gets ₹ 1,500 for a month. Her husband collects scrap metal from house to house and sells it to a factory. They live in a slum area in the outskirts of the city.

Fishing

A Fishing Family

Balbhadrapur is a small village in Bihar. It consists of some fishing families. Pritam gets up at 4 O'clock in the morning and goes to the nearby river Kamala for fishing. He comes back at around 8 O'clock with his catch. He keeps aside some fish for the family and auctions the rest. He keeps one-fourth of the auction money for equipment like boats, nets, etc. Recently, he has taken a loan from the bank to purchase an engine to fix on the boat so that he can get a better catch. In the afternoon, Pritam and his relatives gather to repair their nets. Some village women buy fish from them and carry it in baskets to sell in nearby villages. Every year during the monsoon season, these people do not go to the river to catch fish because this is the season when the fish breed. During these months, they survive by borrowing money from the traders. For this, they are bound to sell the fish to traders at lower rates than the market price.

Women selling fish

Garment Factory Worker

Kishan works as a tailor in an export garment factory. He works as a casual labourer. The factory where he works manufactures winter garments for people living in foreign countries like Russia, USA, UK, Saudi Arabia, etc. He goes to the factory in a crowded bus. He has to work for very long hours for some months in the year. A normal working day begins at 9 a.m. and ends by 9 p.m. Sometimes, he has to stay even later. He works 6 days a week. When the factory owner gets large orders, he has to work on Sundays also. He gets ₹ 80 a day for eight hours and ₹ 40 extra for working late. In the off season, the factory reduces its staff. For about 3 to 4 months in a year, Kishan has to sit idle. There is no work for him in the factory. He has to find some other work. Kishan is also interested in community work. He takes an active part in cleanliness drives, plantation drives and other cultural programmes conducted by the community.

Workers in a garment factory

Bank Employee

Priya works in a bank. She attends her office from 9:30 a.m. to 5:30 p.m. She gets ₹ 50,000 as a regular monthly salary. In addition to the salary, she gets other allowances. She does not go to the office on Sundays. This is a paid holiday. When she joined work, she was given an appointment letter that includes all the terms and conditions of work. She enjoys the security of employment. She is entitled to get

Bank employees

facilities like drinking water and a safe working environment. In the evenings, Priya teaches the daughter of her maid and helps her with English and Science. For this, Priya does not take any money from her maid.

Teacher

Seema works as a teacher in a school. Her school starts at 7:00 a.m. and gets over by 1:30 p.m. She is given a regular salary for her job as a teacher. After returning home, she cooks lunch for her family, does the laundry, helps her children with their homework, waters the plants in her small garden, goes to the market to buy the essentials for the next day, prepares dinner and finally cleans the utensils for morning. She does so much work throughout the day at home but is not paid for this work.

A teacher taking class

You must be quite familiar with the work done by the people in the above examples like selling vegetables, fishing, working in a factory or bank and teaching. Apart from these, people are also engaged in activities like farming, driving, weaving, tailoring, etc. Some people work as potters, doctors, nurses, engineers, scientists, soldiers, policemen, etc.

Think & Answer

Think of two other economic activities that are performed in your surroundings but are not mentioned above.

All the above mentioned activities are broadly divided into two categories : Economic activities and non-economic activities.

ECONOMIC ACTIVITIES

Economic activities are those activities that are done to earn a livelihood and generate income. They involve the production, distribution and consumption of goods and services. *For example,* a street vendor selling vegetables, a domestic servant working in exchange for money, a fisherman selling fish, a garment factory worker manufacturing garments, a bank employee and a teacher giving their services in exchange for money.

> **Think & Answer**
>
> Think of some other non-economic activities that your family members do for you. How are they different from economic activities ?

NON-ECONOMICS ACTIVITIES

Non-economic activities are done not for money, but for personal satisfaction or out of gratitude, love, respect, or a desire to contribute to society. In the examples given above, you read that Kishan takes an active part in cleanliness drives, plantation drives and other cultural programmes conducted by the community, Priya teaches the daughter of her maid and Seema cooks lunch for her family, does the laundry, helps her children with their homework, waters the plants, etc. Kishan, Priya and Seema do these activities either for personal satisfaction, love for their family members, or contribution to society. They do not get any salary for these activities.

Women cooking at home

Helping children with homework

Watering the plants

A man planting trees

TYPES OF ECONOMIC ACTIVITIES

Every day, the village of Sundarpur bustles with different kinds of activities in the morning. Along with the sounds of birds, the hustle and bustle of people going for their work and children going to school make the atmosphere of the village lively. People perform different economic activities and contribute to the well-being of the village.

A farmer in field

Suraj is a farmer. His day starts in the fields. He grows rice, wheat, cotton and vegetables that he supplies to the entire village. He does not have any fixed salary but gets money when he sells his grain and vegetables. People give him money in **Cash.** There are many other farmers like Suraj in the village who own their fields. But, most of the other people engaged in agriculture are landless labourers who

Landless labourers working in fields

work in the fields of big farmers to earn their living. Their work is not permanent and they get a daily **wage** after working throughout the day in the fields. They are removed from work when there is not enough work in the fields.

A general store in village

Asha owns a general store in the village where she sells general items, grocery, stationery, toys, etc. Because of this store, people get most of the things in the village itself. She has kept a helper to assist her in the shop. Asha also offers services like money transfer and deliveries to distant villages for which she charges money from her customers.

A little ahead of the general store, Anil and his family run a small textile factory. They buy cotton from Suraj's farm and spun it into fabric. In their factory, people use machines to weave cloth, which they sell to markets in the neighbouring towns.

A textile factory

Aman runs a computer centre in the village. He has knowledge of computers and teaches a few students of the village for which he charges a nominal fee. The students of landless labourers do not pay fees but bring milk, farm vegetables and fruits for Aman. The milk, vegetables and fruits that Aman gets in exchange for teaching is called **payment in Kind.**

Rashmi is a teacher in the government school, while Anu is a doctor in the village government dispensary. They both have fixed working hours and are paid a fixed salary for their work. Rashmi and Anu also give tuition to the village children in the evenings for which they charge no money.

A computer centre

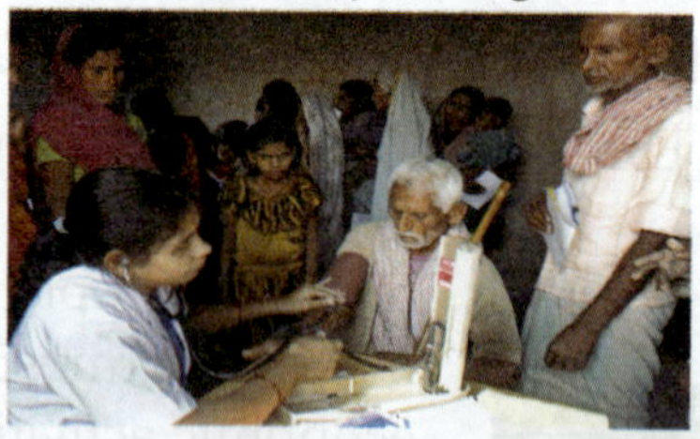

A doctor in village

A teacher in village

The village administration decided to build a road to connect the village to the nearby town. So, there are a number of construction workers in the village nowadays with large machines like cranes, bulldozers and excavators. The road will be a boon for the village as it will facilitate the movement of people and goods from the village to other towns.

Road construction with big machines

Check Your Progress

Understanding

State whether True or False

1. The shops of street vendors are temporary.
2. Economic activities are those activities that are done to earn a livelihood.
3. Economic activities do not involve production or consumption.
4. Work done out of love and respect is an example of economic activity.
5. Teaching someone in exchange for money is a non-economic activity.

Value Addition

In the story of village Sundarpur, we see that people are engaged in many different types of economic activities and each activity has value in terms of money. Value addition in economic activities refers to the process of enhancing the value or worth of a product at each stage of production, distribution or consumption. The more valuable a product becomes, the more profitable, useful and desirable it is. Value addition occurs when an individual or businessperson takes a raw material or a product and improves it by modifying, refining or processing, making it more useful and valuable for the customers.

Let's understand the concept of value addition by an example of making a book (product) from paper (raw material).

The different steps involved in making a book are as follows :

- **Buying Raw Material :** Good quality paper is required for making a book. This paper is produced from wood pulp or recycled materials.
- **Typesetting :** The manuscript for the book is prepared by authors. It is typeset and the text is formatted with appropriate fonts, margins and spacing.
- **Illustrations and Graphics :** The required diagrams, photographs, maps, illustrations, etc. are also placed alongside the text to make them appealing to the readers.

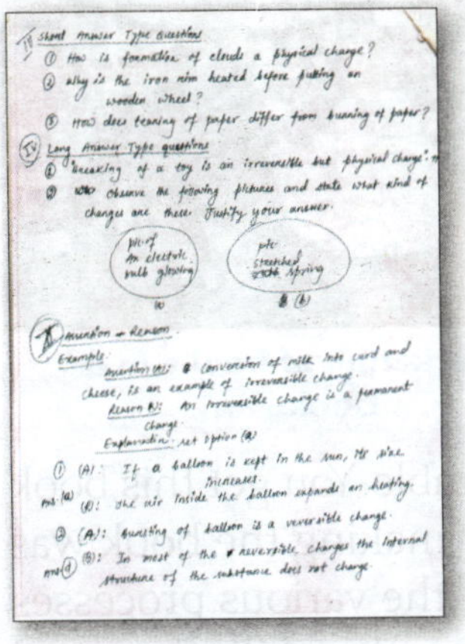

A Manuscript

Proof reading

Final copy

- **Proof Reading and Editing :** It improves the quality of content, ensuring that there are no factual errors, misspellings, or mistakes in grammar and punctuation in the book.

- **Cover Designing :** A graphic designer is appointed to make an attractive, relevant and appealing book cover that aptly describes the content of the book. The cover is laminated for durability and visual appeal.

Cover designing

- **Printing :** High quality ink and advanced printing techniques are used for printing.

Printing

- **Binding :** The printed pages are then collected and sent for binding.

Book binding

Packaging and Storage

- **Packaging and Distribution :** The finished books are finally packed to keep them secure during transportation.
- **Marketing and Promotion :** The publisher finally appoints sales persons who promote the books in different book shops, libraries and schools. Books are also promoted through advertising, social media, book fairs, etc. Books are finally sold through bookstores, online marketplaces, book exhibitions, etc.

Marketing of books in a Book Fair

You must have now understood how your book is enhanced in quality at each step of its production. The final book that you get in your hands is high-quality, visually appealing and durable. You get this book for ₹ 500 while the price of the paper bought for making the book was just ₹ 200. So, the remaining ₹ 300 is the cost of the various processes that are involved in making the book, including the skill, time and effort of the writers, publishers, sales persons, etc. From buying the paper to selling the book, all the different activities added value to the final book and involved payment.

The final look of book

THE IMPORTANCE OF NON-ECONOMIC ACTIVITIES

Although the non-economic activities do not involve money, they are important for our emotional wellbeing and social development. They focus on our social, cultural, educational, recreational and personal development and thus influence our overall personality.

Non-economic activities involve social activities like community service, social gatherings, meetings, etc. You must have witnessed "Seva" or selfless service in temples, gurudwaras, mosques and churches where people voluntarily participate in clean up drives, arrange shoes of devotees and serve food to people through langars or community kitchens. These volunteers are not paid anything for their service, yet they feel a sense of satisfaction for their work. In the examples you studied above, Rashmi and Anu were doing selfless service by teaching some children free of cost.

Think & Answer

Figure out some activities that are performed in your surroundings. Differentiate them into economic and non-economic. Explain how some of the activities you have mentioned add value to your life or create money.

Langars in Gurudwara

Reading

Writing

Celebrating festivals

Drawing

Non-economic activities also include Cultural activities (*e.g.*, celebrating festivals, attending exhibitions, concerts and plays, visiting museums, etc.), Educational activities (Reading, writing, research, attending workshops and seminars and skill development), Recreational activities (developing hobbies, playing games, watching movies, listening to music, etc.) and Personal Development activities (Painting, drawing, doing yoga and meditation, cycling, etc.). All these activities bring us a sense of satisfaction, relaxation, enjoyment and play an important part in shaping our personalities. They make us stress free, bring us closer to our families and communities, help preserve our religious and cultural traditions and contribute to personal happiness and well-being. The emotional and mental well-being we gain from non-economic activities affects our productivity in a positive manner and brings more value to economic activities.

Yoga and Meditation

Cycling

Gardening

The Strength of Community Participation

Community participation is an important aspect of the development and decision making process. It empowers individuals by giving them a voice and ensures that diverse needs of the community are taken into account. Community led programmes have the support of the majority members of the community and therefore give more sustainable, longer lasting and effective solutions. They also help strengthen social bonds and build trust among community members.

Community clean-up days, Community gardens, Community health initiatives, Community art programmes, Youth mentorship programs, Educational workshops are some examples of Community Participation.

The recent **"Ek Ped Maa Ke Naam"** initiative is a meaningful effort to honour mothers by planting trees in their names, while also contributing to environmental conservation and sustainability. It is a community driven programme that encourages participation of all members of the community and makes them aware towards the importance of a greener environment. The campaign also educates people about the benefits of planting and conserving trees. For this, tree planting events are organised in which all members of the community can come and plant trees at designated areas in the loving memory of their mothers or a loved one. Each tree planted is dedicated to a mother, with a small plaque or marker that bears her name. The campaign also focuses on the care and maintenance of planted trees to ensure their survival and growth. Apart from paying tribute to mothers, the campaign also brings people together, fostering a sense of community and unity for environmental conservation.

Ek Ped Maa Ke Naam

You must have heard of **Swachh Bharat Abhiyan** or the Clean India Mission that was launched by the Government of India in 2014, with the aim of achieving a cleaner, healthier and more sustainable India. The campaign increased awareness among citizens and encouraged people to switch to more cleaning habits both in their homes and in their surroundings. People across India took an active part in the cleanliness drives, rallies and awareness campaigns conducted under this Mission. The success of this mission is mainly attributed to the mass participation of people who have come together to clean their parks, schools, railway stations, streets and other public places. The mission became a national movement towards a cleaner India through community participation.

Swachh Bharat Abhiyan

The **Joint Forest Management** (JFM) is another community-driven forest conservation program in India. In this program, the local communities work with the government to sustainably manage and protect forest resources. The communities are allowed to collect non-timber forest products like fruits, medicinal plants, honey and firewood in a sustainable manner. In return, the community protects the forest from illegal logging, grazing, or other harmful activities.

The communities also participate in planting trees and regenerating degraded forest areas. *For example,* in West Bengal and Odisha, the efforts of communities have improved the forest cover and conserved biodiversity. Communities also help protect wildlife by maintaining habitats and prevent poaching. Community members act as forest guards and monitor illegal activities like hunting or logging. Communities have also improved their economic well being by selling the forest produce.

In West Bengal, the local villagers regenerated the Sal trees in the Arabari Forest with the help of the Forest Department. In return, they were allowed to collect firewood and other forest produce. The regenerated forest helped to maintain ecological balance as well as improved the economic conditions of the villagers.

Joint Forest Management

Think & Answer

Think of any community driven program that took place in your neighbourhood. What activities were performed under the program and what was their outcome ? Did you participate in the program ? If yes, then write your experience.

MORE TO KNOW

Van Mahotsav is an annual tree-planting festival celebrated in India, typically during the first week of July. The festival was initiated in 1950 by K.M. Munshi, the then Union Minister for Agriculture and Food. The main objective of the festival was to raise awareness about the importance of trees and encourage afforestation to combat deforestation and environmental degradation. The festival educates people about the benefits of trees and their role in our lives. Tree plantation drives, awareness campaigns, forest conservation initiatives, water conservation, organic farming, etc. are the main activities performed during Van Mahotsav. It is a community driven initiative that brings together people of all ages to work towards environmental conservation.

Tree plantation under Van Mahotsav

K.M. Munshi

Check Your Progress

Understanding

Fill in the blanks

1. Value addition makes a product more __________ and __________ for customers.
2. The raw material for making a book is __________.
3. The Swachh Bharat Abhiyan was launched in the year __________.
4. __________ trees were regenerated in the Arabari Forest by the communities.
5. __________ is an annual tree-planting festival celebrated in India.

NEW WORDS

- **Obstruction :** Something that blocks or hinders progress.
- **Economic Activities :** Activities performed to earn a livelihood and generate income.
- **Non-Economic Activities :** Activities done not for earning money but for personal satisfaction or social reasons.
- **Self-employed :** People who are not employed by others but run their own businesses or services.
- **Payment in Kind :** Receiving goods or services instead of money as a form of payment.
- **Daily Wage :** Payment received by labourers for working a day.
- **Casual Labourer :** A person employed on a temporary or seasonal basis.
- **Value Addition :** The process of increasing the worth of a product at various stages of production by improving its quality or making it more useful.
- **Community Participation :** Involvement of community members in activities aimed at social welfare or development, such as cleanliness drives or forest conservation efforts.
- **Afforestation :** The process of planting trees to create forests, especially in areas where there was no previous tree cover.
- **Sustainable :** Practices or methods that do not deplete resources or harm the environment, ensuring long-term ecological balance.
- **Livelihood :** The means of securing basic necessities like food, water, shelter and income.
- **Social Bonding :** Strengthening relationships and trust within a community through shared activities and collective efforts.

NUTSHELL

- Economic Activities are performed to earn money, such as farming, vending, fishing and working in factories, banks, or schools.
- Economic Activities involve the production, distribution and consumption of goods and services.
- Non-Economic Activities are not aimed at earning money but done for personal satisfaction, social contribution, or cultural reasons, such as helping family members or community service.
- Non-Economic Activities focus on our social, cultural, educational, recreational and personal development and thus influence our overall personality.
- Value Addition means to enhance the worth of a product at each stage of production, making it more valuable, useful and profitable, like turning raw paper into a finished book.
- Community Participation refers to collective efforts by people to achieve common goals, such as cleanliness drives (*e.g.,* Swachh Bharat Abhiyan) and forest conservation programs (*e.g.,* Joint Forest Management). It strengthens social bonds and helps in sustainable development.
- Community led programmes have the support of the majority members of the community and therefore give more sustainable, longer lasting and effective solutions.

IMPORTANT NCERT TEXTBOOK QUESTIONS (Solved)

Questions, activities and projects

1. How are economic activities different from non-economic activities ?

Ans. **Economic activities** are those activities that are done to earn a livelihood and generate income. They involve the production, distribution and consumption of goods and services.

For example, a street vendor selling vegetables.

Non-economic activities are done not for any money but for personal satisfaction or out of gratitude, love, respect or contribution to society.

For example, cooking lunch for your family.

2. What kind of economic activities do people engage in ? Illustrate with examples.

Ans. People engage in a number of economic activities like

- **Farming :** Growing crops like wheat, rice, corn and vegetables.
- **Mining :** Extraction of minerals like coal, iron ore, gold and other minerals.
- **Manufacturing :** Clothes, cars, toys, computers, etc.
- **Construction :** Building bridges, malls, houses, hospitals, etc.
- **Education :** Teaching in schools or taking tuitions.

3. There is great value attached to people who are engaged in community service activities. Comment on this statement.

Ans. Community participation is an important aspect of the development and decision making process. It empowers individuals by giving them a voice, self-confidence, leadership and communication skills. It also develops problem solving skills as community services also pose many challenges. Community service also gives a sense of satisfaction and thus, has a positive impact on mental health of the individual. It strengthens his bonds with his community and helps in his social development. Therefore, it is true that there is great value attached to people who are engaged in community service activities.

4. What are the various ways in which people are compensated for various economic activities ? Give some examples.

Ans. People are compensated for various economic activities in various ways like :

- Regular monthly salary or daily wages.
- Bonus on exceptional performance, festivals, new year, etc.
- Commissions on the percentage of sales.
- Promotions to higher posts.
- Benefits like retirement plans, health insurance, pensions after retirement, etc.
- Gifts or money for family tours once in a year.

EXERCISES
As per NEP-2020 & NCF-2023

I. OBJECTIVE TYPE QUESTIONS

A. Choose the correct answer.

Conceptual Learning | Critical Thinking

1 *Which of the following is an example of an economic activity ?*
(*a*) Cooking lunch for your family
(*b*) Selling vegetables as a street vendor
(*c*) Helping your child with homework
(*d*) Taking care of sick people at home

2. *Non-economic activities are performed*
(*a*) To earn a livelihood
(*b*) For personal satisfaction and social contribution
(*c*) To increase profits
(*d*) To manufacture a product

3. *Value addition in economic activities refers to*
(*a*) Increase the cost of production
(*b*) Enhance the value of a product at each stage
(*c*) Reduce the price of a product
(*d*) Decrease the value of product

4. *Joint Forest Management (JFM) focuses on*
(*a*) Building factories in forest areas
(*b*) Conserving forests with community and government collaboration
(*c*) Increasing timber exports
(*d*) Increase mining in forests

5. *Which of the following is an example of community participation ?*
(*a*) A shopkeeper selling stationery items
(*b*) People coming together to clean surroundings
(*c*) A person cooking food for family
(*d*) An individual cleaning their own home

B. Mark the option that matches Column A with Column B.

Conceptual Learning | Problem Solving

Column A	Column B
1. Non-economic activities	(*i*) Making a product more valuable at each stage
2. Economic activity	(*ii*) Joint Forest Management (JFM)
3. Value addition	(*iii*) Earning a livelihood by selling goods
4. Community participation	(*iv*) Personal satisfaction

(*a*) **1.**-(*iii*), **2.**-(*i*), **3.**-(*iv*), **4.**-(*ii*)
(*b*) **1.**-(*iv*), **2.**-(*iii*), **3.**-(*i*), **4.**-(*ii*)
(*c*) **1.**-(*ii*), **2.**-(*iv*), **3.**-(*i*), **4.**-(*iii*)
(*d*) **1.**-(*iv*), **2.**-(*i*), **3.**-(*ii*), **4.**-(*iii*)

C. Fill in the blanks

1.

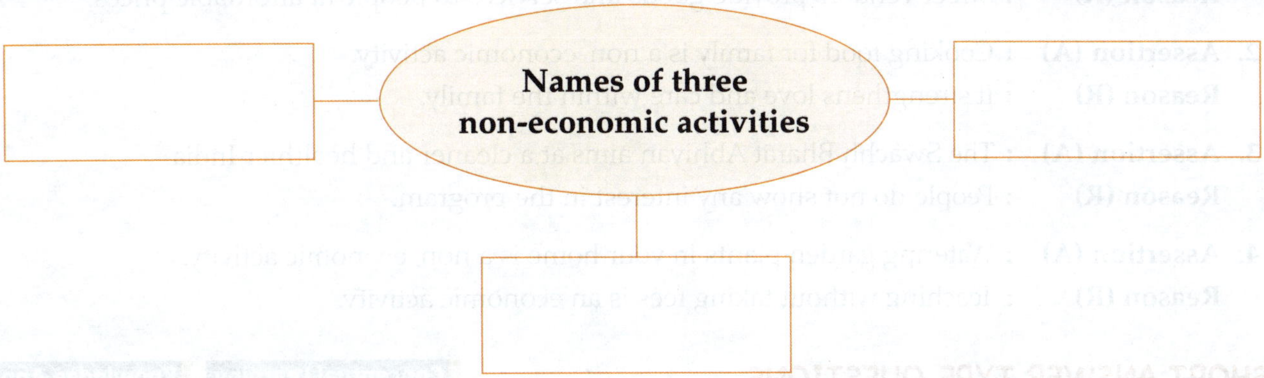

2.

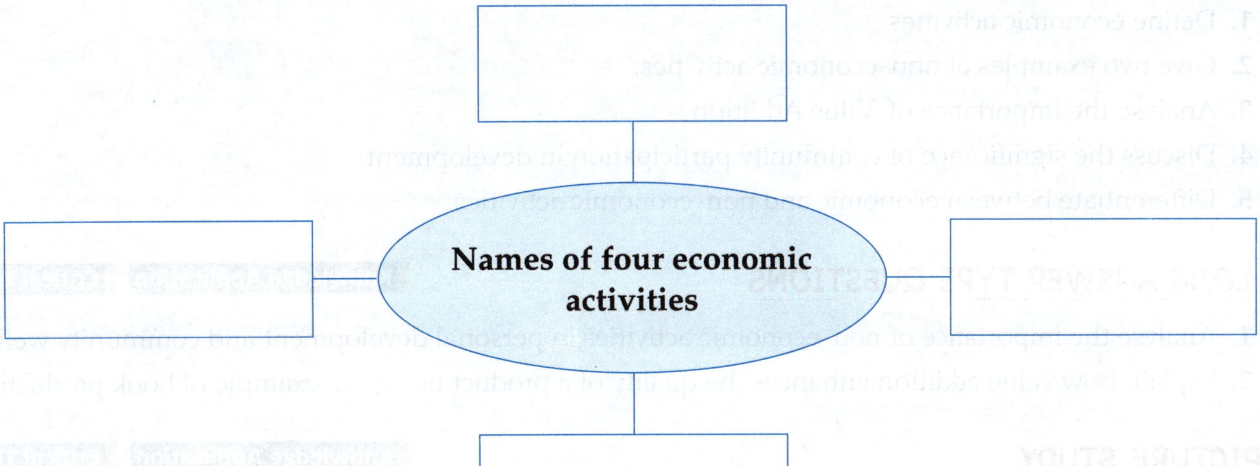

D. State True or False

1. Bank employees and teachers do not receive any salary for their work.
2. Fishing families have work throughout the year.
3. Community services are economic activities.
4. Value addition makes a product more desirable.
5. Community participation decreases social bonds among people.

E. Assertion-Reason

For question numbers 1 to 4, two statements are given—one labelled Assertion (A) and the other labelled Reason (R). Select the correct answer to these questions from the codes *(a)*, *(b)*, *(c)* and *(d)* as given below :

(*a*) Both Assertion (A) and Reason (R) are true and Reason is the correct explanation of the Assertion.

(*b*) Both Assertion (A) and Reason (R) are true but Reason is not the correct explanation of the Assertion.

(*c*) Assertion (A) is true but Reason (R) is false.

(*d*) Assertion (A) is false but Reason (R) is true.

1. **Assertion (A)** : Street vendors are considered an important part of the urban economy.
   Reason (R) : Street vendors provide goods and services to people at affordable prices.
2. **Assertion (A)** : Cooking food for family is a non-economic activity.
   Reason (R) : It strengthens love and care within the family.
3. **Assertion (A)** : The Swachh Bharat Abhiyan aims at a cleaner and healthier India.
   Reason (R) : People do not show any interest in the program.
4. **Assertion (A)** : Watering garden plants in your home is a non-economic activity.
   Reason (R) : Teaching without taking fees is an economic activity.

II. SHORT ANSWER TYPE QUESTIONS

Conceptual Learning | Knowledge Application

1. Define economic activities.
2. Give two examples of non-economic activities.
3. Analyse the importance of Value Addition.
4. Discuss the significance of community participation in development.
5. Differentiate between economic and non-economic activities.

III. LONG ANSWER TYPE QUESTIONS

Knowledge Application | Critical Thinking

1. Analyse the importance of non-economic activities in personal development and community well-being.
2. Explain how value addition enhances the quality of a product using the example of book production.

IV. PICTURE STUDY

Knowledge Application | Critical Thinking

Given here is a picture related to a massive community driven cleanliness initiative launched in India in 2014. Answer the following questions with respect to the picture.

1. Name the initiative.
2. What is the basic purpose of this initiative ?
3. Give two reasons why this programme is so successful in India.
4. Name any other Community driven initiative in India.

V. SOURCE BASED QUESTIONS

Analysing | Conceptual Learning | Understanding

Read the given paragraph and answer the following questions.

Community participation is an important aspect of the development and decision making process. It empowers individuals by giving them a voice and ensures that diverse needs of the community are taken into account. Community led programmes have the support of the majority members of the community and therefore, give more sustainable, longer lasting and effective solutions. They also help strengthen social bonds and build trust among community members.

Community clean-up days, Community gardens, Community health initiatives, Community art programmes, Youth mentorship programs, Educational workshops are some examples of Community Participation.

1. *Which of the following is NOT true about Community Participation ?*
   (*a*) It empowers individuals by giving them a voice.
   (*b*) It has the support of the majority members of the community.
   (*c*) It does not give longer lasting and effective solutions.
   (*d*) It helps strengthen social bonds and build trust among community members.
2. *Which of the following is NOT an example of Community Participation ?*
   (*a*) Community clean-up days
   (*b*) Community gardens
   (*c*) Community health initiatives
   (*d*) Personal health check-up
3. *Which of the following is an example of community participation ?*
   (*a*) Taking solo trips
   (*b*) Volunteering in a local clean-up drive
   (*c*) Shopping in a supermarket
   (*d*) Watching a movie alone

ACTIVITIES & PROJECTS

Multidisciplinary Approach | Creativity and Innovation

1. Talk to the elders in your family and neighbourhood and arrange a Van Mahotsav in your community. Share your experiences in your class.
2. Arrange a debate in your class on the topic " Which is more important : an economic activity or a non-economic activity ?"
3. Talk to some family members and neighbours who are doing some kind of economic activity. Discuss with them their routine and their struggles. Highlight their success stories also. Prepare a report on the same and discuss it in class.
4. Choose any product and research the process of value addition in its production. Create a visual presentation like a poster or PowerPoint showcasing each step of the process and how value is added at each stage. You can choose any clothes, books, decorative items, food items, etc. as your product.
5. Interview a person who takes an active part in community driven activities. Ask him what urges him to take part in such programmes and how he benefits from them.

CHAPTER 14

Economic Activities Around Us

CG-4 : C-4.1; CG-9 : C-9.1

What's new to learn

- **The Classification of Economic Activities into Economic Sectors**
- **Interdependence Among Sectors**

In the last chapter, we studied about the two main types of activities that people perform—Economic activities that are mainly concerned with generating income or having monetary value and non-economic activities that are done for personal satisfaction and social well-being. Both these activities are important for economic growth and a balanced development of society.

In this chapter, we will mainly study about the different types of economic activities and their classification.

THE CLASSIFICATION OF ECONOMIC ACTIVITIES INTO ECONOMIC SECTORS

There are a variety of economic activities related to the production, distribution and consumption of goods and services. Activities having similar features are classified into different economic sectors.

The three main types of economic sectors are : Primary, Secondary and Tertiary Economic Sectors.

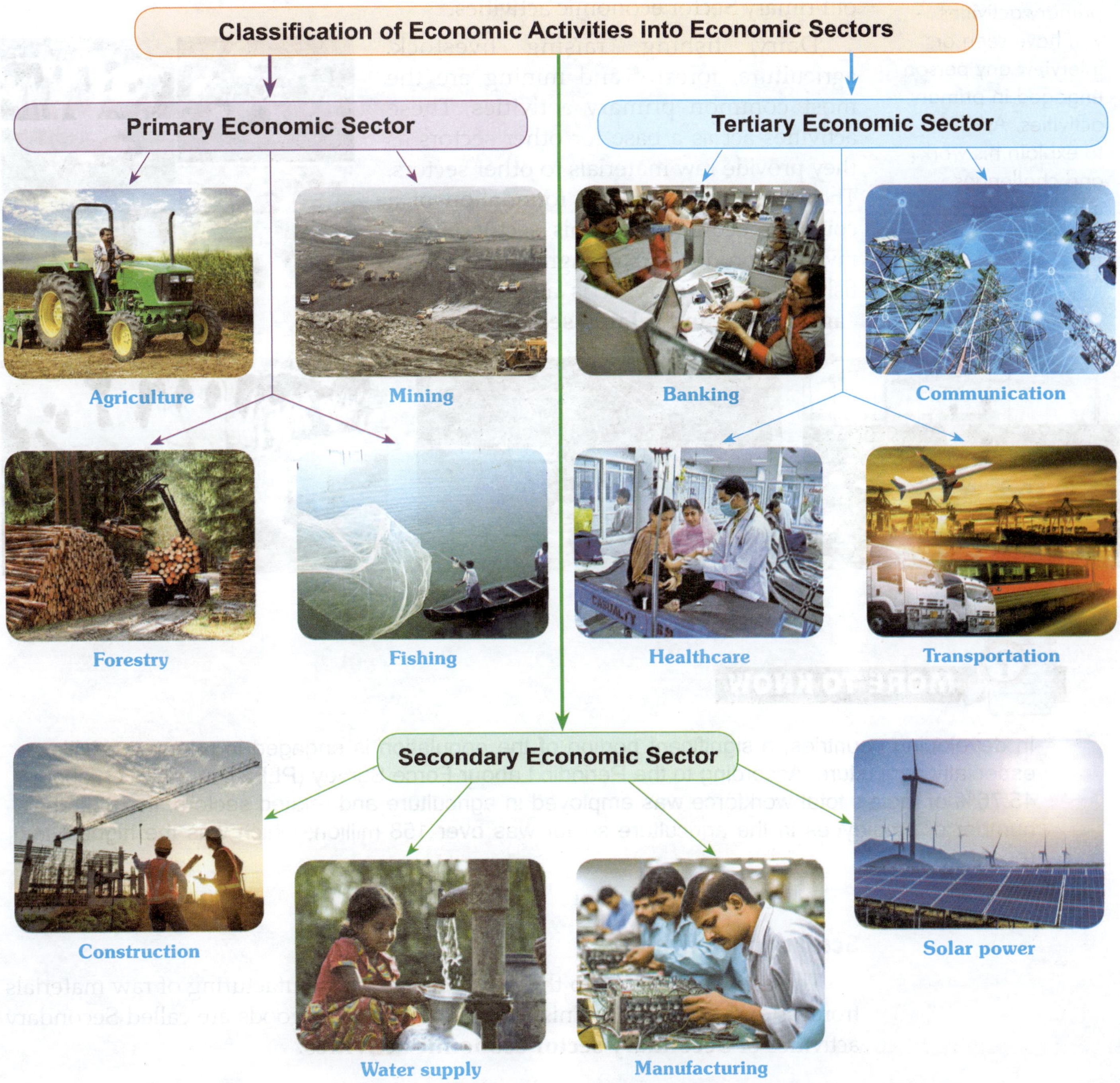

Primary Activities

These activities are directly related to the extraction and production of raw materials from the Earth. Since these activities involve people who are directly dependent on nature for production of goods, they are also called **Primary sector economic activities**. *For example,* the cultivation of wheat is a primary activity as we depend on natural resources like land, rainfall, sunshine and climate for cultivation. Similarly, obtaining milk, meat, wool and eggs, from dairy animals; extracting coal, oil and minerals from mines; catching fish and other seafood from oceans, rivers and lakes; harvesting timber and other forest resources from forests; and cultivating plants, fruits and flowers are all examples of Primary Sector economic activities.

> **Think & Answer**
>
> Think of any two primary activities you have seen or interview any person engaged in primary activities. Ask him to explain his work and challenges in primary sector activities.

Dairy, fishing, raising livestock, agriculture, forestry and mining are the most common primary activities. These activities act as a base for other sectors as they provide raw materials to other sectors. They therefore, form the foundation of a country's economy. As this sector mainly involves products from agriculture, dairy, fishing and forestry, it is also called the "**agriculture and related sector**".

Raising livestock

Greenhouse farming

Forestry

Dairy farming

> **MORE TO KNOW**
>
> In developing countries, a significant portion of the population is engaged in primary activities, especially agriculture. According to the Periodic Labour Force Survey (PLFS), in 2022-23, about 45.76% of India's total workforce was employed in agriculture and related sectors. In 2022, the number of employees in the agriculture sector was over 158 million, which was the highest in recent years.

Secondary Activities

The activities related to the processing and manufacturing of raw materials from primary sector into finished or semi-finished goods are called Secondary activities or **Secondary sector economic activities.**

Manufacturing, Construction, Processing and Production are all Secondary sector economic activities. *For example,* the manufacture of cars, electronic appliances, household appliances and machinery; building infrastructure like roads, bridges, buildings, malls and houses; providing utilities like water, gas and electricity to houses and factories are all secondary sector activities. They also include converting raw materials like fruits and vegetables to packaged foods and beverages; raw cotton or wool into fabrics and clothing; raw resources like coal, oil, natural gas into electricity or refined fuels; as well as converting iron ore into steel used for construction and manufacturing. Other examples of secondary sector activities include manufacture of chemicals, pharmaceuticals, fertilizers and plastics, as well as the processing of metals and chemicals into useful products such as machinery, electronic components and construction materials.

Electricity production

DO YOU KNOW?

The Industrial Revolution (late 18th and 19th centuries) transformed secondary activities by introducing mass production and machinery, increasing productivity and the global spread of industries.

Trade and logistics

Automobile factory

Pharmaceutical factory

This sector is important for the economy as it adds value or worth to raw materials by converting them into useful products. This sector gives a wide range of job opportunities to people ranging from unskilled labour to skilled technicians and managers. This sector fully utilises the skills and expertise of workers along with technology to transform raw materials into finished or semi-finished goods. As this sector involves different industries, it is also called the **"industrial sector".**

Textile factory

MORE TO KNOW

The Economic Survey of 2024 states that 11.4% of India's workforce is employed in manufacturing, 28.9% in services and 13.0% in construction. These figures highlight the importance of these sectors in the country's overall labour market.

Tertiary Activities

The activities that support the functioning of the primary and secondary sectors by improving efficiency through services are called Tertiary activities or **Tertiary sector economic activities.** This sector is not involved in production but provides services to both the primary and secondary sectors. These services are essential for the production, distribution and consumption of goods. Thus, this sector gives support to businesses, individuals and society at large.

Everyday you see vegetable vendors providing fruits and vegetables at your doorsteps, truck drivers transporting goods from one city to another, your teachers, doctors and nurses doing their duties efficiently. All these are examples of tertiary sector activities.

Other important tertiary sector activities that provide services and make our lives easier include selling goods to consumers by shopkeepers; transporting goods, documents, and people by road, air and waterways; providing financial aid, investments, saving accounts and other services by banks; offering medical treatment by doctors and nurses; providing education and vocational training by schools, colleges and universities; offering tours and travel packages by tour operators; providing legal advice by lawyers; offering telephone, internet and data services, as well as call centres; providing vehicle repair, home repair and electronics repair services; providing entertainment through television, radio and other media; and services rendered by cobblers, barbers, washermen and others.

Think & Answer

Your teacher's profession also comes under tertiary sector economic activity. You must have seen your teachers doing a variety of tasks that help them in teaching you effectively. Write a note on the various tasks your teachers perform in school.

MORE TO KNOW

In developed countries, the tertiary sector contributes the largest share to the GDP. *For example*, in the United States, the service sector accounts for over 75% of the economy.

Barber

Cobbler

The tertiary sector is a link between the primary and the secondary sectors. *For example,* it helps in the transportation of raw materials from the fields to the factories and then transports the manufactured products from the factories to the markets for sale. As this sector provides services rather than goods to both the primary and secondary sectors, it is also known as the "Service Sector".

Teaching

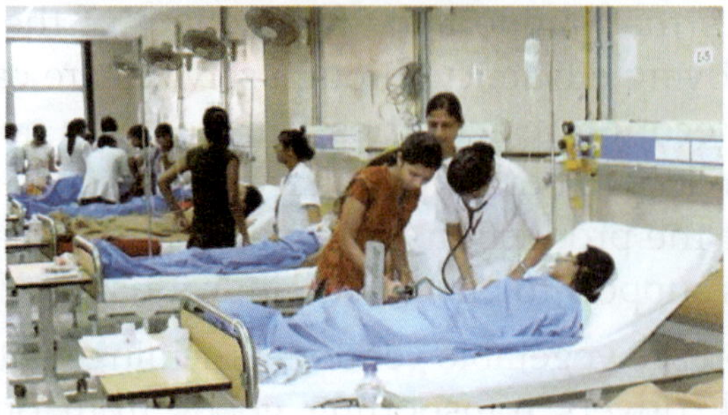

Doctors attending patients

Lawyers fighting cases

The following table summarizes the three economic sectors and the activities related to them.

Economic Sector	Description	Examples
Primary Activities	Directly related to the extraction and production of raw materials from nature. These activities depend on natural resources like land, water and minerals.	Agriculture, Dairy farming, Fishing, Forestry, Mining.
Secondary Activities	Involve processing and manufacturing of raw materials into finished or semi-finished goods. This sector adds value to raw materials by transforming them into useful products.	Manufacturing of cars, construction of houses, roads and bridges, production of electricity, textile production, converting iron ore to steel.
Tertiary Activities	Focus on providing services that support both primary and secondary sectors. This sector includes activities that help in distribution, transportation and selling of goods.	Banking, Retail trade, Transportation, Healthcare, Education, Tele-communications, Tourism, Insurance, Legal services, Entertainment.

Check Your Progress — Understanding

State whether True or False

1. Raising livestock is a primary sector activity.
2. Secondary sector is also called the "Agriculture Sector".
3. Providing services comes under the tertiary sector.
4. Secondary sector includes production through machines in factories.
5. Production of sugar from sugarcane comes under the primary sector.

INTERDEPENDENCE AMONG SECTORS

All the three economic sectors are interdependent and interconnected. The primary sector provides raw materials to the secondary sector, which processes these raw materials into finished goods. The tertiary sector supports the production and distribution of these goods by providing essential services.

Amul dairy in Mogar, Gujarat

Let us understand the interdependence of the three sectors by studying the production of milk and milk products in AMUL (Anand Milk Union Limited) dairy situated in Anand district of Gujarat. You all must have heard the name of brand Amul and bought its products like milk, butter, icecream, chocolates, etc. Amul, a brand of the Gujarat

Cooperative Milk Marketing Federation (GCMMF), has a rich history of how a cooperative movement transformed both the dairy industry of India and the lives of millions of farmers.

Origin

The origin of Amul dates back to the 1940s, when the farmers of Anand district stood up against exploitation by middlemen and private suppliers. The farmers went to neighbouring villages to sell their milk on bicycles or on foot. By the time they reached those villages, the milk would spoil especially during hot summers. This resulted in a loss to farmers and they made very little money. These circumstances forced them to sell their milk to middlemen and private suppliers who bought their milk at very low prices and sold it in markets at higher prices. The conditions of the villagers remained the same as they had no bargaining power.

Fed up with this exploitation, the farmers one day approached Sardar Vallabhbhai Patel, a patriotic national leader, for a solution. Sardar Patel asked the farmers to form a cooperative and get rid of middlemen. This would help the farmers to take up procurement, processing and marketing under their control.

The Cooperative

In 1946, the farmers joined hands to form a cooperative—the **Kaira District Cooperative Milk Producers' Union Limited** under the able guidance of **Sardar Vallabhbhai Patel**, **Tribhuvandas Kishibhai Patel**, **Morarji Desai** and later **Dr. Verghese Kurien.** The immediate aim of this cooperative was to get rid of middlemen and control the pricing and distribution of milk. The cooperative which began with just two village dairy cooperative societies and 247 litres of milk is now famous as the brand Amul.

Sardar Vallabhbhai Patel

Tribhuvandas Kishibhai Patel

Morarji Desai

Dr. Verghese Kurien

With the formation of the cooperative, the farmers now owned the dairy. They formed their own rules and policies for production, pasteurisation and distribution of milk. The different tasks were shared by everyone eliminating the need for middlemen. The farmers employed professionals to operate the dairy and manage the different aspects of business. The cooperatives also elected their representatives who managed the village societies and district unions.

The cooperatives were fully aware of the problems and needs of farmers and provided solutions. All these steps gradually led to an increase in the income of farmers.

Role of Dr. Verghese Kurien

A young dairy engineer, Dr. Kurien joined Amul in 1949. He is also known as the **"Milkman of India".** He introduced modern technology and management practices to make India self-sufficient in milk production. He adopted the latest processing techniques for milk and milk products at Amul. Through his efforts, Amul became the first modern dairy cooperative in Anand capable of competing with other established milk industries in the market. Kurien is credited for spearheading India's **White Revolution** which transformed India into the largest producer of milk in the world.

Verghese Kurien (left) and Tribhuvandas Patel (right)

The Birth of Amul and Expansion

The name "Amul" has been derived from the Sanskrit word **"Amulya,"** which means "priceless" or "precious". The brand Amul was launched in 1955 with the introduction of pasteurised milk and butter.

Packaged milk

Cows grazing grass at dairy farm

Milk Collection

In 1965, the National Dairy Development Board (NDDB) was set up with Dr. Kurien as its Chairman. In the 1970s, a national dairy development program was launched under the leadership of Dr. Kurien. Named **Operation Flood,** the program aimed to increase milk production, create a national milk grid and ensure fair prices for farmers. Amul played a key role in the success of Operation Flood.

Packaging Production

Transportation

DO YOU KNOW?

The White Revolution in India, also known as **Operation Flood**, was an initiative launched in 1970 by the **National Dairy Development Board (NDDB)**. Led by Dr. Verghese Kurien, it transformed India from a milk-deficient nation into the world's largest milk producer.

Over the years, Amul has expanded its range of products and produces dairy products like cheese, icecreams, milk powder, yoghurt, butter, ghee, flavoured milk as well as non-dairy products like chocolates and beverages.

Amul is now a national brand with its products available in almost all rural and urban areas. It also exports it's products to international markets.

Amul dairy products

Amul products in retail stores

MORE TO KNOW

The Amul Girl

You must have seen a cheerful, round faced girl dressed in a polka dotted frock in the advertisements of Amul. The Amul Girl was created in 1966 by the advertising agency daCunha Communications, led by Sylvester daCunha and art director Eustace Fernandes.

Amul Girl—Shobha Tharoor

The Amul advertisements featuring the Amul Girl are known as Amul Topical Ads. Each ad features a short, punchy slogan along with a cartoon of the Amul Girl in different scenarios related to the theme. The themes may be political, social, sports events or daily happenings. The Amul Girl has become a part of Indian pop culture, appearing on billboards, in newspapers and on social media.

Sylvester daCunha

The success of Amul led to the formation of many cooperatives in different parts of India, the most prominent being the following :

- **Mother Dairy** (National Dairy Development Board), Delhi-NCR
- **Nandini** (Karnataka Milk Federation - KMF), Karnataka
- **Aavin** (Tamil Nadu Cooperative Milk Producers' Federation), Tamil Nadu
- **Vijaya** (Andhra Pradesh Dairy Development Cooperative Federation), Andhra Pradesh
- **Saras** (Rajasthan Cooperative Dairy Federation - RCDF), Rajasthan
- **Parag** (Uttar Pradesh Cooperative Milk Union), Uttar Pradesh
- **Sudha** (Bihar State Milk Cooperative Federation - COMFED), Bihar

In the story of Amul, you can now easily identify the involvement of all the three economic sectors. The farmers obtain the milk from the cows, which is a natural resource. So, this comes under a primary sector economic activity.

Think & Answer

Who supplies milk at your home ? From where does the milkman get milk to supply at your home ? Do you know any brand of milk other than the ones mentioned above ? Name the brand.

The milk is further taken to plants and factories where it is processed and pasteurised with the help of technology and human skill to make a variety of other products like curd, cheese, butter, icecreams, milk powder, yoghurt, etc. All these come under secondary sector economic activities.

The different products ready for use are then transported through roadways, railways, airways and waterways to different countries, states, cities and villages. They are further sent to retail stores of Amul, other shops, supermarkets and malls to be sold to the consumers. All the activities of transportation, trade and retail come under tertiary sector economic activities.

Think & Answer

Take any food product like sugar or bread. Study the process of its production, procession and transportation and discuss the interdependence of the three sectors in your class.

With the help of images, let's see the interdependence of all the three sectors in the production of a shirt from cotton. Discuss the different activities and differentiate them into the three economic sectors.

From fibre to fabric

Check Your Progress

Understanding

Fill in the blanks

1. Amul dairy is situated in ________________ district of Gujarat.
2. The name "Amul" has been derived from the Sanskrit word ________________.
3. ________________ is famous as the Milkman of India.
4. Mother Dairy is located in ________________.
5. Two products of brand Amul are ________________ and ________________.

NEW WORDS

- **Extraction :** The process of removing or obtaining something from a source, such as minerals from the Earth.
- **Raw Materials :** The basic natural materials from which goods and products are made, such as cotton, coal, or metal ores.
- **Pasteurisation :** The process of heating liquids (*such as milk*) to kill harmful bacteria without affecting the nutritional value or taste.
- **Interdependence :** The mutual reliance between two or more sectors, activities, or entities for survival or growth.
- **Agriculture :** The practice of cultivating land and breeding animals for food, fibre, medicinal plants and other products.
- **Cooperative :** An organization owned and operated by a group of people for their mutual benefit, often used in farming and milk production.
- **Manufacturing :** The process of converting raw materials into finished goods using labour and machinery.
- **Primary Sector :** The sector of the economy that is directly involved in the extraction and use of natural resources.
- **Secondary Sector :** The sector of the economy involved in manufacturing and processing of raw materials into semi-finished or finished goods.
- **Tertiary Sector :** The sector of the economy that provides services rather than goods, including sectors like retail, education and healthcare.
- **Industrial Revolution :** The period during the late 18th and early 19th centuries marked by a shift from manual production to the use of machinery in industries.
- **Infrastructure :** The basic physical and organizational structures needed for the operation of a society or enterprise, such as roads, bridges and power supply.
- **National Milk Grid :** A system of interconnected dairy networks and processing plants that aim to ensure a consistent milk supply across regions.
- **Operation Flood :** A large-scale dairy development initiative launched in India in the 1970s to increase milk production and supply.
- **Anand Milk Union Limited (Amul) :** A famous dairy cooperative in India known for revolutionizing the milk industry.

NUTSHELL

- Economic activities are classified into three sectors : Primary, Secondary and Tertiary.
- Primary activities are directly related to the extraction and production of raw materials (agriculture, mining, fishing, forestry, etc.). These activities rely on natural resources and form the foundation of the economy.
- The activities related to processing and manufacturing of raw materials from primary sector into finished or semi-finished goods are called Secondary activities or Secondary sector economic activities.
- Manufacturing, Construction, Processing and Production are all Secondary sector economic activities. *For example,* the manufacture of cars, electronic appliances, household appliances, machinery, etc.,They add value to raw materials and offer a wide range of job opportunities.
- Tertiary activities provide services that support the primary and secondary sectors (banking, healthcare, education, transportation, etc.). They are essential for the distribution and consumption of goods.

- All three sectors are interconnected. Raw materials from the primary sector are processed in the secondary sector and services from the tertiary sector ensure production and distribution of goods.
- Dr. Verghese Kurien led India's White Revolution, making India the largest producer of milk. He is also known as the "Milkman of India".
- The name "Amul" has been derived from the Sanskrit word "Amulya," which means "priceless" or "precious".
- The brand Amul was launched in 1955 with the introduction of pasteurised milk and butter.
- In 1965, the National Dairy Development Board (NDDB) was set up with Dr. Kurien as its Chairman.
- In the 1970s, a national dairy development program was launched under the leadership of Dr. Kurien. Named Operation Flood, the program aimed to increase milk production, create a national milk grid and ensure fair prices for farmers. Amul played a key role in the success of Operation Flood.
- Amul has a variety of dairy products like cheese, icecreams, milk powder, yoghurt, butter, ghee, flavoured milk as well as non-dairy products like chocolates and beverages.

IMPORTANT NCERT TEXTBOOK QUESTIONS (Solved)

Questions, activities and projects

1. What is the primary sector ? How is it different from the secondary sector ? Give two examples.

Ans. Differences between primary sector and secondary sector :

- The primary sector involves the extraction of raw materials, while the secondary sector involves the processing and manufacturing of these raw materials into finished or semi-finished goods.
- The primary sector activities depend on natural resources like land, water and minerals while the secondary sector uses machinery, technology and labour to transform raw materials.

Examples :

1. Cultivation of cotton (primary activity).

   Manufacturing clothes from cotton (secondary activity).
2. Mining of coal (primary activity).

   Producing electricity from coal (secondary activity).

2. How does the secondary sector depend on the tertiary sector ? Illustrate with a few examples.

Ans. The secondary sector depends heavily on the tertiary sector for services like transportation, banking, communication and marketing.

Examples :

- It is the tertiary sector that transports raw materials to manufacturing units and delivers finished goods to markets or retailers.

- Manufacturers and industrialists often need capital to invest in their business, buy raw materials and machinery, etc. For this they depend on banks (*tertiary sector*) that manage their finances and give loans.
- Effective communication is also required by the secondary sector to check the movement of their raw materials, transport of finished products, proper distribution of finished products to markets and malls, etc. Communication is also a tertiary sector activity.

3. Give an example of interdependence between primary, secondary and tertiary sectors. Show it using a flow diagram.

Ans. The interdependence between primary, secondary and tertiary sectors can be understood through the following flow chart showing the manufacture of a shirt from cotton.

Primary sector → **Secondary sector** → **Tertiary sector**

- **Primary sector:** Cultivation of cotton, Plucking cotton bolls and Ginning
- **Secondary sector:** Spinning, Weaving, Dyeing, Printing, Cutting and Stitching
- **Tertiary sector:** Transporting, Marketing and Shirt for sale in shop

I. OBJECTIVE TYPE QUESTIONS

A. Choose the correct answer.

Conceptual Learning | Critical Thinking

1. *Which of the following is a primary sector activity ?*
   (*a*) Manufacturing cars (*b*) Teaching in school
   (*c*) Mining coal (*d*) Providing banking services
2. *The secondary sector mainly involves*
   (*a*) Extraction of raw materials (*b*) Production and manufacturing of goods
   (*c*) Providing services (*d*) Retail and trade
3. *The secondary sector depends on the tertiary sector for*
   (*a*) Raw material extraction (*b*) Services like transportation and banking
   (*c*) Harvesting crops (*d*) Raising livestock
4. *Which sector of the economy is also referred to as the service sector ?*
   (*a*) Primary sector (*b*) Secondary sector
   (*c*) Tertiary sector (*d*) None of these
5. *Which of the following is a tertiary sector activity ?*
   (*a*) Fishing (*b*) Banking
   (*c*) Construction of houses (*d*) Mining iron ore

B. Mark the option that matches Column A with Column B.

Conceptual Learning | Problem Solving

Column A	Column B
1. 1946	(*i*) Dr. Kurien joined Amul
2. 1949	(*ii*) National Dairy Development Board (NDDB) was set up
3. 1955	(*iii*) Kaira District Cooperative Milk Producers' Union Limited
4. 1965	(*iv*) The brand Amul was launched

(*a*) **1.**-(*iii*), **2.**-(*i*), **3.**-(*iv*), **4.**-(*ii*)
(*b*) **1.**-(*iv*), **2.**-(*iii*), **3.**-(*i*), **4.**-(*ii*)
(*c*) **1.**-(*iv*), **2.**-(*i*), **3.**-(*ii*), **4.**-(*iii*)
(*d*) **1.**-(*iii*), **2.**-(*iv*), **3.**-(*ii*), **4.**-(*i*)

C. Fill in the blanks

Knowledge Application

1.

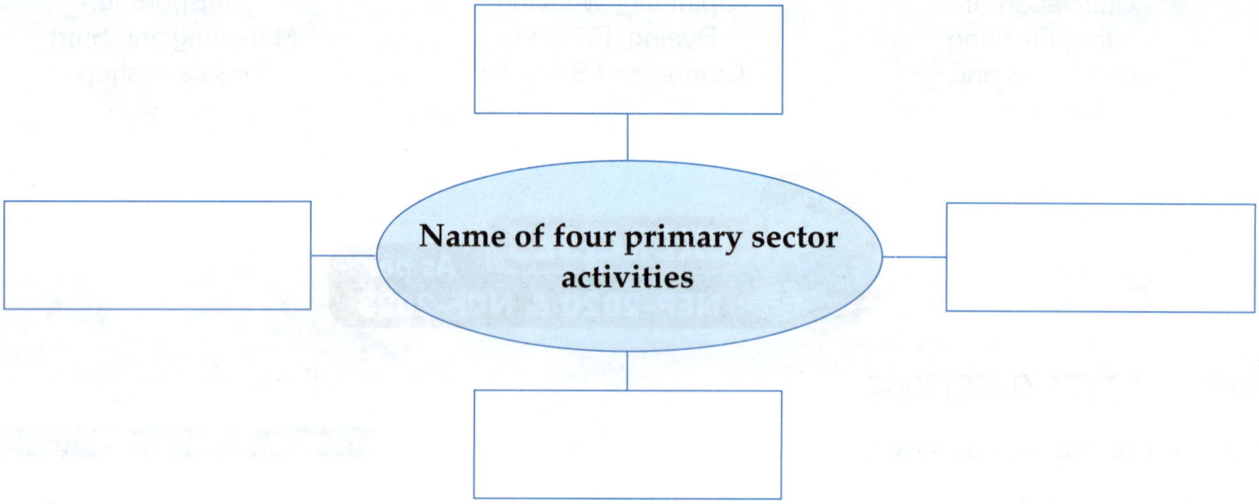

2.

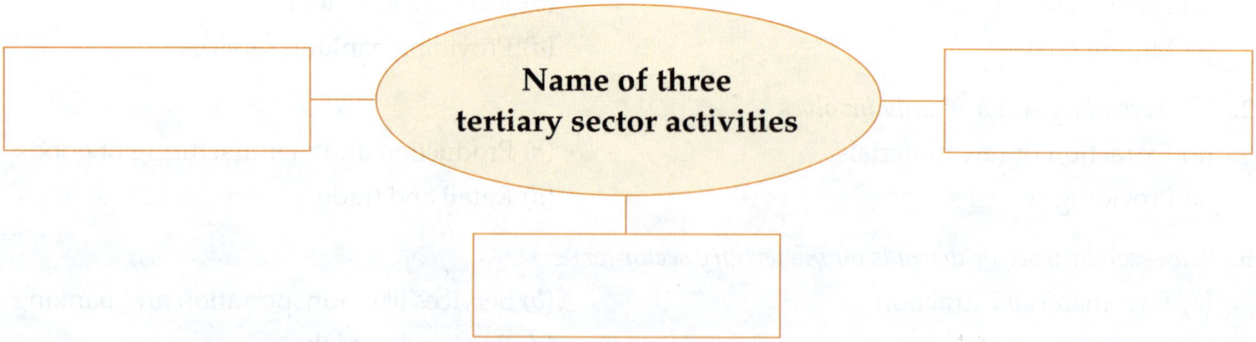

3. Classify the following list of occupations into Primary, Secondary and Tertiary sectors and fill in the columns given below :

(The first column has been done for you)

(*a*) Dairy farming
(*b*) Construction worker
(*c*) Teacher
(*d*) Mining
(*e*) Factory worker (textile)
(*f*) Doctor
(*g*) Fisherman
(*h*) Car manufacturing
(*i*) Bank clerk
(*j*) Retail shop owner

Primary Sector	Secondary Sector	Tertiary Sector
Dairy farming	Construction worker	Teacher

D. State True or False

Knowledge Application | Problem Solving

1. Manufacturing of goods is a part of the tertiary sector.
2. The secondary sector depends on the tertiary sector for services like transportation and banking.
3. Raising livestock is a secondary sector activity.
4. The primary sector is also known as the "industrial sector."
5. The tertiary sector includes services like education, healthcare and banking.

E. Assertion-Reason

Critical Thinking

For question numbers 1 to 4, two statements are given—one labelled Assertion (A) and the other labelled Reason (R). Select the correct answer to these questions from the codes (*a*), (*b*), (*c*) and (*d*) as given below :

(*a*) Both Assertion (A) and Reason (R) are true and Reason is the correct explanation of the Assertion.

(*b*) Both Assertion (A) and Reason (R) are true but Reason is not the correct explanation of the Assertion.

(*c*) Assertion (A) is true but Reason (R) is false.

(*d*) Assertion (A) is false but Reason (R) is true.

1. **Assertion (A)** : The tertiary sector includes services like education, healthcare and banking.
   Reason (R) : It is also called the "Service Sector".
2. **Assertion (A)** : The secondary sector adds value to raw materials by transforming them into finished or semi-finished goods.
   Reason (R) : It is also called the "Agriculture Sector".
3. **Assertion (A)** : The secondary sector depends on the primary sector for raw materials.
   Reason (R) : It does not depend on the tertiary sector for anything.
4. **Assertion (A)** : Washermen and barbers come under primary sectors.
   Reason (R) : Teachers and doctors come under tertiary sectors.

II. SHORT ANSWER TYPE QUESTIONS

Conceptual Learning | Knowledge Application

1. Explain how the primary and secondary sectors are interdependent.
2. Discuss why the tertiary sector is also called the "service sector".
3. Describe the role of the primary sector in the economy of any country.
4. How do education, skill and technology enhance production ? Explain.

III. LONG ANSWER TYPE QUESTIONS

Knowledge Application | Critical Thinking

1. Explain the interdependence of the primary, secondary and tertiary sectors.
2. Why are secondary and tertiary sectors important for a developing country like India ?

IV. DISTINGUISH BETWEEN THE FOLLOWING

Conceptual Learning | Understanding

1. Primary sector and Secondary sector
2. Agriculture sector and Service sector

V. PICTURE STUDY

Knowledge Application | Critical Thinking

The images given here relate to the three sectors of economy. Answer the following questions with respect to the pictures.

1. Which sector does the field, factory and delivery truck represent ?
2. What are the roles of the field, factory and delivery truck ?
3. Are the three sectors interdependent ? Explain how.
4. Which sector is the link between the other two sectors ?

VI. SOURCE BASED QUESTIONS

Analysing | Conceptual Learning | Understanding

Read the given paragraph and answer the following questions.

The origin of Amul dates back to the 1940s, when the farmers of Anand district stood up against their exploitation by middlemen and private suppliers. The farmers went to neighbouring villages to sell their milk on bicycles or on foot. By the time they reached those villages, the milk would spoil especially during hot summers. This resulted in a loss to farmers and they made very little money. These circumstances forced them to sell their milk to middlemen and private suppliers who bought their milk at very low prices and sold it in markets at higher prices. The conditions of the villagers remained the same as they had no bargaining power.

1. *Who exploited the farmers of district Anand ?*

   (*a*) Middlemen (*b*) Private suppliers (*c*) Both (*a*) and (*b*) (*d*) None of these

2. *Which one of the following was NOT related to the farmers of district Anand ?*

(*a*) The farmers went to neighbouring villages to sell their milk on bicycles or on foot.

(*b*) The milk spoiled especially during hot summers.

(*c*) They were forced to sell their milk to middlemen and private suppliers.

(*d*) The middlemen and private suppliers bought the milk at very high prices and the farmers earned huge profits.

3. *The "White Revolution" was related to the production of*

(*a*) Oil (*b*) Butter

(*c*) Milk (*d*) Rice

4. *Who is famous as the "Milkman of India" ?*

(*a*) Sardar Vallabhbhai Patel (*b*) Dr. Verghese Kurien

(*c*) Morarji Desai (*d*) Tribhuvandas Kishibhai Patel

ACTIVITIES & PROJECTS

Multidisciplinary Approach **Creativity and Innovation**

1. You must have gone to a hospital and a bank. Write a report on the different services provided by a hospital and a bank. How do these services affect our lives ?
2. Collect information on the lives of people working in the primary sector and prepare a project report on :
   (*a*) How they earn their livelihood ?
   (*b*) The problems faced by them in their work.
   (*c*) The steps taken by the government to improve their conditions.
   (*d*) The role of secondary and tertiary sectors in their production.
   Paste some relevant pictures also.
3. Suppose you have to start a new factory. Which type of a factory would you prefer and why ? What factors will you keep in mind while setting up the factory ? Which raw materials would you use and how would you utilise the secondary and tertiary sectors in your production ? Prepare a detailed project and discuss it in your class.

ROLE PLAY

Collaboration **Communication**

Divide the class into four groups :

1. People working in the primary sector.
2. People working in the secondary sector.
3. People working in the tertiary sector.
4. Consumers.

Take any textile product, say a Sari/Kurta-Pyjama/Lehenga-Choli, etc. Students will prepare a skit on the working of different sectors, the various processes involved in making the product from the raw materials to bringing it in the market for sale and the expectations of the consumers from the product. After the skit, hold discussions on the importance of different sectors in the class.

Practice Test Paper–I*

(Based on Chapters 1, 2, 4, 7, 9, 10 and 13)

Time : 3 Hours | **Max. Marks : 80**

General Instructions :

1. The question paper comprises **Six Sections**—A, B, C, D, E and F. There are 37 questions in the Question paper. All questions are compulsory.
2. **Section A**—From questions 1 to 20 are MCQs of **1 mark** each.
3. **Section B**—Question no. 21 to 24 are Very Short Answer Type Questions, carrying **2 marks** each. Answers to each question should not exceed 40 words.
4. **Section C**—Question no. 25 to 29 are Short Answer Type Questions, carrying **3 marks** each. Answers to each question should not exceed 60 words.
5. **Section D**—Question no. 30 to 33 are Long Answer Type Questions, carrying **5 marks** each. Answers to each question should not exceed 120 words.
6. **Section E**—Question no. 34 to 36 are Source Based Questions with three sub questions and are of **4 marks** each. Answers to each question should not exceed 100 words.
7. **Section F**—Question no. 37 is Map Based, carrying **5 marks** with two parts, 37(*a*) from **Theme-B (2 marks)** and 37(*b*) from **Theme-A (3 marks)**.
8. There is no overall choice in the question paper. However, an internal choice has been provided in few questions. Only one of the choices in such questions must be attempted.

SECTION-A. (Multiple Choice Questions) [20 × 1 = 20]

Choose the correct answer.

1. *A map of India showing its states, towns and cities is an example of a*
   (*a*) Physical map (*b*) Political map (*c*) Thematic map (*d*) None of these
2. *"North-East" is a*
   (*a*) Scale (*b*) Sketch
   (*c*) Cardinal Direction (*d*) Intermediate Direction
3. *Black colour on the map is used to denote*
   (*a*) Mountains (*b*) Plateaus (*c*) Roads (*d*) Settlement
4. *Mariana Trench lies in the*
   (*a*) Pacific Ocean (*b*) Atlantic Ocean (*c*) Indian Ocean (*d*) Arctic Ocean
5. *Powerful storms driven by heat and moisture from the ocean are called*
   (*a*) Tsunamis (*b*) Hurricanes (*c*) Floods (*d*) Earthquakes

*Chapters are choosen according to five themes covering each aspect of the subject.

6. *People who study the history of life on Earth through the study of fossils are called*
(*a*) Archaeologists (*b*) Genealogists (*c*) Palaeontologists (*d*) Geologists

7. *Which of the following is a source to study history ?*
(*a*) Monuments (*b*) Coins (*c*) Manuscripts (*d*) All of these

8. *The first Homo sapiens (modern humans) appeared on the Earth in the continent of*
(*a*) Asia (*b*) North America (*c*) Africa (*d*) Australia

9. *"Saraswati" is the Goddess of*
(*a*) Wisdom (*b*) Dawn (*c*) Night (*d*) Fire

10. *The 'Book of Sacrificial Prayers' is the*
(*a*) Rig Veda (*b*) Sam Veda (*c*) Yajur Veda (*d*) Atharva Veda

11. *The second Buddhist Council was held at*
(*a*) Rajgir (*b*) Vaishali (*c*) Kashmir (*d*) Pataliputra

12. *Consider the statements given below and choose the correct answer.*

Statement I : Tribes have their own language, music, stories and paintings, which are part of their rich and unique cultural traditions.

Statement II : Land, forests, grasslands, water and their usage are regarded as the wealth of the entire tribe.

(*a*) Statement (I) is correct and (II) is incorrect.
(*b*) Statement (I) is incorrect and (II) is correct.
(*c*) Both (I) and (II) are incorrect.
(*d*) Both (I) and (II) are correct.

13. *Which of the following statements is true about a family ?*
I. Members of a family provide emotional support to each other.
II. Multiple generations live together under one roof in a nuclear family.
III. The members of a family share responsibilities amongst themselves.
IV. A family does not teach social behaviour, social ethics and values to its members.
(*a*) Options I & IV (*b*) Options I & III (*c*) Options II & III (*d*) Options II & IV

14. *The "Chipko Movement" took place in*
(*a*) Uttar Pradesh (*b*) Madhya Pradesh (*c*) Uttarakhand (*d*) Himachal Pradesh

15. *Consider the statements given below and choose the correct answer.*

Statement I : Our country has three organs of Government namely, the Legislature, the Executive and the Judiciary.

Statement II : The executive ensures that justice is given in a fair manner.

(*a*) Statement (I) is correct and (II) is incorrect.
(*b*) Statement (I) is incorrect and (II) is correct.
(*c*) Both (I) and (II) are incorrect.
(*d*) Both (I) and (II) are correct.

16. *Match list I with list II and select the correct answer using the codes below in the lists.*

List I	List II
1. Oceans	(*i*) Huge land masses rising above sea level.
2. Isthmus	(*ii*) Piece of land surrounded by water on all side.
3. Continents	(*iii*) Vast stretches of water.
4. Island	(*iv*) A narrow strip of land connecting two large land masses.

(*a*) **1.**-(*ii*), **2.**-(*i*), **3.**-(*iv*), **4.**-(*iii*)
(*b*) **1.**-(*iv*), **2.**-(*ii*), **3.**-(*i*), **4.**-(*iii*)
(*c*) **1.**-(*i*), **2.**-(*iv*), **3.**-(*ii*), **4.**-(*iii*)
(*d*) **1.**-(*iii*), **2.**-(*iv*), **3.**-(*i*), **4.**-(*ii*)

17. *Which of the following statements is true about non-economic activities ?*

I. Non-economic activities do not involve money.
II. They are important for our emotional wellbeing and social development.
III. They bring us a sense of satisfaction.
IV. Working in a bank on a regular salary is a non-economic activity.

(*a*) Options I & II
(*b*) Options I, II & III
(*c*) Options I & IV
(*d*) Options III & IV

18. ____________ *is the imaginary line that divides the Earth into northern and southern hemispheres.*

(*a*) Tropic of Cancer
(*b*) Tropic of Capricorn
(*c*) Equator
(*d*) South Pole

19. *Given here is a picture of one of the sources of history. What is this called ?*

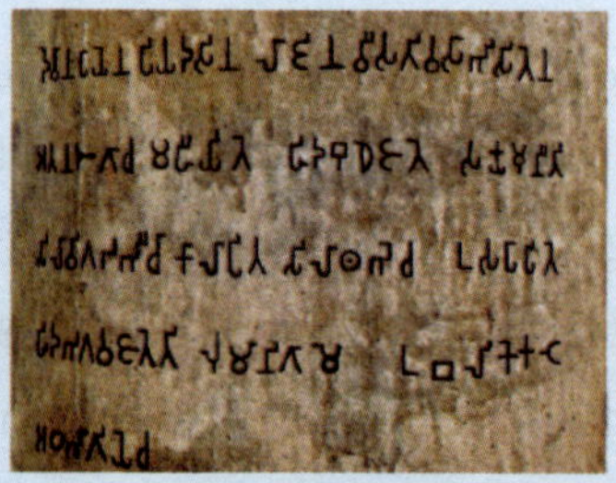

(*a*) Manuscript
(*b*) Inscription
(*c*) Coin
(*d*) Seal

20. *Match list I with list II and select the correct answer using the codes below in the lists.*

List I	List II
1. Rajan	(*i*) Senior-most male member of the family
2. Grihapati	(*ii*) King
3. Gramani	(*iii*) Leader of the army
4. Senani	(*iv*) Leader of the village

(*a*) **1.**-(*ii*), **2.**-(*i*), **3.**-(*iv*), **4.**-(*iii*)
(*b*) **1.**-(*iv*), **2.**-(*ii*), **3.**-(*i*), **4.**-(*iii*)
(*c*) **1.**-(*i*), **2.**-(*iv*), **3.**-(*ii*), **4.**-(*iii*)
(*d*) **1.**-(*iii*), **2.**-(*iv*), **3.**-(*i*), **4.**-(*ii*)

7. *The evidence of cultivation of cotton in the Harappan Civilization has been found from*
(*a*) Harappa (*b*) Mohenjodaro (*c*) Mehrgarh (*d*) Ropar

8. *Which of the following statements about the Harappan civilization is NOT correct ?*
(*a*) Lothal was an important centre for cultivation of rice.
(*b*) Harappans made tools and weapons out of copper and bronze.
(*c*) They did not domesticate animals.
(*d*) The Harappans were the first people to grow cotton in Europe and Asia.

9. *Consider the statements given below and choose the correct answer.*
Statement I : Trade in the Indus Valley was carried on both by land and sea.
Statement II : While external trade was carried on by ships, the internal trade was carried on by bullock carts.
(*a*) Statement (I) is correct and (II) is incorrect.
(*b*) Statement (I) is incorrect and (II) is correct.
(*c*) Both (I) and (II) are incorrect.
(*d*) Both (I) and (II) are correct.

10. *The term, 'unity in diversity' was coined by*
(*a*) Mahatma Gandhi (*b*) Sardar Patel
(*c*) Jawaharlal Nehru (*d*) Lal Bahadur Shastri

11. *Which of the following statements about Unity in Diversity in India are correct ?*
I. India has 22 officially recognized languages, with hundreds of dialects spoken across different states.
II. There is no diversity of food in India.
III. India has a culture of sharing food and dishes with family, friends and neighbours during festivals.
IV. The Saree is worn only in a few regions of India.
(*a*) Options I & II (*b*) Options II & III (*c*) Options I & III (*d*) Options II & IV

12. *The Tamil version of Ramayana is called*
(*a*) Ramcharitmanas (*b*) Ramayana
(*c*) Kamba Ramayanam (*d*) Ramakien

13. *Match list I and II and select the correct answer using the codes below in the lists :*

List I	List II
1. Forestry	(*i*) Secondary Sector
2. Manufacture of cars	(*ii*) Tertiary Sector
3. Banking	(*iii*) Primary Sector

(*a*) **1.**-(*ii*), **2.**-(*i*), **3.**-(*iii*), (*b*) **1.**-(*ii*), **2.**-(*iii*), **3.**-(*i*)
(*c*) **1.**-(*iii*), **2.**-(*ii*), **3.**-(*i*) (*d*) **1.**-(*iii*), **2.**-(*i*), **3.**-(*ii*)

14. *Which of the following statements about the Panchayati Raj System in India is/are correct ?*

I. The Panchayati Raj is a three-tier system.

II. The Zila Parishad works at the district level.

III. In 1992, the Central Government formulated rules for the Panchayati Raj System.

IV. The members of the Gram Panchayat are appointed by the District Commissioner.

(*a*) Option I (*b*) Option II (*c*) Options II & IV (*d*) Options I, II & III

15. *Given here is a picture of an important structure excavated from one of the sites of the Indus-Saraswati Civilization. Identify the structure and the place from where it was found.*

(*a*) Dockyard at Lothal

(*b*) Granary at Harappa

(*c*) Great Bath at Mohenjo Daro

(*d*) Reservoir at Dholavira

16. *Match list I and II and select the correct answer using the codes below in the lists :*

List I	List II
1. Mayor	(*i*) President of the Panchayat
2. Municipal Commissioner	(*ii*) Head of the Municipal Corporation
3. Sarpanch	(*iii*) Link between the Municipal Corporation and the State Government
4. Lekhpal	(*iv*) Measure land and keep land records

(*a*) **1.**-(*ii*), **2.**-(*iv*), **3.**-(*iii*), **4.**-(*i*) (*b*) **1.**-(*ii*), **2.**-(*iii*), **3.**-(*i*), **4.**-(*iv*)

(*c*) **1.**-(*iii*), **2.**-(*ii*), **3.**-(*i*), **4.**-(*iv*) (*d*) **1.**-(*iv*), **2.**-(*i*), **3.**-(*ii*), **4.**-(*iii*)

17. *Consider the statements given below and choose the correct answer*

Statement I : The secondary sector is important for the economy as it adds value or worth to raw materials by converting them into useful products.

Statement II : Fishing and raising livestock come under the secondary sector.

(*a*) Statement (I) is correct and (II) is incorrect.

(*b*) Statement (I) is incorrect and (II) is correct.

(*c*) Both (I) and (II) are incorrect.

(*d*) Both (I) and (II) are correct.

18. *Given here is a picture of a famous type of sari found in India. Identify the state to which it belongs.*

(*a*) Maharashtra

(*b*) Tamil Nadu

(*c*) Telangana

(*d*) Kerala

19. *A harvest festival celebrated in North India that marks the transition of the Sun into the zodiac sign of Capricorn is called*

(*a*) Navratri (*b*) Basant Panchami

(*c*) Naraka Chaturdashi (*d*) Makar Sankranti

20. *"He keeps the map and the corresponding details such as Khata No., Khasra No., etc. He generally uses a long chain for measuring agricultural fields." The above lines describe the functions of a*

(*a*) Secretary (*b*) Sarpanch (*c*) Patwari (*d*) Mayor

ECTION-B. (Very Short Answer Type Questions) [4 x 2 = 8]

21. Write a short note on the challenges people face while living in the mountains.

22. What do you mean by "Sapta Sindhava" ? Where does the name first occur with reference to India ?

Or

India is a land of diversities. Do you agree with this statement ? Justify how.

23. The stories of Panchtantra have a universal appeal. Justify the statement.

24. Mention any two functions of the Gram Sabha.

SECTION-C. (Short Answer Type Questions) [5 x 3 = 15]

25. Discuss the significance of plateaus.

26. Write the chief features of plains

Or

Civilisation means a developed state of human society. Explain the statement.

27. The term, 'unity in diversity' is an appropriate term to describe India. Give examples to prove the statement.

28. All the three economic sectors are interdependent and interconnected. Explain and justify the statement.

29. India has a participatory democracy. Justify this statement with an example.

SECTION-D. (Long Answer Type Questions) [4 x 5 = 20]

30. Plains are ideal for human settlement. Explain this statement. Mention some suitable chief features of plains for human settlement.

Or

Explain the formation of different types of mountains giving one example of each.

31. The ruins of the Indus-Saraswati sites indicate that it was an advanced and well-organised urban civilisation. Justify this statement in the context of town-planning and water management in the civilization.

Or

Both external and internal trade flourished during the Indus-Saraswati Civilization. Justify the statement.

32. Explain how our two great Indian epics, the Ramayana and the Mahabharata reflect—

(*a*) India's traditions and diverse cultures.

(*b*) India's unity in diversity.

Or

The various differences that diversity includes, actually enhance our lives in "many ways". Explair any five ways in which diversity enhances our lives.

33. What is Panchayati Raj System ? Briefly describe its institutions at different levels. How do peopl in the rural areas take part in governance ?

Or

Amit lives in Agra. The road in front of his house has been damaged and has large pothol after the rainy season. Two of the four streetlights on the main road near his house are also n functioning. He and his neighbours are also suffering from the problem of stray animals. Who should Amit and his neighbours approach in such a situation and why ?

SECTION-E. (Source based Questions) [3 × 4 = 12]

34. **Read the source given below and answer the questions that follow :**

The Indus-Saraswati Civilization, one of the world's earliest urban civilizations, flourished from around 2600 to 1900 BCE in what is now Pakistan and western India. Known for its advanced urban planning, the civilization featured well-planned cities like Harappa and Mohenjo-Daro. These cities had sophisticated drainage systems, public baths and granaries, indicating a high level of civic organisation. The Indus-Saraswati people were skilled in various crafts, including pottery, metallurgy and bead-making. They also developed a script, although it remains undeciphered to this day. Trade was a significant aspect of the civilization, with evidence of trade networks extending to Mesopotamia and other regions. The Indus-Saraswati Civilization is notable for its lack of monumental architecture and evidence of social hierarchy, suggesting a more egalitarian society. However, the reasons for its decline are still debated, with theories ranging from environmental changes to invasions.

(*a*) Mention the various crafts of the Indus-Saraswati people.

(*b*) List some key features of urban planning in cities like Harappa and Mohenjo-Daro.

(*c*) What are the theories regarding the decline of Indus-Saraswati Civilization ?

35. **Read the source given below and answer the questions that follow :**

India is a land of great diversity. From the snow-capped mountains of the north to the sandy beaches of the south, from the vast deserts in the west to the dense forests in the east, the country is home to a variety of landscapes. But it is not just the geography that makes India diverse. The people of India belong to many different cultures, languages and religions.

Despite these differences, there is a sense of unity that binds the people of India together. This unity can be seen in the way people celebrate festivals from all religions with equal joy. Diwali, Eid, Christmas and Guru Nanak Jayanti are all celebrated across the country, regardless of which religion one follows. Similarly, different regions have their own traditional dances, music and clothing styles, yet they are all respected and appreciated across the country.

One of the most important reasons for this unity is India's Constitution, which grants equal rights to all citizens, no matter their background. It promotes respect for all religions and cultures, ensuring that everyone is treated fairly. Another reason is the strong belief in the value of harmony and peace. Indians have always believed in the idea of "Vasudhaiva Kutumbakam," which means "the world is one family."

In schools, children learn to respect and understand the customs of others. This helps them grow up with a sense of pride in their own heritage while also appreciating the diversity around them. This spirit of unity in diversity has made India a unique and strong nation, admired by people around the world.

(*a*) List some of the diversities that we find in India.

(*b*) How does our Constitution promote unity among all citizens ?

(*c*) How do children learn about unity in diversity in schools ?

36. **Read the source given below and answer the questions that follow :**

India is a large country and managing it is a big responsibility. To ensure that every part of the country is well-governed, the government is divided into two main types : central and local. The local government plays an important role in taking care of the needs of people living in both rural and urban areas.

In rural areas, the local government is called the Panchayati Raj system. It has three levels : Gram Panchayat, Block Samiti and Zila Parishad. The Gram Panchayat is the first and most important level. It takes care of small villages and is made up of members elected by the villagers. The Panchayat makes decisions about things like building roads, providing clean drinking water and improving schools in the village. The next level, Block Samiti, looks after a group of villages and helps the Gram Panchayats by providing resources. Finally, the Zila Parishad works at the district level and ensures that government schemes are carried out properly.

In urban areas, the local government is known as the Municipal Corporation in big cities and Municipalities in smaller towns. Like the Panchayats, members of the Municipalities and Municipal Corporations are also elected by the people. They are responsible for things like maintaining roads, providing street lights, collecting garbage and ensuring that the city is clean. They also work on providing health services, public parks and schools in cities and towns.

Local governments in both rural and urban areas are important because they understand the needs of the people better. They are closer to the people and can address issues quickly. The system also encourages people to take part in the decision-making process by voting in elections.

(*a*) What is the importance of local government in India ?

(*b*) Discuss the three levels of the Panchayati Raj System.

(*c*) Describe the role of Gram Panchayats in villages.

SECTION-F. (Map Skill-based Questions) [1 x 5 = 5]

37. (*a*) **Two places A and B have been marked on the given outline map of India. Identify them and write their correct names on the lines drawn near them.**

(*i*) The site where a dockyard was found in the Indus-Saraswati Civilization.

(*ii*) The site from where fire altars were discovered in Rajasthan.

(b) On an outline map of the world, locate and label any three of the following :

(*i*) Deccan Plateau in India.

(*ii*) The Himalayan range in India.

(*iii*) The Great Dividing Range in Australia

(*iv*) The Northern Plains in India.